I ♥
John Taylor

Duran Duran

Phsuedo Echo

Power Station

Billy Idol

Simon Le Bon

Madonna

John Taylor

Dude

Nick Rhodes

Dean
Rebel without out a cause

Shelly Hime

Go to P 10

Nerd

Never Ending Radical Dude!

Mathematics Around Us skills and applications

L. Carey Bolster
Gloria Felix Cox
E. Glenadine Gibb
Viggo P. Hansen
Joan E. Kirkpatrick
Charles R. McNerney
David F. Robitaille
Harold C. Trimble
Irvin E. Vance
Ray Walch
Robert J. Wisner

Scott, Foresman and Company

Glenview, Illinois; Dallas, Texas;
Oakland, New Jersey; Palo Alto,
California; and Tucker, Georgia

Follow these Pages
12

Authors

L. Carey Bolster
Supervisor of Mathematics
Baltimore County Public Schools
Towson, Maryland

Gloria Felix Cox
Principal
Los Angeles Unified School District
Los Angeles, California

E. Glenadine Gibb
Professor of Mathematics Education
The University of Texas at Austin
Austin, Texas

Viggo P. Hansen
Professor, Mathematics Education
California State University
Northridge, California

Joan E. Kirkpatrick
Associate Professor,
Elementary Education
University of Alberta
Edmonton, Alberta, Canada

Charles R. McNerney
Associate Professor of Mathematics
University of Northern Colorado
Greeley, Colorado

David F. Robitaille
Assistant Professor
of Mathematics Education
University of British Columbia
Vancouver, British Columbia, Canada

Harold C. Trimble
Professor of Education
Ohio State University
Columbus, Ohio

Irvin E. Vance
Associate Professor
of Mathematics
New Mexico State University
Las Cruces, New Mexico

Ray Walch
Former Teacher of Mathematics
Public Schools
Westport, Connecticut

Robert J. Wisner
Professor of Mathematics
New Mexico State University
Las Cruces, New Mexico

Consultant

Sidney Sharron
Coordinator,
Educational Communications
and Media Branch
Los Angeles Unified School District
Los Angeles, California

Acknowledgments

For permission to reproduce the photographs on the pages indicated, acknowledgment is made to the following:

Jeff Albertson/Stock Boston, Inc.: 12–13; The Sea Library/Peter Lake: 29; John Running/Stock Boston, Inc.: 38; Gary Wolinsky/Stock Boston, Inc.: 70–71; Mount Wilson and Palomar Observatories: 78–79; NASA: 102–103, 104–105; Daniel Brody/Stock Boston, Inc.: 140–141; NASA: 150–151, 185; The Sea Library/Henry Genthe: 262–263; NASA: 272; Linear design of Seurat's "La Parade" © Encyclopaedia Britannica, 15th edition (1974): 279; Eric M. Sanford Photography: 292–293; Finch/Stock Boston, Inc.: 298–299; Ernest Braun: 304; American Indian Center, Chicago, Illinois: 360–361; Photograph by James L. Ballard taken at Lutheran General Hospital, Park Ridge, Ill.: 364.

ISBN: 0-673-04236-7

Copyright © 1975 Scott, Foresman and Company, Glenview, Illinois.
All Rights Reserved.
Printed in the United States of America.

Regional offices of Scott, Foresman and Company are located in Glenview, Illinois; Dallas, Texas; Oakland, New Jersey; Palo Alto, California; and Tucker, Georgia.

678910-STS-858483828180797877

Unit 1 Patterns, Equations, and Integers

Unit 2 Decimals, Exponents, and Metric System

Unit 3 Fractions, Mixed Numbers, and Coordinate Graphs

Unit 4　Geometry and Measurement

Unit 5 Proportion, Percent, and Applications

Unit 6 Counting, Probability, and Statistics

Unit 1

Patterns, Equations, and Integers

$$\begin{array}{r} 36 \\ \times\ 38 \\ \hline 288 \\ 1080 \\ \hline 1368 \end{array}$$

Evaluating Expressions: Addition and Subtraction

A. These are examples of mathematical *expressions*.

$$n + 42$$

$$31 - b$$

In these expressions, n and b are *variables*. A variable is used to represent a number.

B. Evaluate the expression $g + 22$ if g is 36.

$$g + 22$$
$$\downarrow$$
$$36 + 22$$
$$\mathbf{58}$$

For each exercise, evaluate the expression, using the different values for the variable that are shown in the table.

1.

n	$n + 9$
0	9
1	10
5	
9	

5.

a	$a + 45$
13	
27	
46	
89	

2.

x	$x - 7$
7	0
10	
11	
16	

6.

k	$93 + k$
7	
22	
38	
84	

3.

d	$28 + d$
9	
11	
43	
72	

7.

t	$t - 36$
39	
41	
53	
86	

4.

z	$59 - z$
4	
17	
23	
41	

8.

h	$71 - h$
19	
23	
40	
56	

9. Evaluate each expression if c is 23 and w is 49. Then use the code to find the answer to the riddle.

Here's how

$w + c - 34$

$49 + 23 - 34 = 38$ **L**

Code	
43	A
70	B
22	D
54	F
61	I
38	L
99	M
28	N
15	O
86	R
7	T

What would Batman and Robin be called if they were run over by a steam roller?

$w + 5$

$61 - c$

$w - 6$

$w - 42$

$76 + c$

$c + 20$

$77 - w$

$c + w - 29$

$w + c - 44$

$w + c - 50$

$c + 14 + w$

$12 + w$

$c + w - 2$

$7 + c$

$w + c - 57$

$51 - c$

**More practice
Set A, page 62**

Rounding Numbers

In 1972, the circulation of the magazine *Hot Rod* was 817,750.

When working with large amounts, we often use *rounded numbers.*

Round **817,750** to the

nearest hundred thousand.
Is **817,750** nearer **800,000** or **900,000**?
Round down to **800,000**.

nearest ten thousand.
Is **817,750** nearer **810,000** or **820,000**?
Round up to **820,000**.

nearest thousand.
Is **817,750** nearer **817,000** or **818,000**?
Round up to **818,000**.

nearest hundred.
Is **817,750** nearer **817,700** or **817,800**?
It is halfway. Round up to **817,800**.

Complete the table.

	Magazine	Circulation	Circulation rounded to the			
			nearest hundred thousand	nearest ten thousand	nearest thousand	nearest hundred
1.	Sports Illustrated	2,201,022				
2.	Seventeen	1,503,372				
3.	'Teen	750,021				
4.	Popular Mechanics	1,701,742				
5.	Senior Scholastic	2,914,250				
6.	TV Guide	17,698,537				

Estimating Sums

Use rounded numbers to estimate sums.

2836 + 8021

3000 + 8000 = 11,000

2836 + 8021 ≈ 11,000

≈ means "is approximately equal to."

Give an estimate for each sum. Round three-digit numbers to the nearest hundred, and four-digit numbers to the nearest thousand.

1. 721 + 385
2. 674 + 219
3. 3918 + 4095
4. 7312 + 5613
5. 2958 + 7862
6. 8842 + 6155
7. 5017 + 1125
8. 3562 + 9471
9. 9983 + 2075
10. 2103 + 3964

Round each number to the nearest hundred thousand. Then estimate the sum of the morning and evening circulations for each newspaper.

	Newspaper	Circulation	
		Morning	Evening
11.	Baltimore Sun	180,217	204,348
12.	Boston Globe	278,128	184,493
13.	Fort Worth Star-Telegram	96,660	139,048
14.	Omaha World-Herald	130,741	119,009
15.	Santa Ana Register	66,298	124,157

Order of Operations: Addition and Subtraction

When parentheses are used with addition and subtraction, start with the computation inside the parentheses.

A. $36 + (95 - 7)$

$\quad$ $36 + 88$

$\quad\quad$ 124

B. $(24 + 3) - (17 - 5)$

$\quad$ $27 - 12$

$\quad\quad$ 15

When parentheses are *not* used with addition and subtraction, compute from left to right.

C. $75 - 3 + 14 - 23$

$\quad$ $72 + 14 - 23$

$\quad\quad$ $86 - 23$

$\quad\quad\quad$ 63

Compute each answer.

1. $19 - (13 - 6)$
2. $(19 - 13) - 6$
3. $(10 - 4) + 3$
4. $10 - (4 + 3)$
5. $27 + (9 - 8)$
6. $27 + 9 - 8$
7. $56 + 9 - 15 + 20$
8. $(56 + 9) - (15 + 20)$
9. $98 - 23 + 49$
10. $58 + 27 - 14$
11. $(81 - 13) - (42 + 7)$
12. $6 + 12 + 90 - 45$
13. $(91 - 25) + 13$
14. $66 - (10 + 38)$
15. $85 - (51 - 46)$
16. $74 - 28 + 6 - 31$
17. $(73 + 59) + (38 - 29)$
18. $(98 - 35) - (64 - 47)$
19. $36 + 58 + (72 - 15)$
20. $80 - (57 - 21) + 3$

This is a game for 2 to 4 players.

Write 20 different numbers between 1 and 100 on slips of paper and put them in a box.

For each round, each player draws 3 numbers. The player uses the numbers and either addition or subtraction symbols to make a number sentence. The players may also use parentheses. For example,
$83 - (24 + 7) = 52$

The player with the sentence having an answer closest to 50 receives one point. If the answers are equally close to 50, both players receive one point. After each round, the numbers are returned to the box.

The player with the most points after five rounds is the winner.

Daisy and Gina played Nifty 50. For each round, compute their answers and score one point for the girl whose answer was closer to 50.

Daisy

Round	
1	64 + 5 − 24
2	7 + 5 + 31
3	86 − 16 − 29
4	68 − 64 + 29
5	92 − (52 − 37)

Gina

Round	
1	74 − 45 + 13
2	88 − (92 − 53)
3	41 + (37 − 16)
4	78 + 5 − 41
5	99 + 29 − 78

Which girl won the game?

A. Find each sum.

$9281 + 6250 = $ ▦

$6250 + 9281 = $ ▦

Are the sums equal?

■ The **commutative property** *of addition says that you can always change the order of the addends and get the same sum.*

$6031 + 155 = 155 + 6031$

B. Find each sum.

$(300 + 450) + 8 = $ ▦

$300 + (450 + 8) = $ ▦

Are the sums equal?

■ The **associative property** *of addition says that you can always change the grouping of the addends and get the same sum.*

$(11 + 8) + 9 = 11 + (8 + 9)$

● **Discuss** Is there a commutative property of subtraction? Is there an associative property of subtraction?

Find each sum. Order and group the addends in any way that makes your work easier. You might look for numbers that are easy to add mentally. You might look for sums of 10 or 100.

1. $7 + 3 + 5 + 9 + 1$

2. $5 + 8 + 2 + 7 + 5$

3. $9 + 19 + 1$

4. $20 + 59 + 60$

5. $42 + 30 + 70$

6. $50 + 48 + 50$

7. $10 + 76 + 10 + 80$

8. $37 + 5 + 95$

9. $18 + 63 + 7$

10. $250 + 34 + 50$

11. $325 + 61 + 75$

12.		14.	
	59		24
	3		58
	41		76
	57		51
	+ 32		+ 22

13.		15.	
	27		83
	85		48
	65		97
	39		60
	71		15
	+ 50		+ 5

Multiplying Whole Numbers

The Mayfield postmaster received 175 sheets of commemorative stamps honoring famous artists. There were 32 stamps on each sheet. How many commemorative stamps did the postmaster receive?

Find 32 × 175.

$$
\begin{array}{r}
\mathbf{175} \\
\times\ \ \mathbf{32} \\
\hline
\mathbf{350} \\
\mathbf{5250} \\
\hline
\mathbf{5600}
\end{array}
$$

350   2 × 175
5250   30 × 175
5600   350 + 5250

The postmaster received 5600 commemorative stamps.

Multiply.

1. 40
× 9

2. 78
× 4

3. 65
× 7

4. 590
× 3

5. 601
× 8

6. 927
× 9

7. 30
× 20

8. 17
× 50

9. 86
× 60

10. 310
× 50

11. 807
× 40

12. 362
× 90

13. 70
× 13

14. 65
× 97

15. 48
× 36

16. 120
× 19

17. 409
× 82

18. 634
× 59

19. 700
× 300

20. 820
× 600

21. 931
× 800

22. 200
× 890

23. 406
× 380

24. 727
× 160

25. 725 × 410

26. 349 × 202

27. 256 × 881

28. 7 × 6215

29. 80 × 3000

30. 7200 × 90

31. 25 × 9000

32. 46 × 6100

33. 2007 × 83

34. 98 × 4580

35. 200 × 6000

36. 500 × 3900

37. 4620 × 700

38. 1000 × 830

39. 710 × 2600

40. 980 × 7100

41. 842 × 4790

42. 9 × 26,105

43. 238 × 5772

44. 50,000 × 72

45. 43 × 62,180

**More practice
Set B, page 62**

P 85

46. About 27 billion stamps are issued each year in the United States. How many stamps are issued in 3 years?

47. There are 100 air mail stamps on one sheet. How many stamps are on 125 sheets?

48. There are 500 regular stamps in a roll. How many stamps are in 75 rolls?

49. A person in the United States receives an average of about 400 pieces of mail per year. About how many pieces of mail are received in one year by a city of 16,250 people?

50. About 7,200,000,000 pieces of mail are handled by the U.S. Postal Service each month. How much mail is handled in 12 months?

Estimating Products

A. A forest ranger used rounded numbers to estimate the number of trees in the forest preserve.

873 acres in the forest preserve. About 312 trees on each acre.

873 × 312

↓   ↓

900 × 300 = 270,000

873 × 312 ≈ 270,000

The ranger estimated that there were about 270,000 trees in the forest preserve.

B. Estimate the product 450 × 650.

Both numbers end in 50. You will get a better estimate if you round one number up and the other number down.

450 × 650

↓   ↓

500 × 600 = 300,000

450 × 650 ≈ 300,000

Page 24

Estimate each product. Round
three-digit numbers to the nearest
hundred and four-digit numbers to
the nearest thousand.

1. 297 × 412

2. 301 × 517

3. 250 × 650

4. 795 × 891

5. 932 × 474

6. 135 × 682

7. 984 × 216

8. 326 × 179

9. 501 × 309

10. 421 × 487

11. 613 × 785

12. 850 × 150

13. 198 × 594

14. 975 × 631

15. 350 × 350

16. 821 × 868

17. 1002 × 7109

18. 5921 × 8854

19. 2952 × 6135

20. 3218 × 4703

Estimate each answer.

21. 28 trees destroyed by insects
per month.
12 months in a year.
How many trees destroyed in a year?

22. 250 pine trees.
150 pine cones per tree.
How many pine cones?

23. 991 acres of forest.
102 animals per acre.
How many animals in the forest?

24. 243 acres inspected per day.
365 days in a year.
How many acres inspected in a year?

Order of Operations: Addition, Subtraction, and Multiplication

A. 7(8) is another way of writing 7×8.

$$7(8) = 56$$
$$(15)4 = 60$$

B. When you are working with addition, subtraction, and multiplication, follow these rules.

First do all computations inside parentheses.

Then do all remaining multiplications.

Then do all remaining additions and subtractions.

Do the computation inside parentheses.	$65 - 4(21 - 9)$
	$65 - 4(12)$
Then multiply.	$65 - 48$
Then subtract.	17

Compute each answer.

1. $9(6 - 2)$
$9(\blacksquare)$
$\blacksquare$

2. $9(6) - 2$
$\blacksquare - 2$
$\blacksquare$

3. $14 + 2(30)$
$14 + \blacksquare$
$\blacksquare$

4. $(14 + 2)30$
$(\blacksquare)30$
$\blacksquare$

5. $9(7) - 6(3)$
$\blacksquare - \blacksquare$
$\blacksquare$

6. $8 + 4(6) - 7$
$8 + \blacksquare - 7$
$\blacksquare - 7$
$\blacksquare$

7. $2(7 - 3) + 6$
$2(\blacksquare) + 6$
$\blacksquare + 6$
$\blacksquare$

8. $9(8)$

9. $3(6)(7)$

10. $(54)5$

11. $6(7 + 9)$

12. $6(7) + 9$

13. $5(12 - 4)$

14. $5(12) - 4$

15. $1 + 8(3)$

16. $(1 + 8)3$

17. $6(9) - 2(7)$

18. $4(20) + 3(8)$

19. $15 + 6(7) - 1$

20. $10(4) - 13 + 6$

21. $28 + 15 - 2(7)$

22. $3(9 + 16 - 2)$

23. $(42 - 9 - 8)6$

24. $14 + 7(6)(3)$

25. $9(2)(4) - 22$

26. $80 - 8(13 - 9)$

27. $19 + (7 + 4)3$

28. $55 - (16 - 8)2$

29. $18 + 7(32 - 6)$

30. $5(18 - 9) - 42$

Evaluating Expressions:
Addition, Subtraction, and Multiplication

A. $8n$ is another way of writing $8 \times n$.

When n is 3, $8n$ is 24.

B. These tables show values of the expressions for different values of the variables.

n	$9n$	
6	54	9(6)
3	27	9(3)
11	99	9(11)
100	900	9(100)

t	$3t + 5$	
0	5	3(0) + 5
4	17	3(4) + 5
10	35	3(10) + 5
15	50	3(15) + 5

b	$7(b - 1)$	
2	7	7(2 − 1)
9	56	7(9 − 1)
21	140	7(21 − 1)
25	168	7(25 − 1)

Complete.

1.

a	$16a$
0	
1	
10	
12	

2.

z	$4z + 2$
0	
7	
8	
20	

3.

h	$6(h - 3)$
7	
11	
15	
23	

4.

c	$(c + 6)5$
1	
6	
9	
20	

5.

v	$63 - 2v$
0	
4	
20	
31	

When y is 5, find the value of

6. $12y$

7. $12 - y$

8. $12 + y$

9. $3y - 7$

10. $4 + 9y$

11. $6y + 11$

12. $56 - 2y$

13. $8(y + 1)$

14. $6(y - 2)$

15. $6y - 2$

16. $5(y - 5)$

17. $7(30 - y)$

18. $(y + 8)3$

19. $(2y + 4)8$

20. $10(3y - 6)$

When g is 4 and k is 7, find the value of

21. gk

22. $3gk$

23. $2k + g$

24. $5gk - 9$

25. $6k + 8g$

TIME OUT

Tell how you could cut a doughnut into 12 pieces with exactly 3 straight slices.

Commutative and Associative Properties of Multiplication

A. Find each product.

$29 \times 14 = $ ▦

$14 \times 29 = $ ▦

Are the products equal?

■ The *commutative property of multiplication* says that you can always change the order of the factors and the product remains the same.

$46 \times 30 = 30 \times 46$

B. Find each product.

$(8 \times 2) \times 23 = $ ▦

$8 \times (2 \times 23) = $ ▦

Are the products equal?

■ The *associative property of multiplication* says that you can always change the grouping of the factors and the product remains the same.

$(9 \times 7) \times 5 = 9 \times (7 \times 5)$

Find each product. Order and group the factors in any way that makes your work easier.

1. $81 \times 2 \times 5$
2. $50 \times 77 \times 2$
3. $48 \times 2 \times 3$
4. $40 \times 28 \times 10$
5. $8 \times 12 \times 5$
6. $25 \times 98 \times 4$
7. $4 \times 6 \times 38$
8. $21 \times 5 \times 6$
9. $20 \times 18 \times 30$
10. $66 \times 200 \times 5$
11. $50 \times 80 \times 7$
12. $20 \times 36 \times 50$
13. $4 \times 25 \times 63$
14. $56 \times 19 \times 0$
15. $3 \times 250 \times 4 \times 6$
16. $7 \times 20 \times 8 \times 5$
17. $17 \times 2 \times 25 \times 4$
18. $50 \times 3 \times 24 \times 2$
19. $500 \times 8 \times 2 \times 9$
20. $18 \times 35 \times 0 \times 7$

Distributive Property

A. Compute each answer.

$6(8 + 2) = $ ▨

$6(8) + 6(2) = $ ▨

$7(30 + 9) = $ ▨

$7(30) + 7(9) = $ ▨

Are the answers equal in each pair of exercises?

■ When you write $5(7 + 3)$ as $5(7) + 5(3)$ you are using the **distributive property**.

B. Sometimes the distributive property can help you compute mentally.

$3(20 + 8)$
84
$3(20) + 3(8)$
$60 + 24$
84

C. Sometimes it is easier to add first and then multiply.

$17(60 + 40)$
1700
$17(100)$
1700

Find each answer. Use the distributive property whenever it makes your work easier.

1. $8(30 + 4)$

2. $9(2 + 8)$

3. $12(10 + 7)$

4. $7(6 + 4)$

5. $9(35 + 5)$

6. $7(60 + 3)$

7. $72(99 + 1)$

8. $8(48 + 2)$

9. $59(30 + 70)$

10. $6(90 + 1)$

11. $84(25 + 75)$

12. $91(85 + 15)$

13. $22(500 + 500)$

14. $3(100 + 6)$

15. $41(20 + 80)$

16. $5(100 + 30)$

17. $7(1000 + 9)$

18. $9(400 + 70)$

★**19.** $36(25) + 36(75)$

★**20.** $54(800) + 54(200)$

For each exercise, find the answer without computing. The answers are shown below. Use the commutative, associative, and distributive properties to help you.

21. $4(95 + 33)$

22. $7 \times (26 \times 19)$

23. $(26 \times 7) \times 19$

24. $15(3 + 41)$

25. $7(26 + 19)$

26. $(4 \times 95) \times 33$

27. $(53 \times 9) \times 75$

28. $9(53) + 9(75)$

29. $15 \times (3 \times 41)$

30. $15 \times (41 \times 3)$

Answers
$7(26) + 7(19) = 315$
$(7 \times 26) \times 19 = 3458$
$15(3) + 15(41) = 660$
$(15 \times 3) \times 41 = 1845$
$4 \times (95 \times 33) = 12{,}540$
$4(95) + 4(33) = 512$
$9(53 + 75) = 1152$
$(9 \times 53) \times 75 = 35{,}775$

Dividing Whole Numbers

A. In a race, Ria and Nan sailed 135 kilometers in 9 hours. They sailed about how many kilometers per hour?

Find 135 ÷ 9.

```
     15
9) 135
  −9
   45
  −45
    0
```

They sailed about 15 kilometers per hour.

B. A spinnaker is a large, colorful, balloon-shaped sail. It takes about 28 square meters of nylon to make a spinnaker. How many spinnakers could be made with 3000 square meters of nylon? How much nylon would be left?

Find 3000 ÷ 28.

```
       107 R4
28) 3000
   −28
    200
   −196
      4
```

107 spinnakers could be made. There would be 4 square meters of nylon left.

Divide.

1. $3\overline{)261}$

2. $9\overline{)548}$

3. $4\overline{)823}$

4. $6\overline{)4384}$

5. $7\overline{)6002}$

6. $2\overline{)7912}$

7. $8\overline{)64253}$

8. $7\overline{)28048}$

9. $5\overline{)197106}$

10. $9\overline{)649197}$

11. $24\overline{)75}$

12. $46\overline{)92}$

13. $71\overline{)355}$

14. $65\overline{)525}$

15. $37\overline{)777}$

16. $92\overline{)5260}$

17. $94\overline{)3666}$

18. $59\overline{)2383}$

19. $31\overline{)6217}$

20. $52\overline{)19864}$

21. $43\overline{)38528}$

22. $76\overline{)45710}$

23. $29\overline{)102196}$

24. $88\overline{)440300}$

25. $67\overline{)273963}$

26. $403\overline{)953}$

27. $621\overline{)1945}$

28. $258\overline{)7998}$

29. $742\overline{)41558}$

30. $539\overline{)161774}$

31. A boat can be docked every 3 meters along one side of a dock. How many boats can be docked along 108 meters?

32. Ms. Fox has $125 to spend on safety equipment for her boat. How many $16 life vests can she buy? How much money will she have left?

33. On a spinnaker with horizontal stripes, each stripe is 104 centimeters high. How many stripes are on a spinnaker that is 1248 centimeters high?

34. There are 38 people who want to cross the lake in sailboats. Only 4 people can ride in each boat. How many boats are needed?

More practice
Set C, page 62

Order of Operations

A. A bar can be used to indicate division, $\frac{18}{3}$ is another way of writing $18 \div 3$.

$$\frac{18}{3} = 6$$

B. When you are working with more than one operation, follow these rules.

First do all operations inside parentheses and above and below division bars.

Then do all remaining multiplications and divisions.

Then do all remaining additions and subtractions.

$$17 - \frac{2(5+3)}{4}$$

Do the operation inside parentheses.

$$17 - \frac{2(8)}{4}$$

Then do the operation above the division bar.

$$17 - \frac{16}{4}$$

Then divide.

$$17 - 4$$

Then subtract.

$$13$$

Compute each answer.

1. $\dfrac{24}{6} = \blacksquare$

2. $\dfrac{5(8)}{2} = \dfrac{\blacksquare}{2} = \blacksquare$

3. $\dfrac{28}{4}(3) = \blacksquare(3) = \blacksquare$

4. $\dfrac{9+7}{2} = \dfrac{\blacksquare}{2} = \blacksquare$

5. $\dfrac{36}{3(7-3)} = \dfrac{36}{3(\blacksquare)} = \dfrac{36}{\blacksquare} = \blacksquare$

6. $\dfrac{72}{8}$

7. $\dfrac{(3)10}{2}$

8. $\dfrac{6(8)}{2(4)}$

9. $\dfrac{29-2}{9}$

10. $\dfrac{21}{7} + 38$

11. $\dfrac{40}{4} - \dfrac{56}{7}$

12. $\dfrac{8(1+11)}{16}$

13. $\dfrac{75}{3(9-4)}$

14. $\dfrac{45}{3(5)} - 1$

15. $7 + \dfrac{35-25}{2}$

16. $\dfrac{72}{9} - \dfrac{21+3}{4}$

17. $\dfrac{4(9)}{3(6)} + \dfrac{10(7)}{2(5)}$

18. $\dfrac{25}{5} + \dfrac{3(7-5)}{2}$

19. $\dfrac{6(9+1)}{3} - 11$

Evaluating Expressions

These tables show values of three expressions for different values of the variables.

t	$\dfrac{24}{t}$	
2	12	$\dfrac{24}{2}$
8	3	$\dfrac{24}{8}$
24	1	$\dfrac{24}{24}$

n	$\dfrac{7n}{3}$	
0	0	$\dfrac{7(0)}{3}$
9	21	$\dfrac{7(9)}{3}$
30	70	$\dfrac{7(30)}{3}$

c	$\dfrac{3(c+1)}{4}$	
3	3	$\dfrac{3(3+1)}{4}$
7	6	$\dfrac{3(7+1)}{4}$
79	60	$\dfrac{3(79+1)}{4}$

Complete each table.

1.

n	$\dfrac{n}{6}$
12	
42	
60	
96	

2.

m	$\dfrac{360}{m}$
3	
6	
12	
90	

3.

d	$\dfrac{5d}{2}$
4	
12	
20	
32	

4.

w	$\dfrac{7(w-2)}{3}$
5	
14	
32	
41	

Find the value of each expression when a is 3 and b is 5.

5. $\dfrac{6a}{9}$

6. $\dfrac{60}{a} - 16$

7. $\dfrac{b+7}{6}$

8. $19 - \dfrac{8a}{12}$

9. $\dfrac{80}{4(b-3)}$

10. $\dfrac{a+b}{2}$

11. $\dfrac{ab}{15}$

12. $\dfrac{10a}{b}$

13. $\dfrac{2(b+1)}{a}$

14. $\dfrac{36}{b-a}$

15. $\dfrac{25}{b} - \dfrac{2(a+7)}{4}$

CAREERS Hair Stylist

In a certain hair salon, the hair stylists schedule appointments every 20 minutes, or 3 appointments per hour.

What is the greatest number of appointments a hair stylist could schedule in

1. 3 hours?

2. 8 hours?

3. 16 hours?

4. 35 hours?

5. 40 hours?

These are the prices in the salon.

Haircut	$ 9
Shampoo and set	$ 8
Permanent wave A	$17
Permanent wave B	$30
Hair color	$18
Manicure	$ 3

What should a stylist charge for

6. a haircut and a shampoo and set?

7. permanent wave B and a shampoo and set?

8. a haircut, shampoo and set, and manicure?

9. a shampoo and set, hair color, and manicure?

10. permanent wave A, a haircut, shampoo and set, and manicure?

The hair stylists mix a solution for sterilizing their combs and brushes. They mix a given amount of antiseptic with 4 times as much water.

How much water should be mixed with

11. 100 milliliters of antiseptic?

12. 225 milliliters of antiseptic?

13. 500 milliliters of antiseptic?

14. 750 milliliters of antiseptic?

15. 1000 milliliters of antiseptic?

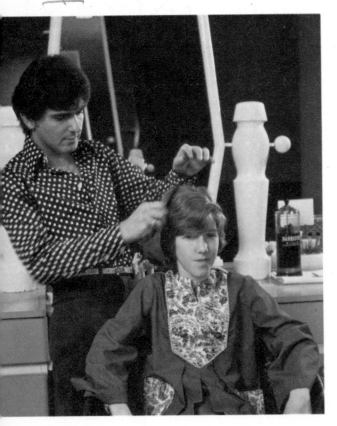

Laboratory Activity

Dora used rounded numbers to estimate the amount of time she spends caring for her hair in one year.

129 minutes spent in one week.
52 weeks in one year.

129×52
$\downarrow \quad \downarrow$
$130 \times 50 = 6500$

Dora estimated that she spends about 6500 minutes per year caring for her hair.

Then she gave the estimate in hours.

$$\begin{array}{r} 108 \text{ R}20 \\ 60\overline{)6500} \end{array}$$

6500 minutes is 108 hours 20 minutes.

1. Estimate the number of hours each student spent caring for his or her hair in one year.

Student	Minutes spent in one week
Tammy	295
Chang	75
Lars	148
Sally	201

2. Keep a record of the time you spend caring for your hair in one week. Then estimate the number of hours you spend caring for your hair in one year.

Chapter 1 Test
Number Patterns, Pages 4-23

Adding and subtracting, pages 4-9

Find the value of each expression when a is 9.

1. $a + 10$

2. $a - 6$

3. $22 - a$

Compute each answer.

4. $15 - (11 - 3)$

5. $(17 + 9) - 6$

Estimate the sum.

6. $7858 + 4115$

Multiplying, pages 10-17

Multiply.

7.
$$\begin{array}{r} 200 \\ \times\quad 8 \\ \hline \end{array}$$

8.
$$\begin{array}{r} 72 \\ \times 53 \\ \hline \end{array}$$

9.
$$\begin{array}{r} 639 \\ \times\quad 84 \\ \hline \end{array}$$

10.
$$\begin{array}{r} 904 \\ \times 652 \\ \hline \end{array}$$

Estimate the product.

11. 417×388

Compute each answer.

12. $9(7)$

13. $6(27 + 3)$

14. $8(3) - 2(9)$

15. $75 - (12 - 10)5$

Find the value of each expression when n is 3.

16. $8n$

17. $4n - 5$

18. $7(n + 6)$

Dividing, pages 18-21

Divide.

19. $6\overline{)4328}$

20. $37\overline{)60219}$

21. $523\overline{)4184}$

Compute each answer.

22. $\dfrac{5(4)}{10}$

23. $\dfrac{3(2 + 4)}{9}$

Find the value of each expression when w is 4.

24. $\dfrac{16}{w}$

25. $\dfrac{6w}{8} - 1$

26. $\dfrac{3(w + 6)}{5}$

129 centimeters

n centimeters

43 centimeters

$43 + n = 129$

Writing mathematical expressions for word phrases can help you with problem solving.

Write an expression for each phrase.

A. 6 more than a number n

$$n + 6$$

B. 4 less than a number k

$$k - 4$$

C. 23 increased by a number b

$$23 + b$$

D. A number w decreased by 12

$$w - 12$$

Write a mathematical expression for each description.

E. The price of a professional camera that costs n dollars more than a $21 Instamatic camera.

$$21 + n$$

F. The weight of an Instamatic camera if it weighs 1200 grams less than a professional camera weighing g grams.

$$g - 1200$$

G. The sale price of a camera if the regular price of $38 has been reduced by d dollars.

$$38 - d$$

Write a mathematical expression for each exercise.

1. 9 more than a number a

2. 3 less than a number r

3. 45 subtracted from a number k

4. 15 plus a number m

5. 8 increased by a number w

6. 4 less than a number y

7. 103 decreased by a number g

8. A number t minus 23

9. 5 more than a number h

10. The total length of a camera if the camera body measures 58 millimeters and the lens measures m millimeters.

11. The length of a normal lens if it is n millimeters shorter than a 180-millimeter telephoto lens.

12. The number of seconds for a time exposure that is s seconds longer than a 2-second exposure.

13. The number of flashes left in a flashcube if there are c flashes and 3 of them have been used.

14. The width of camera film that is y millimeters wider than 16-millimeter film.

15. The number of exposures left on a roll of film if there are e exposures and 14 of them have been used.

Solving Addition and Subtraction Equations

A. The length of a white shark is 920 centimeters more than the length of a sand shark. The white shark is 1050 centimeters long. How long is the sand shark?

Let s represent the length of the sand shark. Then $s + 920$ is the length of the white shark. Here is an equation for the problem.

$$s + 920 = 1050$$

$$s + 920 - 920 = 1050 - 920$$

920 is added to s. To "undo" the addition and get s by itself, subtract 920 from $s + 920$. To keep the equation in balance, also subtract 920 from 1050.

$$s = 130$$

The *solution* of $s + 920 = 1050$ is 130. To check the solution, see whether $130 + 920 = 1050$ is a true statement. The sand shark is 130 centimeters long.

B. The weight of an elephant is 7900 kilograms less than the weight of a whale shark. The elephant weighs 5600 kilograms. How much does the whale shark weigh?

Let w represent the weight of the whale shark. Then $w - 7900$ is the weight of the elephant.

$$w - 7900 = 5600$$

$$w - 7900 + 7900 = 5600 + 7900$$

7900 is subtracted from w. To "undo" the subtraction and get w by itself, add 7900 to both sides of the equation.

$$w = 13,500$$

The whale shark weighs 13,500 kilograms.

Find the solution of each equation. You can check an answer by substituting it for the variable in the original equation.

1. $9 + c = 41$

2. $n - 8 = 36$

3. $47 = g - 5$

4. $x + 31 = 104$

5. $k - 12 = 83$

6. $86 + h = 340$

Write an equation. Find the missing number.

13. 16 more than a number t is 35.

14. 8 less than a number r is 15.

15. A number c increased by 12 is 94.

16. A number b decreased by 37 is 5.

17. 42 more than a number y is 63.

18. 14 less than a number d is 51.

7. $v + 102 = 150$

8. $814 = 591 + w$

9. $642 = d - 47$

10. $15 = m - 139$

11. $n + 218 = 533$

12. $904 = 781 + x$

Find each answer.

19. A shark pup weighs 932 kilograms less than its mother. The pup weighs 8 kilograms. How much does its mother weigh?

20. From birth to adulthood, a shark's length increased by 347 centimeters. The adult shark was 408 centimeters long. How long was the newborn shark?

More practice
Set D, page 62

Using Addition and Subtraction Equations to Solve Problems

A. The crew members of a 747 airplane were on board. Then 294 passengers boarded the plane. There were 305 people in all. How many crew members were there?

You can write an equation for the problem.

$$\underset{\text{Crew}}{c} \;+\; \underset{\text{Passengers}}{294} = \underset{\text{Total}}{305}$$

Find c. Since 294 is added to c, subtract 294 from both sides of the equation.

$$c + 294 \;-\; 294 = 305 - 294$$
$$c = 11$$

Answer the question.

There were 11 crew members.

B. After 54,000 kilograms of fuel were burned on a coast-to-coast flight, there were 96,000 kilograms of fuel left. How much fuel was on board to begin with?

One student wrote this equation for the problem.

$$\underset{\substack{\text{Fuel to} \\ \text{begin with}}}{n} - \underset{\substack{\text{Fuel} \\ \text{burned}}}{54{,}000} = \underset{\substack{\text{Fuel} \\ \text{left}}}{96{,}000}$$

Find n. Since 54,000 is subtracted from n, add 54,000 to both sides of the equation.

$$n - 54{,}000 + 54{,}000 = 96{,}000 + 54{,}000$$
$$n = 150{,}000$$

Answer the question.

There were 150,000 kilograms of fuel on board.

1. The 747 plane has 340 seats. There are 30 seats in the first-class section. How many seats are in the coach section?

2. After the pilot checked 180 items in preparation for takeoff, there were 70 items left to check. How many items had to be checked in all?

3. The 1900 meters required for takeoff is 450 meters more than the distance required for landing. What is the distance required for landing?

4. When the plane carries 158,000 kilograms of fuel, luggage, and people, it weighs 322,000 kilograms. How much does the plane weigh empty?

5. The cruising altitude of a Piper Cub is 10,900 meters less than that of a 747. The Piper Cub cruises at about 500 meters. What is the cruising altitude of a 747?

This formula gives a plane's ground speed when flying with a tailwind.

Airspeed	Tailwind speed	Ground speed

$$a + t = g$$

The numbers in exercises 6–9 refer to kilometers per hour.

6. Find t when a is 725 and g is 760.

7. Find a when t is 52 and g is 937.

This formula gives the plane's ground speed when it flies into a headwind.

Airspeed	Headwind speed	Ground speed

$$a - h = g$$

8. Find a when h is 23 and g is 652.

9. Find a when g is 784 and h is 41.

1. A rock-and-roll band went on tour. Complete this table for the tour.

Location	Number of weeks	Pay per week	Total pay
Detroit	3	$3500	
Chicago	4	$3500	
St. Paul	2	$3000	
Omaha	4	$2800	
Wichita	3	$3200	
Total pay for the tour ⟶			

2. For every $100 that the band earns, the manager gets $21. How much does the manager get when the band earns $8500?

3. The band made a record of songs from the tour. How much did 4 hours in the recording studio cost at the rate of $135 per hour?

For each performance, the band plays 40-minute sets with 20-minute breaks between sets.

4. How many sets does the band play in 6 hours?

5. If a song takes an average of 4 minutes, about how many songs can the band expect to play during a set? During six sets?

6. Find the total cost of this equipment for a rock-and-roll band.

Number of items	Item	Cost per item	Total cost
2	Electric guitars	$450	
1	Bass guitar	$425	
3	Guitar amplifiers	$800	
1	Electric piano	$430	
1	Set of drums	$900	
1	PA system	$800	
5	Microphones	$ 85	
Total cost of equipment ⟶			

The sound of middle C has a frequency of 256 cycles per second. Each time the piano player goes up one octave on the scale, the frequency doubles. What is the frequency of a note

7. one octave above middle C?

8. two octaves above middle C?

9. three octaves above middle C?

Each time the piano player goes down one octave, the frequency is divided by 2. What is the frequency of a note

10. one octave below middle C?

11. two octaves below middle C?

Writing Multiplication and Division Expressions

Write a mathematical expression for each word phrase.

A. 5 times a number b

$$5b$$

B. A number n times 4

$$n(4), \text{ or } 4n$$

C. 12 divided by a number t

$$\frac{12}{t}$$

D. A number d divided by 24

$$\frac{d}{24}$$

Write a mathematical expression for each description.

E. Gulliver's height if he is 12 times as tall as a Lilliputian who is n centimeters tall.

$$12n$$

F. The amount of food each Lilliputian carried to Gulliver if k grams of food were divided equally among 6 Lilliputians.

$$\frac{k}{6}$$

G. The distance a Lilliputian walks in g steps if each step is 8 centimeters long.

$$8g$$

Write a mathematical expression for each exercise.

1. 8 times a number a

2. A number v divided by 9

3. 24 divided by a number r

4. A number t multiplied by 12

5. A number w times 7

6. 30 divided by a number e

7. 2 times a number y

8. A number h divided by 14

9. 150 divided by a number x

10. The amount of weight Gulliver can lift if a Lilliputian can lift r grams and Gulliver can lift 144 times as much.

11. The amount of cloth in a Lilliputian shirt if n square centimeters of cloth in Gulliver's shirt can be divided up to make 144 Lilliputian shirts.

12. Gulliver's weight if he weighs 1728 times as much as a Lilliputian who weighs w grams.

13. The amount of time it takes a Lilliputian to walk d meters at a speed of 40 meters per minute.

14. The number of Lilliputian mattresses needed to make a comfortable bed for Gulliver if y stacks of mattresses are needed, with 12 mattresses per stack.

15. The distance that a Lilliputian can cover in a running jump if she is k centimeters tall and can jump 6 times her height.

35

Solving Multiplication and Division Equations

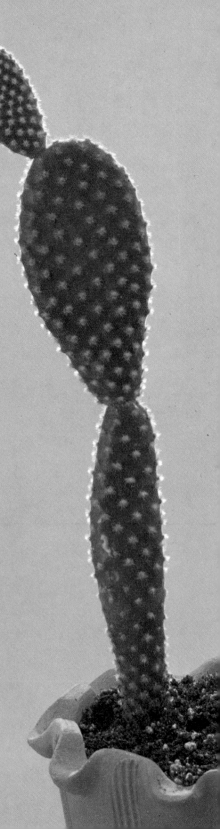

A. Mr. Rizzo's class is growing cactuses. A prickly pear cactus that is 216 millimeters tall is 4 times as tall as a sun cup cactus. How tall is a sun cup cactus?

Let s represent the height of the sun cup cactus. Then $4s$ is the height of the prickly pear cactus. Here is an equation for the problem.

$$4s = 216$$

$$\frac{4s}{4} = \frac{216}{4}$$

s is multiplied by 4. To "undo" the multiplication and get s by itself, divide both sides of the equation by 4.

$$s = 54$$

The sun cup cactus is 54 millimeters tall.

B. Marcia divided some liquid plant food equally among 7 plants. Each plant received 25 milliliters of food. How much food did Marcia use in all?

Let t represent the total amount of food.

Then $\frac{t}{7}$ is the amount of food for each plant.

$$\frac{t}{7} = 25$$

$$(7)\frac{t}{7} = (7)25$$

t is divided by 7. To "undo" the division and get t by itself, multiply both sides of the equation by 7.

$$t = 175$$

Marcia used 175 milliliters of plant food.

Find the solution of each equation.

1. $8a = 112$

2. $\dfrac{n}{6} = 91$

3. $12v = 192$

4. $\dfrac{w}{25} = 2$

5. $108 = 4b$

6. $\dfrac{m}{8} = 160$

7. $3c = 78$

8. $42 = \dfrac{k}{7}$

9. $385 = 11y$

10. $\dfrac{n}{100} = 8$

11. $160 = 32g$

12. $6 = \dfrac{d}{32}$

13. $57t = 342$

14. $95 = \dfrac{v}{5}$

Write an equation. Find the missing number.

15. 6 times a number y is 102.

16. A number b times 9 is 126.

17. A number e divided by 4 is 13.

18. 15 times a number g is 120.

19. A number n divided by 61 is 8.

20. A number m times 32 is 352.

Find each answer.

21. A fishhook cactus with 294 spines has 3 times as many spines as a hedgehog cactus. How many spines does the hedgehog cactus have?

22. Mr. Rizzo divided some flower seeds equally among 5 students. Each student received 14 seeds. How many seeds were distributed?

**More practice
Set E, page 63**

Using Multiplication and Division Equations to Solve Problems

A. This formula is for computing distance traveled.

Rate   Time   Distance

$$rt = d$$

How long does it take the sound of thunder to travel 1660 meters at a rate of 332 meters per second?

Substitute values for r and d in the formula.
$$332t = 1660$$

Find t. Since t is multiplied by 332, divide both sides of the equation by 332.
$$\frac{332t}{332} = \frac{1660}{332}$$
$$t = 5$$

Answer the question.   It takes 5 seconds.

B. This formula is for computing electrical current.

Volts of pressure ⟶ $\dfrac{E}{R} = I$ ⟵ Amperes of current

Ohms of resistance ⟶

How many volts of electrical pressure are in a lightning bolt that has a current of 100,000 amperes with a resistance of 150 ohms?

Substitute values for R and I in the formula.
$$\frac{E}{150} = 100,000$$

Find E. Since E is divided by 150, multiply both sides of the equation by 150.
$$(150)\frac{E}{150} = (150)100,000$$
$$E = 15,000,000$$

Answer the question.   There are 15,000,000 volts.

Use the distance formula for problems 1–3.

1. How fast does electricity travel if it travels 1,198,908 kilometers in 4 seconds?

2. How long does it take a rainstorm to travel 360 kilometers at a rate of 45 kilometers per hour?

3. How far away is lightning if it takes 3 seconds for you to hear the thunder and the sound travels 332 meters per second?

Use the electrical-current formula for problems 4–6.

4. How many volts of pressure are needed to draw 5 amperes of current through a power station with a resistance of 20,000 ohms?

5. How many amperes of current are drawn on a line with 110 volts of pressure by a coffeepot with a resistance of 22 ohms?

6. How many volts of pressure are needed to draw 20 amperes of current through an oven with a resistance of 11 ohms?

Use this formula for problems 7–10.

Watts of power	Amperes of current	Volts of pressure

$$W = IE$$

7. How many amperes of current are in a lightning bolt with 10,000,000 volts of pressure and 500,000,000,000 watts of power?

8. How many amperes of current are drawn by a 550-watt spotlight on a line with a pressure of 110 volts?

9. How many volts of pressure are needed to draw 4 amperes of current through an 880-watt power saw?

10. How many amperes of current are drawn by an 1100-watt toaster on a line with a pressure of 110 volts?

LABORATORY ACTIVITY

This formula can be used to find the speeds of various objects.

Rate   Time   Distance

$$rt = d$$

Measure a distance of 50 meters, or 5000 centimeters, along a sidewalk. Time how many seconds it takes for each object listed below to travel that distance. Then substitute the values you found in the formula and compute the average speed, or rate, of each object in centimeters per second.

1. Your speed when you are walking

2. Your speed when you are hopping on one foot

3. Your speed when you are running

4. The speed of a bicycle that is moving slowly

5. The speed of a bicycle that is moving fast

6. The speed of a car

7. The speed of a running dog

8. The speed of a rolling ball

Time Out

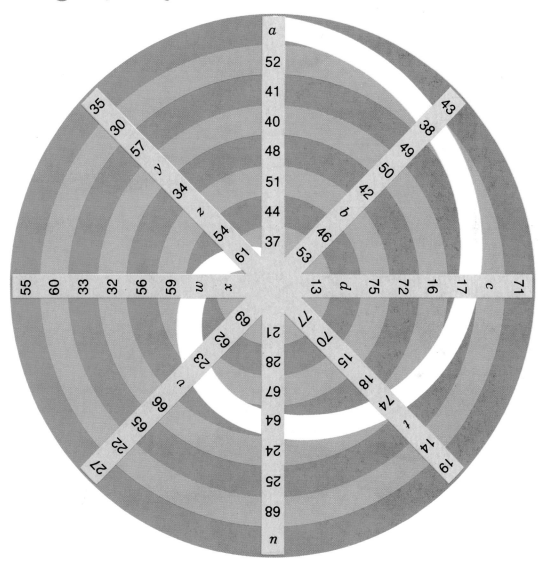

Find the missing numbers. The sum of the numbers along each of the eight spokes is 360. The sum around each ring is also 360.

The sum of the numbers in the spiral is 360. Find another set of numbers that form a spiral with a sum of 360.

Equations Involving Multiplication and Addition

A stagecoach is 42 kilometers from Fort Laramie. It is traveling away from Fort Laramie at a speed of 12 kilometers per hour. In how many hours will it be 150 kilometers from Fort Laramie?

Let h represent the number of hours. Then $12h$ is the distance traveled in h hours, and $12h + 42$ is the distance from Fort Laramie in h hours.

Here is an equation for the problem.

First find $12h$. Since 42 is added to $12h$, subtract 42 from both sides of the equation.

Then find h. Since h is multiplied by 12, divide both sides of the equation by 12.

$$12h + 42 = 150$$
$$12h + 42 - 42 = 150 - 42$$
$$12h = 108$$
$$\frac{12h}{12} = \frac{108}{12}$$
$$h = 9$$

Answer the question.

The stagecoach will be 150 kilometers from Fort Laramie in 9 hours.

Find the solution of each equation. Remember, you can check an answer by substituting it for the variable in the original equation.

1. $6g + 9 = 33$

2. $4e + 7 = 27$

3. $64 = 9y + 10$

4. $8v + 6 = 38$

5. $58 = 7b + 9$

6. $8n + 16 = 128$

7. $2d + 17 = 65$

8. $7a + 5 = 96$

9. $149 = 4s + 45$

10. $170 = 30t + 50$

11. $10p + 21 = 91$

12. $50w + 7 = 357$

13. $99 = 20u + 19$

14. $6c + 42 = 120$

15. $8n + 27 = 227$

16. $195 = 21t + 6$

17. $208 = 35g + 68$

18. $29k + 75 = 162$

Find each answer.

19. A lookout scout for the stagecoach is 75 kilometers from Fort Laramie and is riding away from the fort at 35 kilometers per hour. In how many hours will the scout be 180 kilometers from Fort Laramie?

20. The stagecoach is 1482 kilometers from San Francisco and is averaging 36 kilometers per day. In how many days will it be in Boston if Boston is 5190 kilometers from San Francisco?

21. There is $200,000 worth of gold on the stagecoach. How many $25,000 bags of gold would have to be added to make the total shipment worth $350,000?

22. The stagecoach driver has $32 and saves $4 per month. In how many months will the driver have $100?

Equations Involving Multiplication and Subtraction

The Chamber of Commerce is sponsoring a Frontier Days Rodeo.
Tickets sell for $3. It costs $4700 to sponsor the rodeo.
How many tickets must the sponsors sell to make a profit of $10,000?

Let t represent the number of tickets. Then $3t$ is the money
collected for t tickets, and $3t - 4700$ is the profit for
t tickets.

Here is an equation
for the problem.

$$3t - 4700 = 10{,}000$$

First find $3t$. Since
4700 is subtracted from
$3t$, add 4700 to both
sides of the equation.

$$3t - 4700 + 4700 = 10{,}000 + 4700$$

$$3t = 14{,}700$$

Then find t. Since t is
multiplied by 3, divide
both sides of the
equation by 3.

$$\frac{3t}{3} = \frac{14{,}700}{3}$$

$$t = 4900$$

Answer the question. They must sell 4900 tickets to make a profit of $10,000.

Find the solution of each equation.

1. $8n - 5 = 19$

2. $6w - 3 = 27$

3. $12 = 4x - 8$

4. $7c - 5 = 44$

5. $9p - 8 = 46$

6. $40 = 5t - 20$

7. $6k - 25 = 53$

8. $72 = 3g - 24$

9. $278 = 9h - 10$

10. $4x - 13 = 55$

11. $21g - 15 = 48$

12. $33e - 27 = 39$

13. $80 = 26y - 50$

14. $30v - 65 = 145$

15. $129 = 6t - 81$

16. $164 = 25s - 36$

17. $47a - 31 = 16$

18. $205d - 3 = 817$

19. $53n - 9 = 309$

20. $221 = 62b - 27$

Find each answer.

21. If the rodeo cost $4700 to sponsor, but tickets sold for $4 each, how many tickets would need to be sold to make a profit of $10,000?

22. The sponsors rented a horse for $30. If they charge $6 per hour for rides, how many hours of riding are needed to make a profit of $24?

23. The Jaycees sold lunches for $2. They spent $650 for the lunches. How many lunches do they need to sell to make a profit of $300?

24. Kazuko won a $10 gift certificate for the Frontier Shop. How many $6 leather belts can she buy with $8 in cash and the certificate?

Expressions, equations, and problems involving addition and subtraction, pages 26-31

Write a mathematical expression.

1. 4 more than a number n

2. 7 less than a number k

3. The price of a text book that costs w dollars more than a $2 paperback book.

Find the solution of each equation.

4. $m + 17 = 42$ 6. $d - 12 = 36$

5. $48 + c = 91$ 7. $18 = x - 67$

8. A bus is 630 centimeters longer than a car. If the bus is 1200 centimeters long, how long is the car?

Expressions, equations, and problems involving multiplication and division, pages 34-39

Write a mathematical expression.

9. 5 times a number b

10. A number r divided by 8

11. Mrs. Mott's age if she is 3 times as old as Kay. Kay is y years old.

Find the solution of each equation.

12. $8w = 120$ 14. $30y = 360$

13. $\dfrac{h}{5} = 14$ 15. $\dfrac{d}{90} = 6$

16. Use this formula to find how long it takes a train to travel 380 kilometers at a rate of 95 kilometers per hour.

Rate   Time   Distance

$$rt = d$$

Equations and problems involving more than one operation, pages 42-45

Find the solution of each equation.

17. $4c + 16 = 52$ 19. $2x - 5 = 23$

18. $47 = 8v + 7$ 20. $60 = 4n - 8$

Find each answer.

21. Lianne has $28 and saves $6 per month. In how many months will she have $70?

22. The student council spent $80 to sponsor a dance. Tickets to the dance sold for $2. How many tickets did the council need to sell to make a profit of $130?

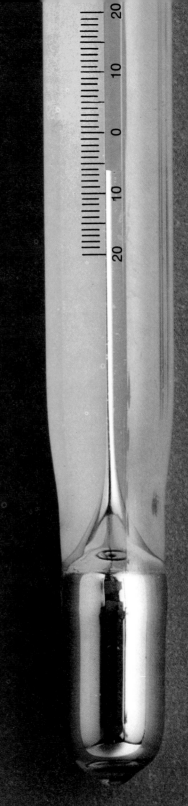

−7°C

Writing and Comparing Integers

A. This number line shows *integers*. It goes on and on in both directions. The integers to the right of zero are *positive integers*. The integers to the left of zero are *negative integers*. Zero is neither positive nor negative.

The integer $^+2$ is "positive two."
The integer $^-3$ is "negative three."

B. For any two integers on a number line like the one shown, the integer farther to the right is greater. The integer farther to the left is less.

$^+4 > {}^+3$	$^+1 > {}^-2$	$^-1 > {}^-4$
$^+3 < {}^+4$	$^-2 < {}^+1$	$^-4 < {}^-1$

C. Positive and negative integers are useful for describing opposite amounts.

Gain of 6 kilograms, **$^+6$**
Loss of 6 kilograms, **$^-6$**

12 blocks east, **$^+12$**
12 blocks west, **$^-12$**

Write the missing number.

1. Gain of 7 yards, $^+7$
Loss of 7 yards, ▥

2. 1000 feet above sea level, $^+1000$
1000 feet below sea level, ▥

3. 15°C below zero, $^-15$
15°C above zero, ▥

4. Deposit of $56, $^+56$
Withdrawal of $56, ▥

5. 13 seconds before blastoff, $^-13$
13 seconds after blastoff, ▥

For each exercise, give the opposite amount.

Here's how

5 blocks north, $^+5$
5 blocks south, $^-5$

6. 21°C above zero, $^+21$

7. 2 floors below ground level, $^-2$

8. Profit of $150, $^+150$

9. 39 kilometers south, $^-39$

10. 5 strokes under par, $^-5$

11. 7 blocks east, $^+7$

12. Price increase of 60 cents, $^+60$

13. Deposit of $28, $^+28$

14. 9 steps backward, $^-9$

15. 500 feet above sea level, $^+500$

Copy the number lines. Use an integer to label each point shown.

16.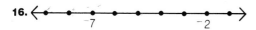

17.

18. ⟨•—•—•—•—•—•—•—•—•—•—•⟩
    ⠀⠀⠀⠀⠀0⠀⠀⠀⠀⠀⠀⠀⁺4

19. ⟨•—•—•—•—•—•—•—•—•—•—•⟩
    ⠀⠀⠀⁻24⠀⠀⠀⠀⠀⠀⁻20

20. ⟨•—•—•—•—•—•—•—•—•—•—•⟩
    ⠀⠀⠀⠀⁺53⠀⠀⠀⠀⠀⠀⁺58

Replace ● with > or <.

21. ⁺6 ● ⁺3   26. ⁺7 ● ⁻7

22. 0 ● ⁺1   27. ⁻11 ● ⁻2

23. 0 ● ⁻8   28. ⁻25 ● ⁺25

24. ⁻3 ● ⁺17   29. ⁺9 ● ⁻37

25. ⁻4 ● ⁻9   30. ⁻82 ● ⁻3

For each exercise, arrange the integers in order from least to greatest.

31. ⁺6, ⁻4, ⁺3, ⁻1

32. ⁻8, 0, ⁻9, ⁺9, ⁺8

33. ⁻2, ⁻10, ⁻7, ⁻1, 0

34. ⁺6, ⁻6, ⁺1, ⁻1, ⁺7, ⁻7

35. ⁻21, ⁻28, ⁺14, ⁺16, ⁻9, ⁻5

Adding Integers

A. Inez was 4 blocks west of the school. She walked 6 blocks east to the bus stop. How far east or west of the school was the bus stop?

4 blocks west is ⁻4.
6 blocks east is ⁺6.

Find ⁻4 + ⁺6.

Use a number line. Find ⁻4 on the number line. ⁺6 is positive. Move 6 units to the right.

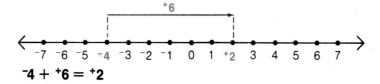

⁻4 + ⁺6 = ⁺2

The bus stop was 2 blocks east of the school.

B. Find ⁻3 + ⁻5.

Find ⁻3 on the number line. ⁻5 is negative. Move 5 units to the left.

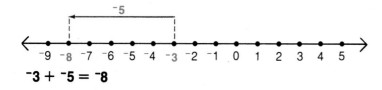

⁻3 + ⁻5 = ⁻8

C. Find ⁺2 + ⁺7.

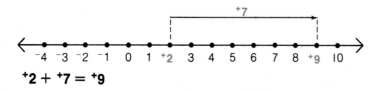

⁺2 + ⁺7 = ⁺9

Use a number line to find each sum.

1. ⁺7 + ⁺1

2. ⁺3 + ⁺8

3. ⁺6 + ⁺7

4. ⁺9 + ⁺3

5. ⁺2 + ⁺8

6. ⁺4 + ⁺9

7. ⁺5 + ⁺7

8. ⁺13 + ⁺4

9. Is the sum of two positive integers positive, or is it negative?

10. ⁻5 + ⁻1

11. ⁻9 + ⁻4

12. ⁻6 + ⁻8

13. ⁻3 + ⁻7

14. ⁻10 + ⁻4

15. ⁻5 + ⁻6

16. ⁻7 + ⁻8

17. ⁻11 + ⁻9

18. Is the sum of two negative integers positive, or is it negative?

19. $^-8 + {}^+3$

20. $^+4 + {}^-5$

21. $^-6 + {}^+1$

22. In exercises 19–21, are the sums positive or negative? In each exercise, is the positive addend or the negative addend farther from zero on the number line?

23. $^+10 + {}^-2$

24. $^-3 + {}^+4$

25. $^+9 + {}^-7$

26. In exercises 23–25, are the sums positive or negative? In each exercise, is the positive addend or the negative addend farther from zero on the number line?

27. $^+6 + {}^-6$

28. $^-2 + {}^+2$

29. $^+10 + {}^-10$

30. In exercises 27–29, what do you notice about the sums? In each exercise, what do you notice about the addends?

Find each sum.

31. $^+8 + {}^+1$

32. $^+20 + {}^+50$

33. $^+13 + {}^+74$

34. $^-6 + {}^-4$

35. $^-30 + {}^-12$

36. $^-65 + {}^-24$

37. $^-6 + {}^+2$

38. $^-40 + {}^+10$

39. $^-24 + {}^+18$

40. $^+4 + {}^-9$

41. $^+80 + {}^-90$

42. $^+57 + {}^-64$

43. $^+90 + {}^-60$

44. $^+85 + {}^-54$

45. $^-10 + {}^+20$

46. $^-17 + {}^+67$

47. $^+75 + {}^-75$

48. $^-36 + {}^+36$

49. $^-10 + {}^-5 + {}^+8$

50. $^+15 + {}^-16 + {}^-3$

**More practice
Set F, page 63**

Find each answer.

51. Gloria was 10 blocks east of school. She walked 12 blocks west. How far east or west of the school was she then?

52. The temperature was 11 degrees below zero. It rose 9 degrees. What was the new temperature?

53. Raul was on the 35th floor above ground. He went down 36 floors. Then what floor was he on?

54. The Garcias were 85 kilometers south of Silvis. They drove 100 kilometers north. How far north or south of Silvis were they then?

55. Inger had $10 in the bank. She made these transactions:
Deposit, $15
Withdrawal, $12
Deposit, $9
Withdrawal, $18
What was the balance in her bank account?

Using Patterns to Subtract Integers

Kiku wanted to find $^+7 - {}^-2$. She knew that $^+7 - {}^+2 = {}^+5$. She wrote these problems and studied the pattern. She used addition to check her answers.

Check

$^+7 - {}^+2 = {}^+5$ $^+2 + {}^+5 = {}^+7$

$^+7 - {}^+1 = {}^+6$ $^+1 + {}^+6 = {}^+7$

$^+7 - 0 = {}^+7$ $0 + {}^+7 = {}^+7$

$^+7 - {}^-1 = {}^+8$ $^-1 + {}^+8 = {}^+7$

$^+7 - {}^-2 = {}^+9$ $^-2 + {}^+9 = {}^+7$

In each exercise, study the pattern. Then give the missing numbers.

1.   *Check*

$^+6 - {}^+2 = {}^+4$ $^+2 + {}^+4 = {}^+6$

$^+6 - {}^+1 = {}^+5$ $^+1 + {}^+5 = {}^+6$

$^+6 - 0 = {}^+6$ $0 + {}^+6 = {}^+6$

$^+6 - {}^-1 = $ ▨ $^-1 + $ ▨ $= {}^+6$

$^+6 - {}^-2 = $ ▨ $^-2 + $ ▨ $= {}^+6$

2.   *Check*

$^+3 - {}^+2 = $ ▨ $^+2 + $ ▨ $= {}^+3$

$^+2 - {}^+2 = 0$ $^+2 + 0 = {}^+2$

$^+1 - {}^+2 = {}^-1$ $^+2 + {}^-1 = {}^+1$

$0 - {}^+2 = {}^-2$ $^+2 + {}^-2 = 0$

$^-1 - {}^+2 = $ ▨ $^+2 + $ ▨ $= {}^-1$

$^-2 - {}^+2 = $ ▨ $^+2 + $ ▨ $= {}^-2$

$^-3 - {}^+2 = $ ▨ $^+2 + $ ▨ $= {}^-3$

3.   *Check*

$^+3 - {}^-4 = {}^+7$ $^-4 + {}^+7 = {}^+3$

$^+2 - {}^-4 = {}^+6$ $^-4 + {}^+6 = {}^+2$

$^+1 - {}^-4 = {}^+5$ $^-4 + {}^+5 = {}^+1$

$0 - {}^-4 = $ ▨ $^-4 + $ ▨ $= 0$

$^-1 - {}^-4 = {}^+3$ $^-4 + {}^+3 = {}^-1$

$^-2 - {}^-4 = $ ▨ $^-4 + $ ▨ $= {}^-2$

$^-3 - {}^-4 = $ ▨ $^-4 + $ ▨ $= {}^-3$

Subtracting Integers by Adding the Opposite

A. For each integer there is an opposite integer. On a number line, an integer and its opposite are equally distant from zero.

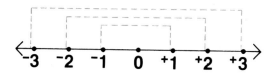

The opposite of $^+1$ is $^-1$.
The opposite of $^-2$ is $^+2$.
Zero is its own opposite.

The sum of an integer and its opposite is zero.
$$^+1 + {}^-1 = 0 \qquad {}^-2 + {}^+2 = 0$$

B. Study these pairs of equations.

$$^+7 - {}^+2 = {}^+5 \qquad {}^-3 - {}^+2 = {}^-5$$
$$^+7 + {}^-2 = {}^+5 \qquad {}^-3 + {}^-2 = {}^-5$$

$$^+6 - {}^-2 = {}^+8 \qquad {}^-3 - {}^-4 = {}^+1$$
$$^+6 + {}^+2 = {}^+8 \qquad {}^-3 + {}^+4 = {}^+1$$

You get the same answer whether you subtract an integer or add its opposite.

■ *To subtract an integer, add its opposite.*

$$^-5 - {}^-1 = \text{▦}$$
$$^-5 + {}^+1 = {}^-4$$

Name the opposite of each integer.

1. $^-9$
2. $^+13$
3. 0
4. $^-45$
5. $^+250$

Change each subtraction problem to an addition problem.

Here's how

$$^+6 - {}^+4$$
$$\mathbf{^+6 + {}^-4}$$

6. $^+7 - {}^+1$
7. $^-5 - {}^-9$
8. $^+10 - {}^-7$
9. $^-2 - {}^+5$
10. $^-1 - 0$
11. $^+8 - {}^-6$
12. $^-11 - {}^-30$
13. $^+16 - {}^+6$
14. $0 - {}^+75$
15. $^-21 - {}^+15$

Subtract.

16. $^+6 - {}^+5$
17. $^+9 - {}^-4$
18. $^-7 - {}^+8$
19. $^-5 - {}^-3$
20. $^+2 - {}^-7$
21. $^-12 - {}^-3$
22. $^+10 - {}^-15$
23. $^+32 - {}^+17$
24. $0 - {}^-53$
25. $^+14 - {}^-8$
26. $^-9 - {}^-11$
27. $^+20 - {}^-10$
28. $^-50 - {}^+30$
29. $^+12 - {}^+20$
30. $^-80 - {}^-50$
31. $^+16 - {}^+38$
32. $^-50 - {}^+29$
33. $^-65 - {}^+28$
34. $^+43 - {}^-36$
35. $^-58 - {}^+18$

More practice
Set G, page 63

Using Subtraction of Integers

If you traveled to the mesosphere from the bottom of the ocean, what would be the drop or the rise in temperature?

Find ⁻93 − ⁺5.

Temperature at destination	Temperature at starting point	Drop or rise in temperature
⁻93	− ⁺5 =	⁻98

The change in temperature would be a drop of 98°C.

Use the temperatures shown. Find the drop or the rise in temperature for each trip. Subtract the temperature at the starting point from the temperature at the destination.

	Destination	Starting point
1.	Death Valley	Great Plains
2.	Bottom of ocean	Mt. McKinley
3.	Mesosphere	Great Plains
4.	Stratosphere	Troposphere
5.	Thermosphere	Mantle
6.	Mantle	Mesosphere
7.	Great Plains	Inner core
8.	Troposphere	Bottom of ocean
9.	Thermosphere	Outer core
10.	Inner core	Mt. McKinley

Thermosphere ⁺1500°C

Mesosphere ⁻93°C

Stratosphere ⁻3°C

Troposphere ⁻56°C

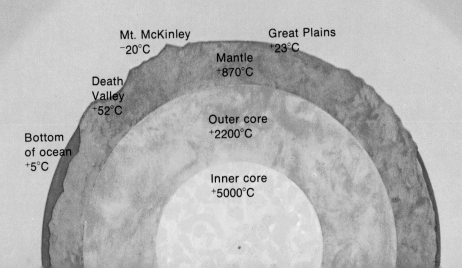

Mt. McKinley ⁻20°C

Great Plains ⁺23°C

Mantle ⁺870°C

Death Valley ⁺52°C

Outer core ⁺2200°C

Bottom of ocean ⁺5°C

Inner core ⁺5000°C

Make a slide rule for subtracting integers.

Cut two strips of paper about 28 centimeters
long and 3 centimeters wide. Mark them as shown.

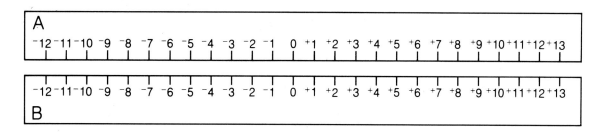

To find ⁻2 − ⁻5, follow these steps.

Find the first
number on the
A scale.

Find the second number
on the B scale. Then
slide the scale so that
the second number is
directly under the first.

Read the answer from
the A scale. The
answer is the number
directly above the
zero on the B scale.

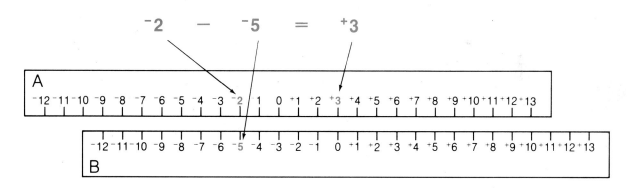

Use your slide rule to find the answers.

1. ⁺6 − ⁺4   4. ⁻3 − ⁻2   7. ⁻5 − ⁺6

2. ⁻9 − ⁺1   5. ⁺7 − ⁻5   8. ⁻12 − ⁻12

3. ⁺8 − ⁻3   6. ⁺9 − ⁺10   9. ⁺8 − ⁺13

Multiplying Integers

A. Complete the pattern.

$^+5 \times {}^+4 = {}^+20$

$^+5 \times {}^+3 = {}^+15$

$^+5 \times {}^+2 = {}^+10$

$^+5 \times {}^+1 = {}^+5$

$^+5 \times 0 = 0$

$^+5 \times {}^-1 = {}^-5$

$^+5 \times {}^-2 = {}^-10$

$^+5 \times {}^-3 = $ ▦

$^+5 \times {}^-4 = $ ▦

■ *The product of two positive integers is positive.*

$^+7 \times {}^+3 = {}^+21$

■ *The product of a positive integer and a negative integer is negative.*

$^+7 \times {}^-3 = {}^-21$

$^-7 \times {}^+3 = {}^-21$

B. Complete the pattern.

$^-5 \times {}^+4 = {}^-20$

$^-5 \times {}^+3 = {}^-15$

$^-5 \times {}^+2 = {}^-10$

$^-5 \times {}^+1 = {}^-5$

$^-5 \times 0 = 0$

$^-5 \times {}^-1 = {}^+5$

$^-5 \times {}^-2 = {}^+10$

$^-5 \times {}^-3 = $ ▦

$^-5 \times {}^-4 = $ ▦

■ *The product of two negative integers is positive.*

$^-7 \times {}^-3 = {}^+21$

Find each product.

1. $^+9 \times {}^+8$

2. $^-9 \times {}^-8$

3. $^+9 \times {}^-8$

4. $^-9 \times {}^+8$

5. $^+6 \times {}^+9$

6. $^+7 \times {}^+6$

7. $^+20 \times {}^+4$

8. $^-5 \times {}^-7$

9. $^-3 \times {}^-9$

10. $^-8 \times {}^-40$

11. $^+8 \times {}^-7$

12. $^+5 \times {}^-6$

13. $^+90 \times {}^-4$

14. $^-6 \times {}^+8$

15. $^-4 \times {}^+8$

16. $^-2 \times {}^+60$

17. $^+12 \times {}^+35$

18. $^-34 \times {}^-96$

19. $^+17 \times {}^-52$

20. $^-24 \times {}^+39$

21. $^-42 \times {}^-68$

22. $^-73 \times {}^+81$

More practice
Set H, page 63

Multiply across.
Multiply down.

23.

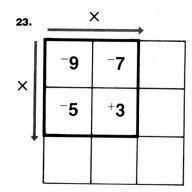

	×	
⁻9	⁻7	
⁻5	⁺3	

24.

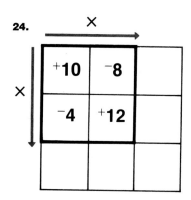

	×	
⁺10	⁻8	
⁻4	⁺12	

25.

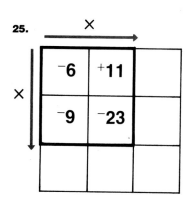

	×	
⁻6	⁺11	
⁻9	⁻23	

TIME OUT

Here are pictures of the same block in different positions.

What color is opposite red?

What color is opposite white?

What color is opposite yellow?

Dividing Integers

Multiplication and division are related. You can learn to divide integers by looking at multiplication of integers.

$$^+5 \times {}^+3 = {}^+15$$

$$^+15 \div {}^+3 = {}^+5$$

$$^-5 \times {}^+3 = {}^-15$$

$$^-15 \div {}^+3 = {}^-5$$

$$^+5 \times {}^-3 = {}^-15$$

$$^-15 \div {}^-3 = {}^+5$$

$$^-5 \times {}^-3 = {}^+15$$

$$^+15 \div {}^-3 = {}^-5$$

■ *If two integers are positive, their quotient is positive.*

$^+54 \div {}^+6 = {}^+9$

■ *If one integer is positive and the other negative, their quotient is negative.*

$^+54 \div {}^-6 = {}^-9$ $^-54 \div {}^+6 = {}^-9$

■ *If two integers are negative, their quotient is positive.*

$^-54 \div {}^-6 = {}^+9$

Find each missing number.

1. $^+7 \times$ ▦ $= {}^+42$
   $^+42 \div {}^+7 =$ ▦

2. $^+8 \times$ ▦ $= {}^-72$
   $^-72 \div {}^+8 =$ ▦

3. $^+6 \times$ ▦ $= {}^-30$
   $^-30 \div {}^+6 =$ ▦

4. $^-8 \times$ ▦ $= {}^-32$
   $^-32 \div {}^-8 =$ ▦

Divide.

5. $^+56 \div {}^+8$

6. $^-56 \div {}^-8$

7. $^-56 \div {}^+8$

8. $^+56 \div {}^-8$

9. $^+36 \div {}^-4$

10. $^+48 \div {}^-6$

11. $^-80 \div {}^+8$

12. $^-36 \div {}^+6$

13. $^-28 \div {}^-7$

14. $^-45 \div {}^-9$

15. $^+70 \div {}^+10$

16. $^+30 \div {}^+3$

17. $^+35 \div {}^+7$

18. $^-40 \div {}^+5$

19. $^+20 \div {}^-4$

20. $^-63 \div {}^+9$

21. $^+45 \div {}^+3$

22. $^-99 \div {}^-9$

23. $^-65 \div {}^-13$

24. $^-343 \div {}^+7$

25. $^-336 \div {}^-56$

26. $^+253 \div {}^-11$

More practice, Set I, page 63

A. Numbers that are multiplied to give a product are called *factors*.

Factor		Factor		Product
6	×	2	=	12
3	×	4	=	12
1	×	12	=	12

The factors of 12 are 1, 2, 3, 4, 6, and 12.

B. A positive number that has exactly two different factors is a *prime number*. A positive number that has more than two different factors is a *composite number*.

Factors of 2 ⟶ 1, 2

Factors of 8 ⟶ 1, 2, 4, 8

2 is a prime number. 8 is a composite number.

The number 1 is neither prime nor composite.

C. Every composite number can be expressed as a product of prime factors.

A factor tree can be used to find prime factors.

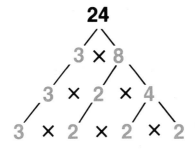

24 = 3 × 2 × 2 × 2

1. List all the prime numbers that are less than 50.

Express each of these numbers as a product of prime factors. Use factor trees to help you.

2. 16

3. 20

4. 66

5. 90

6. 72

7. 125

8. 130

9. 62

10. 148

11. 300

12. 282

13. 1000

Chapter 3 Test
Integers, Pages 48-59

Writing and comparing integers,
pages 48-49

Write the missing number.

1. 500 meters above sea level, $^+500$
   500 meters below sea level, ▦

2. Withdrawal of $30, $^-30$
   Deposit of $30, ▦

Replace ● with > or <.

3. $^+9$ ● $^+7$ 5. $^-3$ ● $^-1$

4. $^+8$ ● $^-11$ 6. $^-5$ ● 0

Adding integers, pages 50-51

7. $^+8 + {}^+7$ 10. $^+4 + {}^-10$

8. $^+9 + {}^-6$ 11. $^-24 + {}^+24$

9. $^-5 + {}^-3$ 12. $^-52 + {}^+17$

Subtracting integers, pages 52-54

13. $^+7 - {}^+9$ 16. $^-10 - {}^+3$

14. $^+8 - {}^-4$ 17. $^-5 - {}^-12$

15. $^-6 - {}^-2$ 18. $^-43 - {}^+29$

Multiplying integers, pages 56-57

19. $^+7 \times {}^+5$ 21. $^-8 \times {}^-6$

20. $^+3 \times {}^-9$ 22. $^-25 \times {}^+14$

Dividing integers, page 58

23. $^+60 \div {}^-6$ 25. $^+49 \div {}^+7$

24. $^-27 \div {}^-3$ 26. $^-160 \div {}^+5$

Problem solving, pages 50, 51, 54

27. José was 10 kilometers south of
    Peoria. He drove 25 kilometers
    north. How far north or south of
    Peoria was he then?

28. The temperature in Milwaukee is
    $^-5$°C. The temperature in Houston
    is $^+15$°C. If you travel from
    Milwaukee to Houston, what is
    the drop or rise in temperature?

Unit 1 Test

Number patterns, pages 4–23

Find the value of each expression when n is 6.

1. $n + 37$

2. $5(n - 2)$

3. $\dfrac{7(n + 8)}{2}$

Compute each answer.

4. $36 - (58 - 42)$

5. $4(23 - 12 + 5)$

6. $93(25 + 75)$

7. $\dfrac{2(34 - 14)}{5}$

Multiply.

8. $\begin{array}{r} 3246 \\ \times \quad 9 \\ \hline \end{array}$

9. $\begin{array}{r} 561 \\ \times \quad 78 \\ \hline \end{array}$

Divide.

10. $8\overline{)73856}$

11. $74\overline{)37444}$

Expressions, equations, and problem solving, pages 26–45

Write a mathematical expression.

12. 7 more than a number n

13. 2 less than a number g

14. 9 times a number k

15. A number w divided by 20

Find the solution of each equation.

16. $d + 28 = 52$

17. $b - 75 = 9$

18. $6h = 108$

19. $\dfrac{m}{4} = 13$

20. $3a + 14 = 50$

21. $9t - 15 = 93$

Find each answer.

22. Jean's leg is 27 centimeters longer than her arm. If her leg is 75 centimeters long, how long is her arm?

23. How long does it take a car to travel 440 kilometers at a rate of 88 kilometers per hour?

24. Doris has 140 green stamps and saves 60 green stamps per week. In how many weeks will Doris have 560 green stamps?

Integers, pages 48–59

Replace ● with $>$ or $<$.

25. $^+7$ ● $^-3$

26. $^-5$ ● $^-2$

Find each answer.

27. $^+11 + {}^-9$

28. $^-16 - {}^+7$

29. $^-8 \times {}^+6$

30. $^-45 \div {}^-9$

More Practice

Set A

Find the value of each expression when n is 138.

1. $n + 85$

2. $356 - n$

3. $n - 99$

4. $76 + n$

5. $284 - n$

6. $n + 491$

7. $530 + n$

8. $n - 65$

9. $427 - n$

Find the value of each expression when w is 243 and z is 192.

10. $w + z$

11. $w + 114 - z$

12. $z + w - 328$

13. $w + z + 84$

14. $z + 547 - w$

15. $w + z - 269$

16. $z + w + 153$

17. $w + 416 + z$

18. $z + 395 + w$

Set B

1. 8×74

2. 65×43

3. 124×4636

4. 14×129

5. 9178×572

6. 463×535

7. 614×43

8. 8354×1675

9. 49×8

10. 729×2808

11. 98×2222

12. $423 \times 94{,}118$

13. $63{,}990 \times 8329$

14. 9828×44

15. $3542 \times 18{,}448$

16. $30{,}967 \times 830$

17. 156×60

18. 8450×155

19. 104×726

20. $97 \times 10{,}179$

21. 892×4868

22. 922×516

23. $17{,}874 \times 91$

24. 2496×3570

Set C

1. $8\overline{)92}$

2. $29\overline{)73}$

3. $109\overline{)863}$

4. $7\overline{)4239}$

5. $158\overline{)20296}$

6. $34\overline{)675}$

7. $29\overline{)7473}$

8. $144\overline{)849}$

9. $5\overline{)36487}$

10. $156\overline{)4661}$

11. $237\overline{)873}$

12. $78\overline{)8227}$

13. $57\overline{)530}$

14. $709\overline{)28071}$

15. $6\overline{)454618}$

16. $48\overline{)71445}$

17. $287\overline{)223772}$

18. $40\overline{)925471}$

Set D

Find the solution of each equation.

1. $d + 22 = 74$

2. $v - 65 = 160$

3. $g + 72 = 95$

4. $97 + w = 261$

5. $b - 42 = 76$

6. $x + 72 = 141$

7. $45 = k - 436$

8. $187 = 95 + y$

9. $n + 40 = 188$

10. $158 = c - 58$

11. $t + 45 = 656$

12. $r - 54 = 184$

13. $15 + d = 90$

14. $142 = z - 37$

15. $195 = 71 + p$

16. $34 + a = 71$

17. $r - 86 = 106$

18. $463 = m - 74$

19. $145 = 59 + t$

20. $e - 57 = 96$

21. $239 = s - 67$

22. $112 = 64 + b$

More Practice

Set E

Find the solution of each equation.

1. $7c = 126$

2. $\dfrac{p}{4} = 19$

3. $529 = 23v$

4. $4 = \dfrac{s}{35}$

5. $36g = 1008$

6. $\dfrac{e}{9} = 13$

7. $204 = 6x$

8. $8 = \dfrac{d}{26}$

9. $11m = 187$

10. $\dfrac{z}{21} = 6$

11. $287 = 41b$

12. $17 = \dfrac{y}{8}$

13. $18r = 216$

14. $\dfrac{k}{16} = 7$

15. $336 = 24n$

16. $9 = \dfrac{w}{13}$

17. $15a = 135$

Set F

1. $^-7 + {}^+11$

2. $^+16 + {}^-13$

3. $^+21 + {}^+24$

4. $^-17 + {}^+3$

5. $^+14 + {}^-21$

6. $^-11 + {}^-24$

7. $^-28 + {}^+18$

8. $^+5 + {}^-20$

9. $^-25 + {}^+13$

10. $^+27 + {}^-18$

11. $^+23 + {}^+6$

12. $^-14 + {}^+20$

13. $^+12 + {}^-2$

14. $^-22 + {}^-26$

15. $^-29 + {}^+17$

16. $^+26 + {}^-8$

17. $^-15 + {}^+28$

18. $^+7 + {}^-19$

19. $^-12 + {}^+22$

20. $^+19 + {}^-23$

21. $^+2 + {}^-6 + {}^+9$

22. $^-7 + {}^-3 + {}^+5$

23. $^-4 + {}^+5 + {}^-7$

24. $^+9 + {}^+6 + {}^-8$

Set G

1. $^-4 - {}^-13$

2. $^+14 - {}^+1$

3. $^+5 - {}^+16$

4. $^-10 - {}^-19$

5. $^-17 - {}^-5$

6. $^+9 - {}^+11$

7. $^+17 - 0$

8. $^-9 - {}^+18$

9. $^-14 - {}^-11$

10. $^+20 - {}^+2$

11. $^-3 - {}^+15$

12. $^-16 - {}^-8$

13. $^+6 - {}^+12$

14. $^-2 - {}^+22$

15. $^-12 - {}^-15$

16. $^+23 - {}^-7$

17. $^+3 - {}^+19$

18. $^+24 - {}^+7$

19. $^+10 - {}^-20$

20. $^-6 - {}^-18$

21. $^-22 - {}^+4$

22. $^+21 - {}^+8$

23. $^+13 - {}^-23$

24. $^-21 - {}^-1$

Set H

1. $^-12 \times {}^+12$

2. $^-1 \times {}^-45$

3. $^+23 \times {}^+18$

4. $^+58 \times {}^-15$

5. $^-19 \times {}^+1$

6. $^+61 \times {}^-20$

7. $^-7 \times {}^+47$

8. $^-23 \times {}^-30$

9. $^+6 \times {}^-37$

10. $^-25 \times {}^-16$

11. $^-42 \times {}^+34$

Set I

1. $^+84 \div {}^-12$

2. $^-54 \div {}^-1$

3. $^-901 \div {}^+17$

4. $^+18 \div {}^+3$

5. $^-594 \div {}^+18$

6. $^-49 \div {}^-7$

7. $^+414 \div {}^-9$

8. $^-986 \div {}^-29$

9. $^+75 \div {}^-5$

10. $^-91 \div {}^+1$

11. $^-21 \div {}^-7$

Individualized Skills Maintenance

Diagnosis

A. 9542 + 498

6179 + 4422

5440 + 3885

B. 9179 − 274

6000 − 1764

8067 − 98

C. 8 × 46

37 × 505

768 × 958

Practice

Set A (pp. 4–5)

1. 7486 + 735
2. 6734 + 271
3. 373 + 3522
4. 469 + 4023
5. 8973 + 327
6. 3784 + 662
7. 491 + 1743
8. 220 + 8652
9. 1693 + 502
10. 1984 + 881
11. 218 + 3733
12. 657 + 8563
13. 8733 + 146
14. 2691 + 496
15. 4386 + 4833
16. 9882 + 6910
17. 1277 + 5075
18. 7123 + 8290
19. 8782 + 2988
20. 2861 + 7586
21. 3269 + 1038
22. 8903 + 9524
23. 7231 + 2406

Set B (pp. 4–5)

1. 2525 − 324
2. 2167 − 94
3. 6790 − 6741
4. 4919 − 992
5. 1379 − 909
6. 8670 − 6146
7. 2910 − 1055
8. 4977 − 3238
9. 2917 − 139
10. 4000 − 76
11. 9404 − 1778
12. 3475 − 2327
13. 7731 − 477
14. 5550 − 98
15. 2298 − 688
16. 4838 − 900
17. 3200 − 54
18. 7240 − 357
19. 3655 − 991
20. 2441 − 1182
21. 3886 − 536
22. 4943 − 2286
23. 9356 − 3806

Set C (pp. 10–11)

1. 9 × 41
2. 5 × 37
3. 7 × 12
4. 8 × 81
5. 6 × 443
6. 7 × 531
7. 8 × 116
8. 94 × 75
9. 29 × 89
10. 63 × 41
11. 19 × 610
12. 21 × 734
13. 31 × 124
14. 82 × 973
15. 51 × 209
16. 545 × 925
17. 865 × 897
18. 451 × 222
19. 298 × 595
20. 775 × 269
21. 803 × 544
22. 314 × 938
23. 572 × 517

Unit 2

Decimals, Exponents, and Metric System

Exponents and Expanded Notation: Whole Numbers

A. $10^2 = 10 \times 10 = 100$

The *exponent* 2 tells how many times 10 is used as a factor.

10^2 is read "ten to the second power."

B. $3^4 = 3 \times 3 \times 3 \times 3 = 81$

"three to the fourth power"

C. $6^1 = 6$

"six to the first power"

■ *The first power of any whole number is that whole number.*

D. $10^0 = 1$

"ten to the zero power"

■ *The zero power of any whole number, except 0, is 1.*

E. The population of Kansas City, Missouri, is 507,087.

Use this place-value chart to help you write 507,087 in expanded notation.

billions period			millions period			thousands period			units period		
hundred billions	ten billions	billions	hundred millions	ten millions	millions	hundred thousands	ten thousands	thousands	hundreds	tens	ones
100,000,000,000	10,000,000,000	1,000,000,000	100,000,000	10,000,000	1,000,000	100,000	10,000	1000	100	10	1
10^{11}	10^{10}	10^9	10^8	10^7	10^6	10^5	10^4	10^3	10^2	10^1	10^0
						5	0	7	0	8	7

507,087

500,000 + 7000 + 80 + 7

(5 × 100,000) + (7 × 1000) + (8 × 10) + (7 × 1)

$(5 \times 10^5) + (7 \times 10^3) + (8 \times 10^1) + (7 \times 10^0)$

Find each answer.

1. 3^2
2. 8^2
3. 4^1
4. 5^3
5. 9^0
6. 2^5
7. 10^1
8. 10^0
9. 10^7
10. 10^5

Write each number using exponents.

Here's how

$5 \times 5 \times 5 \times 5 \quad 5^4$

11. 7×7
12. $8 \times 8 \times 8$
13. $10 \times 10 \times 10$
14. $9 \times 9 \times 9 \times 9 \times 9$
15. 6

Give the missing exponent.

16. $27 = 3^{\blacksquare}$
17. $144 = 12^{\blacksquare}$
18. $16 = 2^{\blacksquare}$
19. $1000 = 10^{\blacksquare}$
20. $10,000 = 10^{\blacksquare}$
21. $100,000 = 10^{\blacksquare}$
22. $1,000,000 = 10^{\blacksquare}$

Write each number in expanded notation using exponents.

	City	Population
23.	Hammerfest, Norway	7248
24.	Anchorage, Alaska	48,081
25.	Würzburg, Germany	120,309
26.	Honolulu, Hawaii	324,871
27.	Memphis, Tennessee	623,530
28.	Warsaw, Poland	1,279,600
29.	Bombay, India	5,970,500
30.	London, England	7,393,600

	Continent	Population
31.	Oceania	21,666,000
32.	Europe	636,529,000
33.	Asia	2,075,726,000

Exponents and Expanded Notation: Decimal Numbers

A. You can use *negative exponents* to write powers of 10.

$$.1 = 10^{-1}$$

$$.01 = 10^{-2}$$

$$.001 = 10^{-3}$$

$$.0001 = 10^{-4}$$

$$.00001 = 10^{-5}$$

Notice that the negative exponent helps you tell how many digits there are to the right of the decimal point.

B. The atomic weight of the gas helium is 4.0026.

Use this place-value chart to help you write 4.0026 in expanded notation.

hundreds	tens	ones	tenths	hundredths	thousandths	ten thousandths	hundred thousandths	millionths	ten millionths	hundred millionths
100	10	1	.1	.01	.001	.0001	.00001	.000001	.0000001	.00000001
10^2	10^1	10^0	10^{-1}	10^{-2}	10^{-3}	10^{-4}	10^{-5}	10^{-6}	10^{-7}	10^{-8}
		4.	0	0	2	6				

4.0026

$$4 + .002 + .0006$$

$$(4 \times 1) + (2 \times .001) + (6 \times .0001)$$

$$(4 \times 10^0) + (2 \times 10^{-3}) + (6 \times 10^{-4})$$

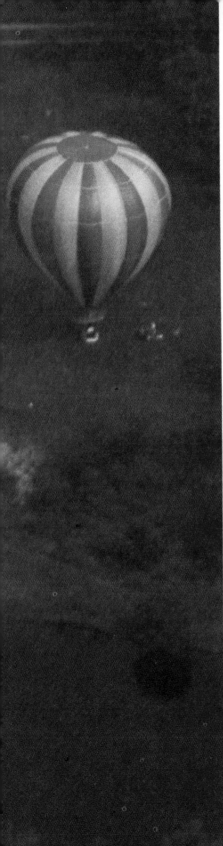

Write each number as a decimal.

1. 10^{-3}
2. 10^{-5}
3. 10^{-1}
4. 10^{-6}
5. 10^{-2}
6. 10^{-8}
7. 10^{-4}
8. 10^{-7}

Write each decimal as a power of 10.

9. .0001
10. .01
11. .001
12. .1
13. .00001
14. .0000001
15. .00000001
16. .000001

Write each number in expanded notation using exponents.

	Chemical element	Atomic number
17.	Calcium	40.08
18.	Nickel	58.71
19.	Carbon	12.011
20.	Mercury	200.59
21.	Silicon	28.086
22.	Hydrogen	1.0079
23.	Nitrogen	14.0067
24.	Oxygen	15.9994
25.	Magnesium	54.9380
26.	Sodium	22.98977

Pagel 98

Multiplying Powers of 10

A. $1000 \times 100 = 100{,}000$

$10^3 \times 10^2 = 10^5$ $\quad$ $10^{3+2} = 10^5$

B. $.001 \times .1 = .0001$

$10^{-3} \times 10^{-1} = 10^{-4}$ $\quad$ $10^{-3+-1} = 10^{-4}$

C. $.01 \times 1000 = 10$

$10^{-2} \times 10^3 = 10^1$ $\quad$ $10^{-2+3} = 10^1$

■ *To multiply powers of 10, add the exponents.*

Find each missing exponent.

1. $10^4 \times 10^5 = 10^{\square}$
2. $10^2 \times 10^2 = 10^{\square}$
3. $10^3 \times 10^1 = 10^{\square}$
4. $10^2 \times 10^4 = 10^{\square}$
5. $10^0 \times 10^3 = 10^{\square}$
6. $10^{-1} \times 10^{-2} = 10^{\square}$
7. $10^{-3} \times 10^{-4} = 10^{\square}$
8. $10^{-2} \times 10^0 = 10^{\square}$
9. $10^{-3} \times 10^4 = 10^{\square}$
10. $10^2 \times 10^{-3} = 10^{\square}$
11. $10^{-3} \times 10^3 = 10^{\square}$
12. $10^0 \times 10^{-2} = 10^{\square}$

Multiply. Write each product as a power of ten.

Here's how

$100 \times 100{,}000$ $\quad$ $10^2 \times 10^5 = 10^7$

13. 10×1000
14. $10{,}000 \times 100$
15. 1000×1000
16. $1{,}000{,}000 \times 10$
17. $.1 \times .01$
18. $.001 \times .001$

19. $100 \times .1$
20. $.001 \times 10$
21. $10{,}000 \times 1000$
22. $1000 \times .0001$
23. $.01 \times 10{,}000$
24. 1×1000

More practice
Set A, page 126

Dividing Powers of 10

A. $1000 \div 100 = 10$

   $10^3 \div 10^2 = 10^1$

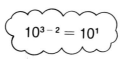
$10^{3-2} = 10^1$

B. $.0001 \div .01 = .01$

   $10^{-4} \div 10^{-2} = 10^{-2}$

$10^{-4--2} = 10^{-2}$

C. $100 \div .001 = 100{,}000$

   $10^2 \div 10^{-3} = 10^5$

$10^{2--3} = 10^5$

■ *To divide powers of 10,*
subtract the exponents.

Find each missing exponent.

1. $10^3 \div 10^1 = 10^{\Box}$

2. $10^4 \div 10^2 = 10^{\Box}$

3. $10^5 \div 10^3 = 10^{\Box}$

4. $10^3 \div 10^5 = 10^{\Box}$

5. $10^4 \div 10^0 = 10^{\Box}$

6. $10^2 \div 10^3 = 10^{\Box}$

7. $10^5 \div 10^{-1} = 10^{\Box}$

8. $10^{-4} \div 10^2 = 10^{\Box}$

9. $10^{-2} \div 10^1 = 10^{\Box}$

10. $10^0 \div 10^{-2} = 10^{\Box}$

11. $10^0 \div 10^3 = 10^{\Box}$

12. $10^{-5} \div 10^{-4} = 10^{\Box}$

Divide. Write each quotient
as a power of ten.

Here's how

$1000 \div .01 \qquad 10^3 \div 10^{-2} = 10^5$

13. $100 \div 10$

14. $1000 \div 10$

15. $1000 \div 100$

16. $10{,}000 \div 10$

17. $10 \div 1000$

18. $100 \div 10{,}000$

19. $.01 \div 10$

20. $.01 \div 100$

21. $.001 \div 1000$

22. $100 \div .001$

23. $10 \div .01$

24. $.01 \div .001$

More practice
Set B, page 126

73

Comparing and Ordering Decimals

A. Compare .78 and .8.

.78 ⬤ .8

.78 < .80

.78 < .8

> .8 = .80
> Seventy-eight hundredths
> is less than
> eighty hundredths.

B. Compare .423 and .42.

.423 ⬤ .42

.423 > .420

.423 > .42

> .42 = .420
> Four hundred twenty-three
> thousandths is greater
> than four hundred twenty
> thousandths.

Replace ⬤ with >, <, or =.

1. .23 ⬤ .24
2. .49 ⬤ .48
3. .2 ⬤ .28
4. .5 ⬤ .59
5. .2 ⬤ .33
6. .6 ⬤ .59
7. 2.68 ⬤ 2.62
8. .616 ⬤ .619
9. .315 ⬤ .311
10. .4096 ⬤ .4089
11. .903 ⬤ .9030

12. .071 ⬤ .017
13. .304 ⬤ .403
14. 5.06 ⬤ 5.060
15. .8 ⬤ .800
16. 765.1 ⬤ 76.51
17. .190 ⬤ .20
18. 6.74 ⬤ 6.749
19. .9030 ⬤ .9003
20. .87 ⬤ .8700
21. .8142 ⬤ .8412
22. .5730 ⬤ .5370

74

For each exercise, arrange the numbers in order from least to greatest.

23. 6.85 7.05 6.83 7.16

24. .503 .530 .529 .513

25. .7132 .7213 .7123

26. .080 .810 .008 .018

Here are some finishing times in the women's speed skating events in the 1972 winter Olympics. The time 4:52.14 is read "four minutes fifty-two and fourteen hundredths seconds."

For each exercise, list the skaters and their times in order. Begin with the lowest time.

27. 500 meters

Vera Krasnova	44.01
Ludmilla Titova	44.45
Anne Henning	43.33

28. 1000 meters

Monika Pflug	1:31.40
Anne Henning	1:31.62
Atje Keulen-Deelstra	1:31.61

29. 1500 meters

Stien Baas-Kaiser	2:21.05
Dianne Holum	2:20.85
Atje Keulen-Deelstra	2:22.05

30. 3000 meters

Dianne Holum	4:58.67
Atje Keulen-Deelstra	4:59.91
Stien Baas-Kaiser	4:52.14

LABORATORY ACTIVITY

Form five-member relay teams. Have each team member push a pencil eraser with his or her nose across a desk.

Using a stopwatch or a clock with a second hand, record the total time for each team to move the eraser across the desk five times. If the eraser falls on the floor, that team member must push the eraser across the desk again.

The winner is the team with the shortest total time. Which team won? Which team was second? Third? Fourth?

Rounding Decimals

A. Round 2.3481 to the nearest thousandth.

Look at the digit directly to the right of the thousandths place. Is that digit less than 5? It is, so round *down*.

$\downarrow$

2.3481

2.3481 ≈ 2.348

B. Round .8673 to the nearest hundredth.

Look at the digit directly to the right of the hundredths place. Is that digit 5 or more? It is, so round *up*.

$\downarrow$

.8673

.8673 ≈ .87

Round to the nearest tenth.

1. 4.83	**5.** 4.09
2. .55	**6.** 5.555
3. 313.77	**7.** .46516
4. 402.575	**8.** .907

Round to the nearest hundredth.

9. 13.255	**13.** 215.9256
10. 71.341	**14.** .06437
11. 6.008	**15.** 10.1058
12. .7193	**16.** .00835

Round to the nearest thousandth.

17. 100.0063	**21.** 3.2165
18. 82.6814	**22.** .83671
19. 12.0322	**23.** .62041
20. 1.7815	**24.** 4.00054

In the FORTRAN IV programming language, the programmer determines the number of decimal places in the answer to be printed by the computer. For example, the symbol F6.3 instructs the computer to print the answer with three decimal places.

The symbol F8.4 means the answer should have four decimal places.

This table shows how some answers would be written in FORTRAN IV programming language.

Result of computation	FORTRAN IV symbol	Number printed by computer
6.3785	F10.2	6.38
2.1460	F5.2	2.15
0.8340	F6.3	.834
1.68752	F8.4	1.6875

How many decimal places will be printed for each symbol?

1. F4.1
2. F10.4
3. F9.2
4. F12.7
5. F7.3
6. F8.5

Complete the table.

	Result of computation	FORTRAN IV symbol	Number printed by computer
7.	12.63	F6.1	
8.	14.863	F8.2	
9.	11.9750	F7.2	
10.	2.361	F5.1	
11.	7.4874	F9.3	
12.	3.60567	F10.3	
13.	1.60783	F12.4	
14.	1.005865	F11.5	
15.	2.010101	F9.5	

NUMBER	ROUNDED NUMBER
19.51	19.5
15.782	15.78
10.9640	10.96
3.471	3.5
8.9433	8.943
4.30867	4.309
1.61481	1.6148
1.003782	1.00378
8.909000	8.90900

Multiplying by Negative and Positive Powers of 10

A. The star Epsilon Eridani is .000025 times as bright as the sun. The star Sirius A is 1000 times as bright as Epsilon Eridani. Sirius A is how many times as bright as the sun?

Find $1000 \times .000025$.

$$1000 \times .000025 = .025$$

Sirius A is .025 times as bright as the sun.

Notice that 1000 is 10^3. To multiply .000025 by 10^3, move the decimal point three places to the right.

$$10^3 \times .000025 = .025$$ .000025

B. The star Lalande 21185 is .04 times as bright as the sun. Barnard's Star is .01 times as bright as Lalande. Barnard's Star is how many times as bright as the sun?

Find $.01 \times .04$.

$$.01 \times .04 = .0004$$

Barnard's Star is .0004 times as bright as the sun.

Notice that .01 is 10^{-2}. To multiply .04 by 10^{-2}, move the decimal point two places to the left.

$$10^{-2} \times .04 = .0004$$ 00.04

■ To multiply a decimal by a positive power of 10, move the decimal point to the right the number of places indicated by the exponent of 10.

■ To multiply a decimal by a negative power of 10, move the decimal point to the left the number of places indicated by the exponent of 10.

Multiply.

1. 45.3×10^1
2. 1.86×10^1
3. 9.35×10^2
4. $.652 \times 10^2$
5. $.5 \times 10^2$
6. 4.683×10^3
7. 2.0064×10^3
8. $.2895 \times 10^4$
9. 6.308×10^4
10. $.470316 \times 10^5$
11. $.296 \times 10^5$
12. $.001 \times 10^1$
13. $10^3 \times .4634$
14. $10^6 \times .0001$
15. $10^4 \times 64.329$

16. 6.3×10^{-1}
17. $.45 \times 10^{-1}$
18. 36.4×10^{-2}
19. 8.1×10^{-2}
20. 156.2×10^{-3}
21. 70.3×10^{-3}
22. 7184.3×10^{-4}
23. 12.55×10^{-4}
24. 8063.1×10^{-5}
25. 9.784×10^{-3}
26. $.217 \times 10^{-4}$
27. 92.35×10^{-2}
28. $10^{-1} \times .8$
29. $10^{-3} \times 67.5$
30. $10^{-6} \times 684.2$

31. The star Epsilon Eridani is .000025 times as bright as the sun. The star Ross 128 is 10 times as bright as Epsilon Eridani. Ross 128 is how many times as bright as the sun?

32. The star 61 Cygni B is .033 times as bright as the sun. The star Luyten 726-8B is .001 times as bright as 61 Cygni B. Luyten 726-8B is how many times as bright as the sun?

33. The star Sirius B is .0017 times as bright as the sun. The star Procyon A is 100 times as bright as Sirius B. Procyon A is how many times as bright as the sun?

34. The star Epsilon Indi is .1 times as bright as the sun. The star Ross 248 is .001 times as bright as Epsilon Indi. Ross 248 is how many times as bright as the sun?

Scientific Notation: Large Numbers

Very large numbers are sometimes expressed in *scientific notation*.

A. The customers of a large power company used 117,000,000 kilowatt hours of electric power on September 18, 1974.

Here is 117,000,000 expressed in scientific notation.

$$1.17 \times 10^8$$

■ *A number written in scientific notation is a number between 1 and 10 multiplied by a power of 10.*

B. The customers of the same power company used 161,000,000 kilowatt hours of electric power on April 3, 1974.

Express 161,000,000 in scientific notation.

Place the decimal point to get a number between 1 and 10.   **1.61**

Count the digits from the decimal point in 1.61 to the decimal point in 161,000,000.

1.61000000

moved 8 digits

The number of digits the decimal point was moved is the exponent of 10.

$$10^8$$

Express the original number as a product of 1.61 and the power of 10.

$$1.61 \times 10^8$$

The number 161,000,000 expressed in scientific notation is 1.61×10^8.

In each exercise, tell whether the number is expressed in scientific notation.

1. 23,500

2. 6.89×10^2

3. 14.85×10^3

4. $.48 \times 10^2$

5. 1.367×10^5

6. 5.0×10^3

7. 18×10^4

8. 324.95×10^3

9. 1.06378×10^8

Give each missing exponent.

10. $7400 = 7.4 \times 10^{\blacksquare}$

11. $313,000 = 3.13 \times 10^{\blacksquare}$

12. $560,000 = 5.6 \times 10^{\blacksquare}$

13. $406,300 = 4.063 \times 10^{\blacksquare}$

14. $7,540,000 = 7.54 \times 10^{\blacksquare}$

15. $9,019,000 = 9.019 \times 10^{\blacksquare}$

16. $84,300,000 = 8.43 \times 10^{\blacksquare}$

17. $561,000,000 = 5.61 \times 10^{\blacksquare}$

18. $4,960,000,000 = 4.96 \times 10^{\blacksquare}$

Write each number in scientific notation.

Here's how

830,000 8.3×10^5

19. 3600

20. 49,400

21. 80,100

22. 579,200

23. 3,083,000

24. 72,651,000

25. 260,000,000

26. 5,230,000,000

★ 27. 1415.9

★ 28. 96,481.7

Here are more data on the number of kilowatt hours used by customers of the power company. Write each number in scientific notation.

	Date	Kilowatt hours
29.	August 27, 1973	250,000,000
30.	July 19, 1974	237,000,000
31.	September 18, 1974	167,000,000
32.	September 1–7, 1974	1,013,961,000
33.	September 1–30, 1974	4,674,040,000

**More practice
Set C, page 126**

Scientific Notation: Numbers Between 0 and 1

Scientific notation can also be used to express very small numbers.

A. The average wavelength of infrared light is 0.000001407 meter.

Here is .000001407 written in scientific notation.

$$1.407 \times 10^{-6}$$

B. The average wavelength of ultraviolet light is 0.000000268 meter.

Express .000000268 in scientific notation.

Place the decimal point to get a number between 1 and 10.	**2.68**
Count the digits from the decimal point in 2.68 to the decimal point in .000000268.	**0000002.68** **moved 7 digits**
For the exponent of 10, use the negative of the number of the digits the decimal point was moved.	10^{-7}
Express the original number as a product of 2.68 and the power of 10.	2.68×10^{-7}

The number .000000268 expressed in scientific notation is 2.68×10^{-7}.

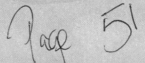

In each exercise, tell whether the number is expressed in scientific notation.

1. .00458

2. 3.15×10^{-3}

3. 78.82×10^{-4}

4. 8.0×10^{-6}

5. $.09 \times 10^{-3}$

6. 1.0607×10^{-5}

7. 61.3

8. 4.8592×10^{-3}

9. $.7316 \times 10^{-3}$

Give each missing exponent.

10. $.00046 = 4.6 \times 10^{\blacksquare}$

11. $.0000575 = 5.75 \times 10^{\blacksquare}$

12. $.000817 = 8.17 \times 10^{\blacksquare}$

13. $.000093 = 9.3 \times 10^{\blacksquare}$

14. $.000000682 = 6.82 \times 10^{\blacksquare}$

15. $.00000914 = 9.14 \times 10^{\blacksquare}$

16. $.000000025 = 2.5 \times 10^{\blacksquare}$

17. $.0000000001 = 1.0 \times 10^{\blacksquare}$

18. $.000000009 = 9.0 \times 10^{\blacksquare}$

Write each number in scientific notation.

Here's how

.000017 1.7×10^{-5}

19. .123

20. .0408

21. .00915

22. .000062

23. .00000173

24. .0000086

25. .00000005

26. .000000257

27. .000000001

28. .0000060841

This table lists the average wavelength of some kinds of radiation. Write each number in scientific notation.

	Kind of radiation	Average wavelength (meters)
29.	violet	0.000000394
30.	blue	0.000000508
31.	yellow	0.00000058
32.	red	0.000000659
33.	X rays	0.000000000482
34.	gamma rays	0.000000000065

**More practice
Set D, page 126**

Chapter 4 Test
Decimals and Exponents, Pages 68-83

Exponents and expanded notation, pages 68-71

Find each answer.

1. 3^4

3. 10^{-2}

2. 6^0

4. 10^{-4}

Give the missing exponent.

5. $36 = 6^{\text{⬚}}$

6. $.001 = 10^{\text{⬚}}$

Write each number in expanded notation using exponents.

7. 726,004

8. 55.10429

Multiplying and dividing powers of 10, pages 72-73

Multiply.

9. $10^3 \times 10^1$

11. $10^{-5} \times 10^0$

10. $10^6 \times 10^{-2}$

12. $10^{-3} \times 10^{-4}$

Divide.

13. $10^6 \div 10^2$

15. $10^5 \div 10^{-1}$

14. $10^{-4} \div 10^3$

16. $10^{-3} \div 10^{-2}$

Comparing, ordering, and rounding decimals, pages 74-76

Replace ⬤ with >, <, or =.

17. 6.3 ⬤ 6.35

18. .05 ⬤ .050

For each exercise, arrange the numbers from least to greatest.

19. 3.13   1.31   3.31   1.33

20. .608   .6081   .6008   .60081

Round to the nearest hundredth.

21. .361

22. .5088

Multiplying decimals by powers of 10, pages 78-79

Multiply.

23. 2.874×10^2

25. 6057.4×10^{-3}

24. $10^3 \times 12.81$

26. $10^{-4} \times 964.1$

Scientific notation, pages 80-83

Write each number in scientific notation.

27. 69,580,000,

29. .000085

28. 203,000,000

30. .000000675

Adding and Subtracting Decimals

Precipitation Record for Greeley, Colorado

Month	Snowfall (centimeters)	Total precipitation (centimeters)
November	40.6	4.10
December	27.0	2.67
January	9.7	0.90
February	5.0	0.58
March	26.4	3.84
April	31.0	8.13

The total precipitation for each month includes snowfall and all other forms of precipitation. About 10 centimeters of snow is equivalent to 1 centimeter of precipitation.

A. What was the total snowfall for January through April?

Find 9.7 + 5.0 + 26.4 + 31.0.

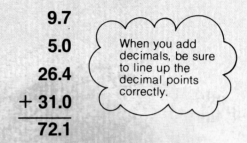

```
  9.7
  5.0
 26.4
+31.0
─────
 72.1
```

When you add decimals, be sure to line up the decimal points correctly.

The total snowfall for January through April was 72.1 centimeters.

B. The total snowfall for the previous January through April was 91 centimeters. How much more snow fell that year?

Find 91 − 72.1.

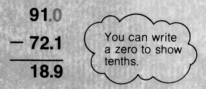

```
 91.0
−72.1
─────
 18.9
```

You can write a zero to show tenths.

18.9 centimeters more snow fell during the previous January through April.

Add.

1. $14.2 + 18.6 + .3$

2. $1.9 + 12.8 + .2$

3. $6.6 + .4 + 21.6 + .3$

4. $18.43 + .77 + .06$

5. $8.92 + 9.82 + 14.11$

6. $1.101 + .027 + 15.989$

7. $.003 + .014 + .533$

8. $9.8 + 18.1 + .44$

9. $.017 + .423 + .718$

10. $3.471 + .083 + .45$

11. $.003 + 1.285 + 7.9111$

12. $.000002 + .00053$

13. $.0055 + 1.8822$

14. $16.4 + 488.32 + .0101$

15. $2395.87 + 342.146$

Subtract.

16. $2.7 - 1.3$

17. $4.8 - 2.2$

18. $36.28 - 5.12$

19. $49.96 - 27.35$

20. $6.17 - 3.29$

21. $9.35 - 4.7$

22. $.638 - .23$

23. $.9 - .49$

24. $.6 - .15$

25. $14.73 - 8.125$

26. $8.21 - 3.756$

27. $.06 - .004$

28. $9.08 - 6.007$

29. $36.326 - 13.0413$

30. $98.581 - 55.08$

Find each answer. Use the table on page 86.

31. What was the total snowfall in Greeley for November and December?

32. What was the total snowfall for November through April?

33. How much more snow fell in April than in January?

34. What was the total precipitation for November through April?

35. How much more total precipitation was recorded in April than in February?

36. How much more total precipitation was recorded in March and April than in November through February?

**More practice
Set E, page 126**

Using Equations to Solve Problems

A. On Monday, 11.52 centimeters of snow fell at Big Timber Ski Resort. This made the total snowfall for the season 243.65 centimeters. What had been the total snowfall before Monday?

Snowfall before Monday	Snowfall on Monday	New total

Write an equation.

$$d + 11.52 = 243.65$$

Find d. Since 11.52 is added to d, subtract 11.52 from both sides of the equation.

$$d + 11.52 - 11.52 = 243.65 - 11.52$$

$$d = 232.13$$

Answer the question.

The total snowfall before Monday had been 232.13 centimeters.

B. On Tuesday, from noon to 4 P.M., the temperature on the slopes dropped 4.8°C. Then the temperature was 1.9°C. What had the temperature been at noon?

Noon temperature	Decrease in temperature	4 P.M. temperature

Write an equation.

$$t \quad - \quad 4.8 = 1.9$$

Find t. Since 4.8 is subtracted from t, add 4.8 to both sides of the equation.

$$t - 4.8 \quad + \quad 4.8 = 1.9 + 4.8$$

$$t = 6.7$$

Answer the question.

The temperature had been 6.7°C at noon.

Solve each equation.

1. $3.7 + a = 5.2$

2. $2.8 + c = 6.4$

3. $d - 1.1 = 3.4$

4. $p - 2.6 = 4.1$

5. $b + 8.6 = 12.5$

6. $r + 7.7 = 11.4$

7. $t - .3 = 6.1$

8. $a - .5 = 7.2$

9. $2.16 + c = 8.5$

10. $f - 6.02 = 7$

11. $3.29 + x = 9.1$

12. $n - 8.17 = 10$

13. $.006 + y = .1$

14. $p - 2.073 = 5.111$

★15. $.2 - n = .09$

★16. $8.03 - r = 2.15$

Find each answer.

17. One of the chair lifts is 788.5 meters long. The distance from the base to the mid-station is 392.7 meters. How far is it from the mid-station to the top?

18. One Monday the snow base was 87.8 centimeters. The next Monday it was 101.6 centimeters. How much had the snow base increased during that week?

19. Tracy saved some money for her ski vacation. She spent $17.44 of the money, and then had $7.56 left. How much had she saved?

20. The main lodge is 1625 meters above sea level. The summit of the mountain is 2019.6 meters above sea level. How much higher is the summit than the lodge?

Estimating Sums

Mikio is estimating the total cost of the things he bought while the salesperson is finding the actual cost.

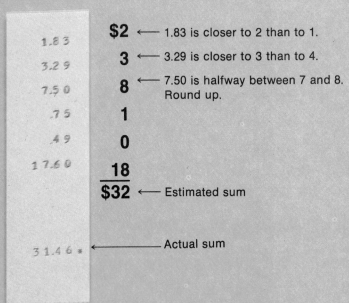

1.83	$2	← 1.83 is closer to 2 than to 1.
3.29	3	← 3.29 is closer to 3 than to 4.
7.50	8	← 7.50 is halfway between 7 and 8. Round up.
.75	1	
.49	0	
17.60	18	
	$32	← Estimated sum
31.46 *		← Actual sum

Estimate the total cost of the purchases on each slip. Then find the actual sum.

1.
1.48
.67
2.39
1.86
3.40
.50

2.
.75
.45
1.25
1.98
.69
.89
1.50
.27
1.38

3.
1.19
2.37
.93
.54
6.10
3.50
1.78

4.
8.02
3.66
2.98
1.29
3.75
6.29

5.
1.89
2.67
.93
.54
6.60
3.50
1.59
.69

6.

1.4 7

4.2 9

2.8 5

.7 9

.2 9

5.4 2

9.6 5

7.

1 6.5 0

7.2 5

9.8 9

1 0.4 9

1 8.7 5

8.

4 1.8 2

2 6.1 4

7 9.5 0

2 3.6 7

2 9.9 5

5 0.2 5

TIME OUT

Using the diagram below, figure out a winning route through the gates to the center. You must start at the outer gate and pass through only six gates. The total number of points must be exactly 138. There is more than one route.

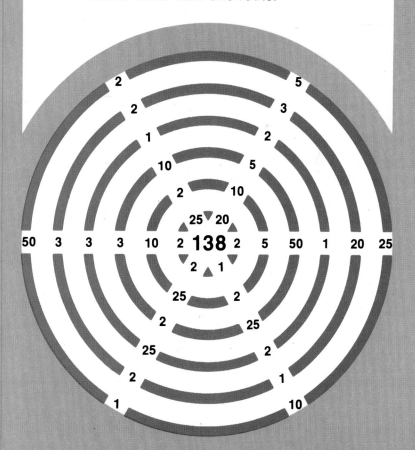

Multiplying Decimals

To multiply decimals, multiply as with whole numbers. The number of decimal places in the product is the sum of the decimal places in the factors.

A.

$$18 \longleftarrow \text{0 decimal places}$$
$$\times .06 \longleftarrow \text{2 decimal places}$$
$$\overline{1.08} \longleftarrow \text{2 decimal places}$$

B.

$$3.64 \longleftarrow \text{2 decimal places}$$
$$\times .83 \longleftarrow \text{2 decimal places}$$
$$\overline{1092}$$
$$29120$$
$$\overline{3.0212} \longleftarrow \text{4 decimal places}$$

When you multiply decimals, sometimes you need to write one or more zeros in the product.

C.

$$.19 \longleftarrow \text{2 decimal places}$$
$$\times .5 \longleftarrow \text{1 decimal place}$$
$$\overline{.095} \longleftarrow \text{3 decimal places}$$

D.

$$.013 \longleftarrow \text{3 decimal places}$$
$$.01 \longleftarrow \text{2 decimal places}$$
$$\overline{.00013} \longleftarrow \text{5 decimal places}$$

Multiply.

1.
$$\begin{array}{r} 23 \\ \times\ .03 \\ \hline \end{array}$$

2.
$$\begin{array}{r} 14 \\ \times\ .08 \\ \hline \end{array}$$

3.
$$\begin{array}{r} 2.5 \\ \times\ .9 \\ \hline \end{array}$$

4.
$$\begin{array}{r} .01 \\ \times\ 9 \\ \hline \end{array}$$

5.
$$\begin{array}{r} 3.27 \\ \times\ .6 \\ \hline \end{array}$$

6.
$$\begin{array}{r} 2.86 \\ \times\ .19 \\ \hline \end{array}$$

7.
$$\begin{array}{r} 5.81 \\ \times\ 1.67 \\ \hline \end{array}$$

8.
$$\begin{array}{r} 6.05 \\ \times\ 5.17 \\ \hline \end{array}$$

9.
$$\begin{array}{r} .003 \\ \times\ 13 \\ \hline \end{array}$$

10. 7.03×2.11

11. $21 \times .001$

12. 3.72×20.2

13. $.012 \times .03$

14. $.082 \times .07$

15. 2.5×6.1

16. 1.61×6.5

17. 2.34×3.42

18. $.23 \times .3$

19. $.002 \times 27$

20. $.013 \times .07$

21. $2.1 \times .0004$

22. 84.3×3.01

23. $3.7 \times .0072$

24. $.94 \times .81$

25. $.85 \times .077$

26. $316 \times .015$

27. $4.013 \times .08$

28. $16.07 \times .005$

29. 12.009×2.8

30. $.0075 \times .41$

More practice
Set F, page 127

Using Multiplication: Anthropology

The chart shows how the lengths of several human bones are related to a person's height.

HEIGHTS (centimeters)
MALE
(2.89 × humerus) + 70.640 cm
(3.27 × radius) + 85.926 cm
(1.88 × femur) + 81.305 cm
(2.38 × tibia) + 78.664 cm
FEMALE
(2.75 × humerus) + 71.476 cm
(3.34 × radius) + 81.224 cm
(1.95 × femur) + 72.845 cm
(2.35 × tibia) + 74.775 cm

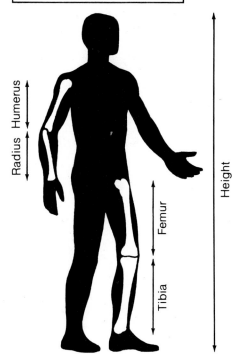

With only a bone as a clue, anthropologists can determine about how tall the person was. For example, suppose a 36.1-centimeter humerus bone is found from a human male. The man's former height can be determined as follows.

(2.89 × humerus) + 70.640 cm

(2.89 × 36.1) + 70.640

104.329 + 70.640

174.969

The man was about 175 centimeters tall.

Use the formulas in the chart to help you find the person's height. Round to the nearest tenth of a centimeter.

1. 40.2-centimeter tibia (male)

2. 45.1-centimeter tibia (male)

3. 31.2-centimeter tibia (female)

4. 38.1-centimeter tibia (female)

5. 20.6-centimeter radius (female)

6. 30.5-centimeter humerus (female)

7. 46.9-centimeter femur (male)

8. 40.8-centimeter humerus (male)

9. 25.7-centimeter radius (male)

10. 39.5-centimeter femur (female)

Using Multiplication: Thickness of Paper

One sheet of notebook paper is about 0.0097 centimeter thick. How thick is a stack of paper with

1. 10 sheets?

2. 100 sheets?

3. 1000 sheets?

4. 10,000 sheets?

5. 100,000 sheets?

6. 1,000,000 sheets?

One sheet of paper in a book is about 0.007 centimeter thick. How thick is the paper in a book with

7. 50 sheets (100 pages)?

8. 150 sheets?

9. 278 sheets?

10. 436 sheets?

11. 904 sheets?

12. One sheet of paper in a telephone book is 0.0068 centimeter thick. How thick is the paper in a book with 816 sheets?

13. An unabridged dictionary contains 1360 sheets of paper, each about 0.006 centimeter thick. How thick are the pages in the book?

14. Each cover of the unabridged dictionary is 0.4 centimeter thick. How thick is the dictionary?

LABORATORY ACTIVITY

Use a sheet of notebook paper.

1. **a.** Fold the paper in half so it is two pieces thick.

   b. Fold in half again so it is four pieces thick.

   c. Repeat this procedure as long as you can, and complete the table.

Number of folds	Number of pieces thick
0	$1 = 2^0$
1	$2 = 2^1$
2	$4 = 2^2$
3	$8 = 2^3$
4	$\blacksquare = 2^{\blacksquare}$
5	$\blacksquare = 2^{\blacksquare}$
6	$\blacksquare = 2^{\blacksquare}$

   d. Could you make more folds if you started with a larger sheet of paper?

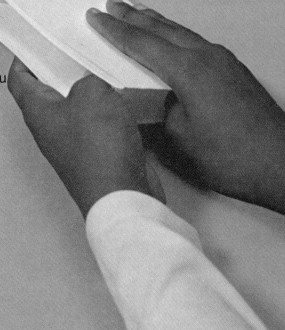

2. Do you see a pattern for finding the number of pieces thick by using powers of 2? If you do, how many pieces thick will it be

   a. after 8 folds?

   b. after 10 folds?

   c. after 15 folds?

3. Suppose that each piece of paper is 0.01 centimeter thick. How thick will the stack be after

   a. 4 folds?

   b. 6 folds?

   c. 10 folds?

4. Suppose that you could make 20 folds. After 20 folds you would have a stack 2^{20} pieces thick.

   a. How many pieces is this?

   b. How thick would the stack be?

Dividing a Decimal by a Whole Number

A. Twelve carnival rides cost $7.20. Find the cost per ride.

Find $7.20 \div 12$.

$$12\overline{)7.20}$$

Place the decimal point for the quotient directly above the decimal point in the dividend.

$$\begin{array}{r} .60 \\ 12\overline{)7.20} \\ -7\,2 \\ \hline 0 \\ -0 \\ \hline 0 \end{array}$$

Then divide the same way you divide whole numbers.

The rides cost $.60 each.

B. The roller coaster ride lasts for 150 seconds ($2\frac{1}{2}$ minutes). Find the cost per second.

Find $.60 \div 150$.

$$\begin{array}{r} .00 \\ 150\overline{)\,.600} \end{array}$$

Sometimes, when you divide decimals, you need to write one or more zeros in the quotient.

$$\begin{array}{r} .004 \\ 150\overline{)\,.600} \\ -600 \\ \hline 0 \end{array}$$

The cost per second is $.004. ($.004 is .4 of a cent.)

Divide. Continue dividing until the remainder is 0.

1. $16.5 \div 5$
2. $4.86 \div 3$
3. $.2 \div 5$
4. $23.32 \div 53$
5. $1.05 \div 7$
6. $214.2 \div 9$
7. $29.16 \div 27$
8. $3.36 \div 48$
9. $139.2 \div 120$
10. $53.04 \div 136$
11. $8.4 \div 15$
12. $737.2 \div 388$

Divide until the quotient is in thousandths. Then give the answer as a tenth of a cent.

13. A package of 60 lemon drops costs $.54. What is the price per lemon drop?

14. A 350-meter spool of thread costs $.70. What is the price per meter?

15. A three-minute (180-second) telephone call between Milwaukee and Minneapolis costs $.90. What is the price per second?

16. A 400-sheet pack of notebook paper costs $.80. What is the price per sheet?

More practice
Set G, page 127

Dividing Decimals by Decimals

A. Find 5.94 ÷ 1.08. Continue dividing until the remainder is 0.

$$1.08\overline{)5.94}$$

Multiply the dividend and the divisor by 100 to make the divisor a whole number.

$$
\begin{array}{r}
5.5 \\
1.08\overline{)5.94\,0} \\
-5\,40 \\
\hline
54\,0 \\
-54\,0 \\
\hline
0
\end{array}
$$

B. Find 8.51 ÷ .0037.

$$.0037\overline{)8.5100}$$

Multiply the dividend and divisor by 10,000.

$$
\begin{array}{r}
2300. \\
.0037\overline{)8.5100} \\
-7\,4 \\
\hline
1\,11 \\
-1\,11 \\
\hline
000
\end{array}
$$

Divide. Continue dividing until the remainder is 0.

1. .35 ÷ .05
2. .105 ÷ .07
3. 7.2 ÷ 1.8
4. 5.684 ÷ 2.03
5. 13.95 ÷ 4.65
6. .567 ÷ .63
7. 2.6 ÷ 1.04
8. .002 ÷ .025
9. 3.1625 ÷ 1.25
10. 105.57 ÷ 1.7
11. 1.065 ÷ 21.3
12. 1.472 ÷ 18.4
13. .3744 ÷ 9.36
14. .02073 ÷ .003
15. .05175 ÷ 4.5
16. .00735 ÷ .525

17. A catalog is 4.5 centimeters thick. It contains 960 sheets. Find the thickness of one sheet of paper.

★ 18. Find the approximate thickness of a sheet of paper in

a. your local telephone book.

b. your mathematics textbook.

**More practice
Set H, page 127**

Rounding Quotients

FILM PROCESSING	
COLOR PRINTS - Cartridge film	
12-exposure cartridge	$3.74
20-exposure cartridge	5.42
COLOR PRINTS - 35-mm film	
20-exposure roll	5.47
COLOR SLIDES - 35-mm film	
20-exposure roll	2.99
36-exposure roll	4.84

Ada paid $5.47 for 20 color prints. Find the price per print. Round to the nearest cent (hundredth).

Find 5.47 ÷ 20.

```
     .273 ≈ .27
20)5.470
  −4 0
    1 47
   −1 40
       70
      −60
       10
```

Divide until the quotient is in thousandths. Then round to the nearest hundredth.

The cost per print is about $.27.

Divide. Round each quotient to the nearest tenth.

1. 3.91 ÷ 12   **3.** 5.17 ÷ .9

2. 1.36 ÷ 1.2   **4.** .3917 ÷ 2.71

Divide. Round each quotient to the nearest hundredth.

5. 17.6 ÷ .7   **7.** 321.11 ÷ 4.6

6. 12.243 ÷ 2.9   **8.** .9137 ÷ .0117

Divide. Round each quotient to the nearest thousandth.

9. 39.1 ÷ .2   **11.** .245 ÷ .09

10. 7.031 ÷ 6   **12.** .7358 ÷ .671

For exercises 13 and 14, round to the nearest cent (hundredth of a dollar).

13. Dan uses cartridge film. Find the cost per print for

 a. the 12-exposure cartridge.

 b. the 20-exposure cartridge.

14. René uses 35-mm film for slides. Find the cost per slide for

 a. the 20-exposure roll.

 b. the 36-exposure roll.

More practice
Set I, page 127

Pages 109

CAREERS Computer Programmer

A computer program is a series of instructions that the computer follows to solve a problem. The person who converts a problem into a set of instructions for the computer is called a programmer. The programmer writes the instructions in a special language; for example, FORTRAN, COBOL, or BASIC.

The program below uses the BASIC language to find the number of amperes (A) of current that flow through a resistance of 9.21 ohms (R) when the voltage (V) is 4.283.

```
10 LET R = 9.21

20 LET V = 4.283

30 LET A = V/R

40 PRINT A

50 END
```

Round to the nearest thousandth.

1. What value will be printed for A when the program is run by the computer?

   The formula $A = V/R$ means $A = V \div R$. To find A, divide 4.283 by 9.21.

For each exercise, find the value printed for A if statements 10 and 20 in the program are changed as shown.

2. 10 LET R = 64
   20 LET V = 115

3. 10 LET R = 98.2
   20 LET V = 18.6

4. 10 LET R = 1.5
   20 LET V = 3.86

Formulas Involving Decimals

A. A one-way coach train ticket from Chicago to New Orleans costs $38.50. The distance is 1477 kilometers. Find the cost per kilometer. Round to the nearest cent.

Use this cost formula.

Substitute values for C and n in the formula.

Cost   Number   Price
         of km   per km

$$C = n \times p$$

$$38.50 = 1477 \ \ p$$

Find p. Since p is multiplied by 1477, divide both sides of the equation by 1477.

$$\frac{38.50}{1477} = \frac{1477}{1477} \ p$$

$$.026 = p$$

Answer the question.

The cost per kilometer is about $.03.

B. The train uses an average of 600 liters of fuel per hour. Find the amount burned in the 17.8-hour trip from Chicago to New Orleans.

Use the fuel consumption formula.

Fuel $\longrightarrow$ $\dfrac{f}{t} = c \longleftarrow$ Fuel consumption rate
Time $\longrightarrow$

Substitute values for t and c in the formula.

$$\frac{f}{17.8} = 600$$

Find f. Since f is divided by 17.8, multiply both sides of the equation by 17.8.

$$(17.8)\,\frac{f}{17.8} = (17.8)\ 600$$

$$f = 10,680$$

Answer the question.

About 10,680 liters of fuel are used.

Solve each equation.

1. $1.1a = 44$

2. $2.3t = 3.68$

3. $.021b = .1071$

4. $1.2m = 1.44$

5. $.63z = 4.41$

6. $.78y = 3.9$

7. $.901r = .1802$

8. $1.8k = .108$

9. $\dfrac{c}{.02} = .12$

10. $\dfrac{d}{.7} = .91$

11. $\dfrac{n}{1.3} = .001$

12. $\dfrac{h}{.5} = .25$

13. $\dfrac{e}{8.7} = 4.3$

14. $\dfrac{t}{3.12} = 18$

15. $\dfrac{q}{28.8} = .16$

Find each answer.

16. A one-way coach ticket on a turbine-powered train between Chicago and St. Louis costs $15.25. The distance is 452 kilometers. Find the cost per kilometer to the nearest cent.

17. The train from Chicago to St. Louis uses an average of 675 liters of fuel per hour. Find the amount of fuel used in the 4.9-hour trip from Chicago to St. Louis.

18. The train travels 452 kilometers in 4.9 hours. How many kilometers does it travel per hour, to the nearest tenth?

19. A one-way coach ticket from New York to Los Angeles costs $147.25. The distance is about 5000 kilometers. Find the cost per kilometer, to the nearest cent.

20. The train from New York to Los Angeles uses an average of 600 liters of fuel per hour. Find the amount of fuel used in the 58.5-hour trip from New York to Los Angeles.

21. The train travels 5000 kilometers in 58.5 hours. How many kilometers does it travel per hour, to the nearest tenth?

Using Scientific Notation to Multiply

Pioneer 10, an unmanned United States spacecraft, was launched March 2, 1972, on a 639-day, 992,000,000-kilometer journey past Jupiter.

A. Pioneer 10 can travel at a top speed of 1.31×10^5 kilometers per hour. At this rate, how far will Pioneer 10 travel in 10^7 hours (about 1141 years)?

Use the distance formula.

Distance   Rate   Time

$$d = r \times t$$
$$d = (1.31 \times 10^5) \times 10^7$$
$$d = 1.31 \times (10^5 \times 10^7) \qquad 10^5 \times 10^7 = 10^{5+7}$$
$$d = 1.31 \times 10^{12}$$

Pioneer 10 will travel about 1.31×10^{12} kilometers.

B. How far will Pioneer 10 travel in 2.5×10^6 hours (over 285 years)?

$$d = r \times t$$
$$d = (1.31 \times 10^5) \times (2.5 \times 10^6)$$
$$d = (1.31 \times 2.5) \times (10^5 \times 10^6)$$
$$d = 3.275 \times 10^{11}$$

Pioneer 10 will travel about 3.275×10^{11} kilometers.

How far will Pioneer 10 travel in

1. 10^4 hours?

2. 10^6 hours?

3. 10^9 hours?

4. 1.3×10^4 hours?

5. 2.1×10^4 hours?

6. 3.2×10^4 hours?

7. 5.2×10^5 hours?

8. 2.4×10^8 hours?

Multiply. Use scientific notation.

9. $(1.8 \times 10^5) \times 10^9$

10. $(4.5 \times 10^2) \times 10^3$

11. $(6.2 \times 10^5) \times 10^2$

12. $(2.1 \times 10^1) \times (1.6 \times 10^4)$

13. $(3.7 \times 10^2) \times (1.8 \times 10^4)$

14. $(5.8 \times 10^4) \times (1.2 \times 10^3)$

★ 15. $(1.9 \times 10^6) \times (4.5 \times 10^{-2})$

★ 16. $(2.4 \times 10^{-5}) \times (3.1 \times 10^{-3})$

Using Scientific Notation to Divide

On July 15, 1972, Pioneer 10 entered the asteroid belt, a region 280 million kilometers wide between Mars and Jupiter.

Width of asteroid belt:

$$280{,}000{,}000 \text{ km} = 2.8 \times 10^8 \text{ km}$$

Speed of Pioneer 10 per hour:

$$131{,}000 \text{ km per hr.} = 1.31 \times 10^5 \text{ km per hr.}$$

A. How long did it take Pioneer 10 to travel through the asteroid belt?

$$\overset{\text{Time}}{\searrow} t = \frac{d}{r} \overset{\text{Distance}}{\nearrow}$$

$$t = \frac{2.8 \times 10^8}{1.31 \times 10^5}$$

$$t = \frac{2.8}{1.31} \times \frac{10^8}{10^5}$$

$$t \approx 2.14 \times 10^3$$

$$\frac{2.8}{1.31} \approx 2.14$$
$$\frac{10^8}{10^5} = 10^{8-5}$$

It took Pioneer 10 about 2.14×10^3 hours to travel through the asteroid belt.

Round this
quotient to
the nearest
hundredth.
↓

B. $\dfrac{3.46 \times 10^{15}}{2.13 \times 10^{6}} = \dfrac{3.46}{2.13} \times \dfrac{10^{15}}{10^{6}}$

$\approx 1.62 \times 10^{9}$

Divide. Round the quotient of the
decimals to the nearest tenth.

Round this
quotient to
the nearest
tenth.

1. $\dfrac{8.4 \times 10^{9}}{2.8 \times 10^{4}}$

2. $\dfrac{7.8 \times 10^{5}}{2.2 \times 10^{1}}$

4. $\dfrac{6.6 \times 10^{7}}{1.4 \times 10^{4}}$

3. $\dfrac{9.3 \times 10^{3}}{7.3 \times 10^{2}}$

5. $\dfrac{2.35 \times 10^{10}}{1.87 \times 10^{3}}$

Divide. Round the quotient of the
decimals to the nearest hundredth.

Round this
quotient to
the nearest
hundredth.

6. $\dfrac{1.7 \times 10^{3}}{1.2 \times 10^{1}}$

7. $\dfrac{4.5 \times 10^{6}}{2.8 \times 10^{2}}$

9. $\dfrac{4.68 \times 10^{10}}{2.11 \times 10^{2}}$

8. $\dfrac{5.55 \times 10^{12}}{1.66 \times 10^{7}}$

★ 10. $\dfrac{3.01 \times 10^{-2}}{2.61 \times 10^{-3}}$

Chapter 5 Test
Decimal Computation, Pages 86–105

Adding and subtracting decimals, pages 86–87

Add or subtract.

1. $13.6 + 5.12 + .005$

2. $2.063 + .0008 + .1$

3. $5.8 + .06 + 15$

4. $12.86 - 5.93$

5. $2.11 - .976$

6. $.09 - .0275$

Multiplying decimals, pages 92–95

Multiply.

7. $45 \times .06$

8. $3 \times .03$

9. 2.6×1.7

10. $2.143 \times .02$

Dividing decimals, pages 96–98

Divide. Give your answers to the nearest tenth.

11. $16.35 \div .5$

12. $3.2 \div 6$

Give your answer to the nearest hundredth.

13. $3.2172 \div .03$

14. $.049 \div 1.6$

Solving equations, pages 88–89, 100–101

Solve each equation.

15. $4.8 + m = 13$

16. $x - .25 = 3.6$

17. $.3a = .63$

18. $\dfrac{n}{.06} = 1.2$

Using scientific notation, pages 102–105

Multiply, using scientific notation.

19. $(2.35 \times 10^3) \times 10^2$

20. $(1.3 \times 10^2) \times (2.5 \times 10^2)$

Divide, using scientific notation.

21. $\dfrac{5.6 \times 10^5}{1.4 \times 10^2}$

22. $\dfrac{4.25 \times 10^7}{1.70 \times 10^3}$

Problem solving, pages 88–89, 100–101

23. Barbara had the oil in her car changed when the odometer read 24,386.7 kilometers. Now the odometer reads 30,009.9 kilometers. How many kilometers has she driven since that oil change?

24. The snowfall in 1973 was 158.3 centimeters. In 1974, the snowfall was 145.9 centimeters. How much less snow fell in 1974?

25. The one-way coach air fare between New York and San Juan is $94.60. The distance is 2575 kilometers. Find the cost per kilometer to the nearest cent.

26. A 747 airplane uses about 11,000 liters of fuel per hour. Find the amount of fuel used in the 3.5-hour trip from New York to San Juan.

36.4 cm

Metric Units of Length

This table shows the relationship of seven metric units of length. The most commonly used units are *kilometer, meter, centimeter,* and *millimeter.*

kilometer (km) 1000 meters	hectometer (hm) 100 meters	dekameter (dam) 10 meters	meter (m) 1 meter	decimeter (dm) 0.1 meter	centimeter (cm) 0.01 meter	millimeter (mm) 0.001 meter
1 km is 10 hm	1 hm is 10 dam	1 dam is 10 m	1 m is 10 dm	1 dm is 10 cm	1 cm is 10 mm	

A. The entries below the table show that each unit of length is ten times as great as the unit to its right. These entries can help you find the relationship between any two units.

1 m = 10 dm

1 m = 100 cm

1 m = 1000 mm

1 km = 100 dam

1 km = 10,000 dm

1 km = 100,000 cm

1 km = 1,000,000 mm

B. The distance between two cars is 1.2 dekameters. How many centimeters is this?

1.2 dam = ▦ cm

> 1 dam is 1000 cm

1.2 × 1000 = 1200

1.2 dam = 1200 cm

It is 1200 centimeters.

■ *To convert from one metric unit to a smaller metric unit, multiply.*

C. The length of a station wagon is 6650 millimeters. How many decimeters is this?

6650 mm = ▦ dm

> 1 dm is 100 mm

6650 ÷ 100 = 66.50

6650 mm = 66.50 dm

It is 66.50 decimeters.

■ *To convert from one metric unit to a larger metric unit, divide.*

Give each missing number.

1. 1 dm = ▦ cm
2. 1 dm = ▦ mm
3. 1 km = ▦ dam
4. 1 km = ▦ dm
5. 1 km = ▦ cm
6. 1 hm = ▦ m
7. 13 cm = ▦ mm
8. 7.5 m = ▦ cm
9. 2.9 km = ▦ m
10. 3.04 m = ▦ mm
11. 1.78 cm = ▦ mm
12. 0.76 hm = ▦ m
13. 63 mm = ▦ cm
14. 807 cm = ▦ m
15. 3816 m = ▦ km
16. 515 mm = ▦ m
17. 0.93 cm = ▦ m
18. 14 dam = ▦ hm
19. 4.6 m = ▦ cm
20. 301 m = ▦ km
21. 76 cm = ▦ mm
22. 76 cm = ▦ m
23. 4.8 km = ▦ m
24. 203 m = ▦ km

Give each answer.

25. Ms. Goldberg commutes 32.4 kilometers per day. How many meters is this?

26. It is 4.5 kilometers to the Jackson Street exit. How many meters is this?

27. The clearance height of the viaduct is 487 centimeters. How many meters is this?

28. The length of a compact car is 4400 millimeters. How many centimeters is this?

Metric Units of Area

Square units are used to measure area.

square kilometer (km²)	square hectometer (hm²)	square dekameter (dam²)	square meter (m²)	square decimeter (dm²)	square centimeter (cm²)	square millimeter (mm²)
1 km² is 100 hm²	1 hm² is 100 dam²	1 dam² is 100 m²	1 m² is 100 dm²	1 dm² is 100 cm²	1 cm² is 100 mm²	

The entries below the table show that each square unit is one hundred times as great as the square unit to its right. These entries can help you convert from one metric unit of area to another.

A. When you convert from one metric unit of area to a smaller metric unit of area, you can multiply.

$6.78 \text{ m}^2 = \text{____} \text{ cm}^2$ (1 m² is 10,000 cm²)

$6.78 \times 10{,}000 = 67{,}800$

$6.78 \text{ m}^2 = 67{,}800 \text{ cm}^2$

B. When you convert from one metric unit of area to a larger metric unit of area, you can divide.

$2{,}457{,}000 \text{ m}^2 = \text{____} \text{ km}^2$ (1 km² is 1,000,000 m²)

$2{,}457{,}000 \div 1{,}000{,}000 = 2.457$

$2{,}457{,}000 \text{ m}^2 = 2.457 \text{ km}^2$

Give each missing number.

1. $1 \text{ km}^2 = \text{____} \text{ m}^2$
2. $1 \text{ m}^2 = \text{____} \text{ cm}^2$
3. $1 \text{ m}^2 = \text{____} \text{ mm}^2$
4. $1 \text{ cm}^2 = \text{____} \text{ mm}^2$
5. $4.32 \text{ m}^2 = \text{____} \text{ cm}^2$
6. $6.7 \text{ cm}^2 = \text{____} \text{ mm}^2$
7. $0.183 \text{ km}^2 = \text{____} \text{ m}^2$
8. $4.35 \text{ m}^2 = \text{____} \text{ mm}^2$
9. $61 \text{ mm}^2 = \text{____} \text{ cm}^2$
10. $372 \text{ m}^2 = \text{____} \text{ km}^2$
11. $6140 \text{ cm}^2 = \text{____} \text{ m}^2$
12. $986 \text{ mm}^2 = \text{____} \text{ m}^2$
13. $1.9 \text{ dm}^2 = \text{____} \text{ cm}^2$
14. $6.85 \text{ hm}^2 = \text{____} \text{ m}^2$
15. $107 \text{ dam}^2 = \text{____} \text{ hm}^2$
16. $358 \text{ dm}^2 = \text{____} \text{ m}^2$

For each postage stamp, multiply
the length times the width to find
the area in square millimeters.
Give the area in square centimeters.

17.

18 mm

29 mm

18.

15 mm

18 mm

19.

24 mm

21 mm

20.

22 mm

18 mm

21.

39 mm

27 mm

LABORATORY
ACTIVITY

1. Cut a piece of string twenty
   centimeters in length. Make
   as many different rectangles
   as you can using the piece
   of string.

   You might want to make
   a table like this one.

Length (cm)	Width (cm)	Area (cm²)
9	1	9
8	2	16
7	3	21

   Which rectangle has the
   greatest area?·

2. Cut a piece of string twenty-
   eight centimeters in length.
   Make as many different
   rectangles as you can using
   the piece of string. Which
   rectangle has the greatest
   area?

3. For a given piece of string,
   what kind of rectangle has
   the greatest area?

Metric Units of Volume

Cubic units are used to measure volume.

cubic kilometer (km³)	cubic hectometer (hm³)	cubic dekameter (dam³)	cubic meter (m³)	cubic decimeter (dm³)	cubic centimeter (cm³)	cubic millimeter (mm³)
1 km³ is 1000 hm³	1 hm³ is 1000 dam³	1 dam³ is 1000 m³	1 m³ is 1000 dm³	1 dm³ is 1000 cm³	1 cm³ is 1000 mm³	

The entries below the table show that each cubic unit is one thousand times as great as the cubic unit to its right. These entries can help you convert from one metric unit of volume to another.

A. When you convert from one metric unit of volume to a smaller metric unit of volume, you can multiply.

$3.75 \text{ m}^3 = \blacksquare \text{ cm}^3$ (1 m³ is 1,000,000 cm³)

$3.75 \times 1,000,000 = 3,750,000$

$3.75 \text{ m}^3 = 3,750,000 \text{ cm}^3$

B. When you convert from one metric unit of volume to a larger metric unit of volume, you can divide.

$408 \text{ cm}^3 = \blacksquare \text{ dm}^3$ (1 dm³ is 1000 cm³)

$408 \div 1000 = .408$

$408 \text{ cm}^3 = 0.408 \text{ dm}^3$

Give each missing number.

1. $1 \text{ dm}^3 = \blacksquare \text{ cm}^3$

2. $1 \text{ dm}^3 = \blacksquare \text{ mm}^3$

3. $1 \text{ m}^3 = \blacksquare \text{ dm}^3$

4. $1 \text{ m}^3 = \blacksquare \text{ cm}^3$

5. $1 \text{ m}^3 = \blacksquare \text{ mm}^3$

6. $1 \text{ cm}^3 = \blacksquare \text{ mm}^3$

7. $1.3 \text{ cm}^3 = \blacksquare \text{ mm}^3$

8. $265 \text{ cm}^3 = \blacksquare \text{ mm}^3$

9. $4.37 \text{ dm}^3 = \blacksquare \text{ cm}^3$

10. $9.7 \text{ m}^3 = \blacksquare \text{ dm}^3$

11. $4.25 \text{ m}^3 = \blacksquare \text{ cm}^3$

12. $313 \text{ mm}^3 = \blacksquare \text{ cm}^3$

13. $96.2 \text{ cm}^3 = \blacksquare \text{ dm}^3$

14. $134 \text{ cm}^3 = \blacksquare \text{ m}^3$

15. $72.6 \text{ dm}^3 = \blacksquare \text{ m}^3$

16. Find the volume of each block by multiplying the length times the width times the height. Then list the volumes in order from least to greatest.

300 mm

240 mm

250 mm

16 cm

40 cm   22 cm

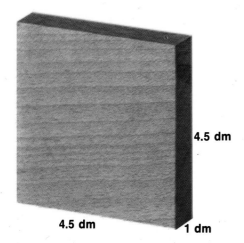

4.5 dm

4.5 dm   1 dm

Complete the table.

	Length	Width	Height	Volume	Volume (m³)
17.	3 cm	3 cm	3 cm		
18.	4.6 dm	3.8 dm	9.1 dm		
19.	48 mm	34 mm	12 mm		
20.	8.1 dam	6.3 dam	2.7 dam		
21.	4 cm	72 mm	8 cm		
22.	9.6 dm	42 cm	184 mm		

Liter and Milliliter

about 1 liter

about 400 milliliters

Liter (ℓ) and *milliliter* (ml) are also metric units
of volume. One liter is equal to one cubic decimeter.
One milliliter is equal to one cubic centimeter.
One liter equals 1000 milliliters.

Match each object in column I with a sensible
measure in column II.

Column I

1. Bathtub
2. Pail
3. Gas tank of an automobile
4. Glass
5. Spoon
6. Swimming pool
7. Thermos bottle

Column II

a. 5 ml
b. 240 ml
c. 1 ℓ
d. 8 ℓ
e. 60 ℓ
f. 400 ℓ
g. 60,000 ℓ

Give each missing number.

Here's how

5000 ml = ▦ ℓ **5**

8. 1700 ml = ▦ ℓ
9. 6000 ml = ▦ ℓ
10. 4.6 ℓ = ▦ ml
11. 0.5 ℓ = ▦ ml
12. 350 ml = ▦ ℓ
13. 8 ℓ = ▦ ml

Metric Units of Mass

about 1 kilogram   **about 35 grams**   **about 900 milligrams**

Kilogram (kg), *gram* (g), and *milligram* (mg) are commonly used units of mass in the metric system.

Kilogram, gram, and milligram are units of mass.

The mass of an object is the same on the moon as it is on the earth. The gravitational force on an object is less on the moon than it is on the earth.

In common usage, the units of mass are often referred to as units of weight. The term *weight* is also used to mean the gravitational force on an object.

Match each object in column I with a sensible measure in column II.

Column I	Column II
1. Volkswagen	a. 95 mg
2. Eyelash	b. 475 mg
3. Tennis ball	c. 56 g
4. Textbook	d. 7 kg
5. Thumbtack	e. 1 kg
6. Bowling ball	f. 41 kg
7. Fourteen-year-old boy	g. 199 kg
8. Tiger	h. 940 kg

Relationship Among the Metric Units

A. A container with a volume of one cubic decimeter holds one liter of water. The mass of one liter of water is one kilogram.

1 dm³
1 ℓ   related measures
1 kg

B. A container with a volume of one cubic centimeter holds one milliliter of water. The mass of one milliliter of water is one gram.

1 cm³
1 ml   related measures
1 g

C. Find the amount of water in the aquarium in cubic decimeters, in liters, and in kilograms.

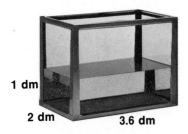

1 dm
2 dm   3.6 dm

Volume = 3.6 × 2 × 1

Volume = 7.2 dm³

The aquarium contains 7.2 dm³ of water. This is 7.2 ℓ of water. The mass of the water is 7.2 kg.

For each exercise, tell which measures are the same amount.

1. 48 ℓ of water

  48 kg   48 g

2. 15 cm³ of water

  15 ℓ   15 ml

3. 64 g of water

  64 cm³   64 dm³

4. 4 dm³ of water

  4 ℓ   4 ml

5. 6.3 kg of water

  6.3 ml   6.3 ℓ

Below are the dimensions of some aquariums. For exercises 6–9, find the amount of water in cubic decimeters, in liters, and in kilograms. For exercises 10–13, find the amount of water in cubic centimeters, in milliliters, and in grams.

6. 14 dm by 13 dm by 8 dm

7. 4 dm by 2.4 dm by 2 dm

8. 4.8 dm by 2.4 dm by 2 dm

9. 3 dm by 5.2 dm by 2.3 dm

10. 50 cm by 20 cm by 10 cm

11. 23 cm by 19 cm by 15 cm

12. 7.6 cm by 7.5 cm by 6 cm

13. 8.3 cm by 9 cm by 6.7 cm

Prefixes in the Metric System

This table shows you the most commonly used prefixes in the metric system.

Prefix	Symbol	Meaning
mega	M	1,000,000
kilo	k	1000
hecto	h	100
deka	da	10
deci	d	0.1
centi	c	0.01
milli	m	0.001
micro	μ	0.000001

You have used most of these prefixes with the units of length, mass, and volume. These prefixes are also used with the following metric units.

Unit	Symbol	Measurement of
second	s	time
ampere	A	electric current

Give the meaning of each symbol.

Here's how

Ms   **megasecond**

1. kA
2. ms
3. μA
4. ks
5. mA

TIME OUT

Sheila has two glasses. One glass holds 500 milliliters. The other glass holds 700 milliliters.

She wants to get exactly 400 milliliters of water. How does she do it?

How would she get exactly 100 milliliters of water?

117

CAREERS Bricklayer

Bricklayers apply mortar between bricks to hold them together.

The mortar consists of one part cement, one part hydrated lime, six parts sand, and enough water to make the mixture soft.

1. If 20.3 kilograms of cement is used, how much lime is needed? How much sand is needed?

2. If 15.5 kilograms of cement is used, how much lime is needed? How much sand is needed?

3. If 87.6 kilograms of sand is used, how much cement is needed? How much lime is needed?

★ 4. If 93 kilograms of sand is used, how much cement is needed? How much lime is needed?

The side of a brick is 20 centimeters long and 10 centimeters wide. The mortar between two bricks is about one centimeter thick.

5. Give the area of one side of a brick.

6. Give the area of two bricks placed side-by-side with mortar between them.

★ 7. Give the area of one row of seven bricks with mortar between the bricks.

Laboratory Activity

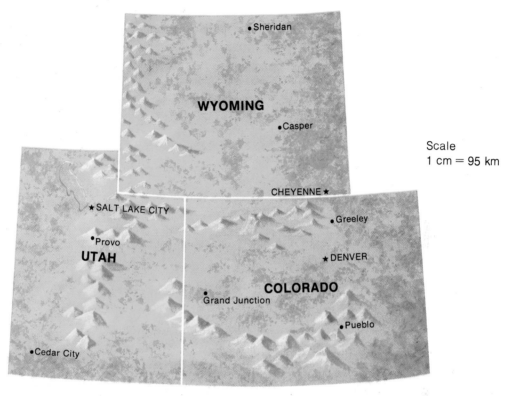

Scale
1 cm = 95 km

Use a centimeter ruler and the scale of the map to help you with these exercises.

1. Give the approximate distance between

   a. Salt Lake City and Casper.

   b. Denver and Pueblo.

   c. Cedar City and Provo.

   d. Cheyenne and Grand Junction.

   e. Greeley and Sheridan.

2. Find the approximate perimeter of each state shown.

3. Find the approximate area of each state shown.

4. Find a map of your state. Find the distance between several cities in the state.

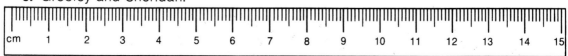

Precision

A. The unit of measure of ruler A is one centimeter.

The goldfish is 6 centimeters long, to the nearest centimeter.

The unit of measure of ruler B is one millimeter.

The goldfish is 58 millimeters long, to the nearest millimeter.

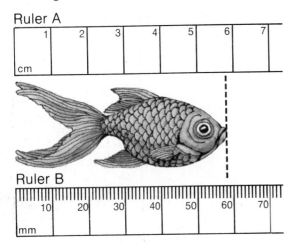

Ruler A

Ruler B

Ruler B is more *precise* than ruler A because the unit of measure is smaller.

■ *The smaller the unit of measure, the more precise the measurement.*

B. After Joni measured the goldfish, she recorded some other measurements in a table.

	Measurement	Unit of measure
Length of blue marlin	2 m	1 m
	1.87 m	0.01 m
Mass of pike	9 kg	1 kg
	9.1 kg	0.1 kg
Length of yellow perch	15 cm	1 cm
	152 mm	1 mm
Length of Atlantic cod	1 m	1 m
	98 cm	1 cm

When 1 meter is used as a unit of measure, the length of the blue marlin is 2 meters, to the nearest meter.

When 0.01 meter is used as a unit of measure, the length of the blue marlin is 1.87 meters, to the nearest 0.01 meter.

The measurement 1.87 meters is more precise than 2 meters because the unit of measure is smaller.

Tell which unit gives
the more precise measure.

1. 1 m   1 km

2. 1 cm   1 mm

3. 1 kg   1 g

4. 1 ml   1 ℓ

5. 0.1 m   0.01 m

6. 1 kg   0.1 kg

7. 0.001 m   0.0001 m

★ 8. 1 m   0.001 cm

For each exercise, give
each unit of measure.
Then tell which measure
is more precise.

9. 5 g   5 kg

10. 3.45 m   4.1 m

11. 2.05 ml   8.64 ml

12. 0.06 kg   0.006 kg

13. 20 mm   20 cm

14. 41 g   8.5 kg

15. 0.604 km   0.84 km

16. 6.4 cm   3.8 mm

17. 1306 ml   24.4 ml

18. 406 kg   398 g

★ 19. 0.93 ℓ   948 ml

★ 20. 6.327 cm   3.4 mm

c. Marie's height to the nearest
0.1 meter is 1.8 meters. Rachel's
height to the nearest 0.01 meter
is 1.67 meters. How much taller
is Marie?

Find 1.8 − 1.67.

$$
\begin{array}{r}
\mathbf{1.8} \\
\mathbf{-\ 1.67} \\
\hline
\mathbf{.13} \approx \mathbf{.1}
\end{array}
$$

nearest 0.1 m

nearest 0.01 m

Round answer to the less precise measure.

Marie is about 0.1 meter taller
than Rachel.

■ *When you add or subtract two measures,
the unit used in the answer should
be the same as the less precise of
the units used in the two measures.*

Add or subtract. Give each answer in
the less precise unit of the two
measures.

21.
$$
\begin{array}{r}
2.81 \ \text{kg} \\
+\ 1.6 \ \ \text{kg} \\
\hline
\end{array}
$$

24.
$$
\begin{array}{r}
2.27 \ \ \text{kg} \\
+\ 1.348 \ \text{kg} \\
\hline
\end{array}
$$

22.
$$
\begin{array}{r}
30.61 \ \ell \\
-\ 13 \ \ \ \ell \\
\hline
\end{array}
$$

25.
$$
\begin{array}{r}
49.8 \ \text{cm} \\
+\ 39 \ \ \text{cm} \\
\hline
\end{array}
$$

23.
$$
\begin{array}{r}
0.0023 \ \ \text{m} \\
-\ 0.00034 \ \text{m} \\
\hline
\end{array}
$$

26.
$$
\begin{array}{r}
14.657 \ \text{km} \\
-\ 8.79 \ \ \ \text{km} \\
\hline
\end{array}
$$

Significant Digits

Sometimes when you work with measures, you need
to know the number of *significant digits*.

Study examples A–E. Then complete the table.
Notice that the significant digits are only those
digits needed to express the number of units
of measure used.

	Measurement	Unit of measure	Number of units of measure used	Significant digits	Number of significant digits
A.	57.35 cm	0.01 cm	5735 units of 0.01 cm	5735	4
B.	0.003 g	0.001 g	3 units of 0.001 g	3	1
C.	46 ml	1 ml	46 units of 1 ml	46	2
D.	520 km	10 km	52 units of 10 km	52	2
E.	520 km	1 km	520 units of 1 km	520	3

1.	0.69 cm	0.01 cm	▦ units of 0.01 cm	69	
2.	82.6 ℓ	0.1 ℓ	▦ units of 0.1 ℓ	826	
3.	0.0004 g	0.0001 g	▦ units of 0.0001 g		
4.	1.05 ml	0.01 ml			
5.	0.3402 mg	0.0001 mg			
6.	25.0 mm	0.1 mm			
7.	4160 km	10 km			
8.	1500 kg	1 kg			
9.	1500 kg	10 kg			
10.	1500 kg	100 kg			

Significant Digits in Computation

A. To the nearest 0.1 centimeter, a rectangle is 17.1 centimeters long and 2.8 centimeters wide. What is the area of the rectangle?

Find 17.1 × 2.8.

$$\begin{array}{r} 17.1 \\ \times\ \ 2.8 \\ \hline 47.88 \end{array}$$

17.1 ⟵ 3 significant digits
× 2.8 ⟵ 2 significant digits
47.88 ≈ 48   Round the answer to 2 significant digits.

The area is about 48 square centimeters.

■ *The product of two measurements should be rounded to the smaller number of significant digits in either factor.*

B. To the nearest 0.01 meter, the area of a rectangle is 16.24 square meters and the width is 3.62 meters. What is the length of the rectangle?

Find 16.24 ÷ 3.62.

Notice that 16.24 has 4 significant digits and 3.62 has 3 significant digits. Round the answer to 3 significant digits.

$$3.62\overline{)16.24\,000} = 4.486 \approx 4.49$$

The length is about 4.49 meters.

■ *The quotient of two measurements should be rounded to the smaller number of significant digits in either the divisor or the dividend.*

Find the area of each rectangle.

These measures are given to the nearest tenth.

1. length: 2.6 cm
width: 1.2 cm

2. length: 24.5 mm
width: 2.8 mm

These measures are given to the nearest hundredth.

3. length: 4.82 km
width: 1.07 km

4. length: 0.73 m
width: 0.58 m

Find the width of each rectangle.

These measures are given to the nearest unit.

5. Area: 39 km²
length: 8 km

6. Area: 375 cm²
length: 26 cm

These measures are given to the nearest tenth.

7. Area: 167.3 km²
length: 14.2 km

8. Area: 0.5 mm²
length: 1.2 mm

Metric units of length, area, volume, and mass, pages 108–116

1 cm = 10 mm
1 m = 100 cm
1 m = 1000 mm

Find each missing number.

1. 6.1 m = ▦ mm

2. 3.9 cm = ▦ mm

3. 47 mm = ▦ cm

1 cm² = 100 mm²
1 m² = 10,000 cm²
1 m² = 1,000,000 mm²

Find each missing number.

4. 6155 mm² = ▦ m²

5. 6.8 cm² = ▦ mm²

6. 237 cm² = ▦ m²

1 cm³ = 1000 mm³
1 m³ = 1,000,000 cm³
1 m³ = 1,000,000,000 mm³

Find each missing number.

7. 385 mm³ = ▦ cm³

8. 1.73 m³ = ▦ cm³

9. 8206 cm³ = ▦ m³

Find the area of the rectangle.

10.

36 mm
11 mm

Find the volume of the prism.

11.

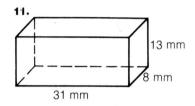

13 mm
8 mm
31 mm

Choose the more sensible measure.

12. Coffee cup

200 ml   20 ml

13. Kitchen sink

4 ℓ   40 ℓ

14. Baseball

224 g   22.4 g

15. Car

773 kg   77.3 kg

Which measures are the same amount?

16. 30 cm³ of water

30 ℓ   30 ml

17. 4.3 ℓ of water

4.3 dm³   4.3 cm³

Precision and significant digits, pages 120–123

Tell which unit gives the more precise measure.

18. 1 mm   1 cm

19. 0.1 m   0.01 m

20. 1 km   0.1 km

Add or subtract. Give each answer to the less precise unit of the two measures.

21.   6.87 m
      + 3.9 m
      ‾‾‾‾‾‾‾

22.   13   cm
      − 4.6 cm
      ‾‾‾‾‾‾‾

Give the number of significant digits in each measure.

23. 92 ml

24. 44.83 cm

25. 0.06 g

Multiply or divide. Round the product or quotient to the correct number of significant digits.

26. 5.8 cm × 9.7 cm

27. 12.6 m² ÷ 4.6 m

Unit 2 Test

Decimals and exponents, pages 68–83

Write each number in expanded notation using exponents.

1. 24,013

2. 661,948

3. .34613

4. 27.159

Multiply.

5. $10^2 \times 10^3$

6. $10^{-4} \times 10^{-1}$

7. $10^{-3} \times 10^1$

Divide.

8. $10^7 \div 10^5$

9. $10^9 \div 10^3$

10. $10^{-3} \div 10^1$

Multiply.

11. $.4938 \times 10^3$

12. 172.1×10^{-2}

Write each number in scientific notation.

13. 4863

14. 804,000

15. .000673

Decimal computation, pages 86–105

Compute.

16. $2.8 + 13.75 + .06$

17. $.0007 + 1.86 + 3.29$

18. $6.03 - 2.6$

19. $.52 - .0089$

20. $19 \times .08$

21. $.35 \times .23$

22. $16.75 \div 2.5$

23. $7.68 \div .03$

Solve each equation.

24. $15.1 + k = 36.9$

25. $n - 4.35 = 7.3$

26. $.8m = .32$

27. $\dfrac{r}{1.5} = 4$

Find each answer.

28. On a toll road, it costs $8.80 to travel 485 kilometers. Find the cost per kilometer to the nearest cent.

29. Juanita paid $3.62 for dinner. Then she had $6.53 left. How much did she have before dinner?

Metric system, pages 108–123

1 cm = 10 mm
1 cm² = 100 mm²
1 cm³ = 1000 mm³

Find each missing number.

30. 85 mm = ▦ cm

31. 0.314 cm² = ▦ mm²

32. 906 mm³ = ▦ cm³

Choose the more sensible measure.

33. Bottle of cola
    500 ml   50 ml

34. Small paper clip
    500 mg   500 g

Tell which unit gives the more precise measure.

35. 1 m   1 cm

36. 0.01 km   0.1 km

37. 1 cm   0.1 cm

Give the number of significant digits in each measure.

38. 14 g

39. 98.37 ℓ

40. 0.03 m

More Practice

Set A

Multiply. Write each product as a power of 10.

1. .01 × 1000
2. 10,000 × 10
3. .0001 × 1000
4. 10 × 10,000
5. .001 × .01
6. 10 × 100,000
7. 1000 × .01
8. 100,000 × 10
9. 100 × 10,000
10. 10 × .0001
11. 1000 × 100
12. .1 × 100,000
13. .01 × .0001
14. 10,000 × .01
15. 100 × 1000

Set B

Divide. Write each quotient as a power of 10.

1. .001 ÷ 10
2. 1000 ÷ .01
3. 10 ÷ 10,000
4. .001 ÷ .1
5. 10,000 ÷ 100
6. .01 ÷ 1000
7. .1 ÷ 10,000
8. 1000 ÷ .001
9. .001 ÷ 100
10. 100 ÷ .01
11. .01 ÷ .01
12. 10,000 ÷ .01
13. .1 ÷ .01
14. 10 ÷ .001
15. 100 ÷ 1000

Set C

Write each number in scientific notation.

1. 720,000
2. 5849
3. 226
4. 574,000,000
5. 9700
6. 2,360,000
7. 547.2
8. 39,000,000
9. 42,000

Set D

Write each number in scientific notation.

1. .00000134
2. .0053
3. .00007435
4. .55
5. .000027
6. .00000086
7. .0421
8. .009576
9. .0007

Set E

1. 8.7 + .00819
2. 72.43 − 48.6
3. .037 + 9.468
4. 6.3 − 2.8
5. .7 + .000564
6. .8 − .37
7. 7.2 + .85
8. .584 − .39
9. .008 + 4.326
10. .063 − .0071
11. .94 + 4.754
12. .4 − .26
13. .025 + .0092
14. 3.8 − 2.1
15. .075 + .8888
16. 61.3 − 36.25
17. .008 + .0009
18. 5.43 − 2.816
19. 36.04 + 5.97
20. 5.04 − 3.006
21. .078 + .8709
22. 30.3 − 3.09
23. 3.9 + .13
24. 22.3 − 14.65

More Practice

Set F

1. .088 × .06
2. 4.5 × .0097
3. 7.84 × 3.89
4. 7.006 × .07
5. 7.18 × 67.3
6. .0064 × .52
7. 4.7 × 4.2
8. 30.03 × 2.85
9. .008 × 16
10. .88 × .74
11. 5.87 × 8.37
12. 42.03 × .007
13. 9.3 × .0008
14. 733 × .012
15. 99 × .001
16. 5.7 × .022
17. 46.7 × 4.03
18. .077 × .03
19. 2.73 × .0054
20. .061 × .09
21. .77 × .042
22. .69 × .6
23. 21.007 × 3.4
24. 7.15 × 2.7

Set G

Continue dividing until the remainder is 0.

1. 5.232 ÷ 6
2. 317.8 ÷ 227
3. .731 ÷ 17
4. 10.85 ÷ 5
5. .2117 ÷ 73
6. 1.87 ÷ 34
7. 3423.8 ÷ 106
8. 4.41 ÷ 3
9. 7.9315 ÷ 145
10. 17.82 ÷ 54
11. 13.692 ÷ 4
12. 13.92 ÷ 348
13. 79.67 ÷ 62
14. 5910 ÷ 125
15. 1.68 ÷ 7
16. 8.424 ÷ 117
17. .1512 ÷ 28
18. 117.6 ÷ 8
19. 71.071 ÷ 91
20. 57.33 ÷ 49
21. 552.64 ÷ 88
22. 671.49 ÷ 9

Set H

Continue dividing until the remainder is 0.

1. 60.49 ÷ 2.3
2. .0121 ÷ .55
3. 3.996 ÷ 1.08
4. 31.35 ÷ 41.8
5. .2244 ÷ 7.48
6. 6.902 ÷ 2.03
7. 261.33 ÷ .62
8. 27.72 ÷ 6.3
9. .657 ÷ .045
10. 1.284 ÷ 32.1
11. 16.017 ÷ 5.7
12. .231 ÷ .003
13. 56.68 ÷ .65
14. 2.144 ÷ 26.8
15. .378 ÷ .54
16. .07875 ÷ 3.5
17. 7.92 ÷ 2.25
18. 1.456 ÷ .04
19. 16.2 ÷ 2.7
20. 21.84 ÷ 5.46
21. .0015 ÷ .025
22. .0171 ÷ .003

Set I

Round each quotient to the nearest hundredth.

1. 4.083 ÷ 8.7
2. .48 ÷ .033
3. 431.75 ÷ 60
4. 9.87 ÷ 2.4
5. 58.725 ÷ 9.2
6. 760.5 ÷ 10.5
7. 5.3 ÷ .77
8. .56 ÷ .83
9. 72.1 ÷ 20.7
10. 45.61 ÷ 9.8
11. .733 ÷ .051
12. 276.8 ÷ 52.3
13. 3.88 ÷ .79
14. 68.36 ÷ 2.56
15. .3725 ÷ .044
16. 4.5 ÷ .83
17. 29.1 ÷ 6.9
18. 183.49 ÷ 5.7
19. .894 ÷ .013
20. 9.207 ÷ .028
21. 7.28 ÷ .0036
22. .046 ÷ .0077

Individualized Skills Maintenance

Diagnosis

A. $5\overline{)3010}$

$8\overline{)19656}$

$9\overline{)8293}$

$7\overline{)35061}$

B. $33\overline{)2871}$

$47\overline{)30174}$

$71\overline{)4986}$

$60\overline{)27513}$

C. $109\overline{)8502}$

$374\overline{)53108}$

$556\overline{)47765}$

$482\overline{)84367}$

Practice

Set A (pp. 18–19)

1. $5\overline{)9580}$
2. $9\overline{)80757}$
3. $7\overline{)9737}$
4. $8\overline{)53672}$
5. $6\overline{)3528}$
6. $7\overline{)33572}$
7. $8\overline{)1832}$
8. $5\overline{)98535}$
9. $7\overline{)9880}$
10. $9\overline{)12778}$
11. $5\overline{)7124}$
12. $6\overline{)87826}$
13. $9\overline{)2863}$
14. $8\overline{)32691}$
15. $6\overline{)8902}$
16. $5\overline{)72313}$
17. $8\overline{)9235}$

Set B (pp. 18–19)

1. $48\overline{)4128}$
2. $32\overline{)93120}$
3. $72\overline{)3528}$
4. $36\overline{)10476}$
5. $24\overline{)9600}$
6. $38\overline{)35720}$
7. $49\overline{)1666}$
8. $93\overline{)71909}$
9. $27\overline{)1500}$
10. $89\overline{)20406}$
11. $76\overline{)3678}$
12. $25\overline{)80010}$
13. $97\overline{)7019}$
14. $29\overline{)10590}$
15. $69\overline{)1696}$
16. $85\overline{)33025}$
17. $62\overline{)3088}$

Set C (pp. 18–19)

1. $856\overline{)5992}$
2. $622\overline{)5598}$
3. $131\overline{)2882}$
4. $779\overline{)12464}$
5. $825\overline{)15675}$
6. $614\overline{)7368}$
7. $294\overline{)6174}$
8. $923\overline{)60095}$
9. $247\overline{)6497}$
10. $416\overline{)36317}$
11. $296\overline{)12878}$
12. $331\overline{)32613}$
13. $135\overline{)9635}$
14. $798\overline{)69626}$
15. $866\overline{)24473}$
16. $495\overline{)79720}$
17. $783\overline{)79333}$

Unit 3

Fractions, Mixed Numbers, and Coordinate Graphs

$$3 \times \frac{3}{4} = 2\frac{1}{4}$$

Equal Fractions

A. The *fraction* $\frac{5}{8}$ gives the width of the nut.

$$\frac{5}{8}$$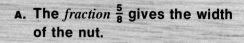

5 ⟵ Numerator

8 ⟵ Denominator

B. The fraction $\frac{10}{16}$ also gives the width of the nut. $\frac{5}{8}$ and $\frac{10}{16}$ are *equal fractions*.

$$\frac{5}{8} = \frac{10}{16}$$

■ *You can multiply or divide the numerator and the denominator of a fraction by the same number to find an equal fraction.*

$$\overset{5 \times 2}{\frac{5}{8}} = \underset{8 \times 2}{\frac{10}{16}}$$

$$\overset{10 \div 2}{\frac{10}{16}} = \underset{16 \div 2}{\frac{5}{8}}$$

For each exercise, multiply to find four fractions equal to the given fraction.

Here's how

$$\frac{3}{4} \quad \frac{6}{8}, \frac{9}{12}, \frac{12}{16}, \frac{15}{20}$$

1. $\frac{1}{2}$ 4. $\frac{7}{10}$ 7. $\frac{5}{6}$

2. $\frac{1}{4}$ 5. $\frac{9}{4}$ 8. $\frac{3}{2}$

3. $\frac{4}{5}$ 6. $\frac{2}{5}$ 9. $\frac{7}{3}$

For each exercise, divide to find an equal fraction.

Here's how

$$\frac{4}{10} \quad \frac{2}{5}$$

10. $\frac{3}{6}$ 12. $\frac{6}{9}$ 14. $\frac{4}{12}$

11. $\frac{8}{10}$ 13. $\frac{4}{16}$ 15. $\frac{10}{15}$

132

Fractions in Lowest Terms

$$\frac{3}{4} = \frac{6}{8} = \frac{9}{12} = \frac{12}{16} = \frac{15}{20} = \frac{18}{24} = \frac{21}{28} = \cdots$$

A. The fraction $\frac{3}{4}$ is in *lowest terms*. A fraction
is in lowest terms when the greatest common
factor of the numerator and the denominator is 1.

$\dfrac{3}{4}$ Factors of 3: **1, 3**
       Factors of 4: **1, 2, 4**

B. The fraction $\frac{18}{24}$ is not in lowest terms because
the greatest common factor of the numerator and
the denominator is 6.

$\dfrac{18}{24}$ Factors of 18: **1, 2, 3, 6, 9, 18**
       Factors of 24: **1, 2, 3, 4, 6, 8, 12, 24**

Two ways to rename $\frac{18}{24}$ in lowest terms are shown
below.

Long way

$$\frac{18}{24} = \frac{6}{8} = \frac{3}{4}$$

$18 \div 3 \quad 6 \div 2$
$24 \div 3 \quad 8 \div 2$

Short way

$$\frac{18}{24} = \frac{3}{4}$$

$18 \div 6$
$24 \div 6$

Rename each fraction in lowest terms.

1. $\frac{8}{16}$ 3. $\frac{6}{18}$ 5. $\frac{6}{15}$ 7. $\frac{15}{40}$ 9. $\frac{21}{28}$ 11. $\frac{6}{36}$ 13. $\frac{16}{20}$ 15. $\frac{30}{35}$ 17. $\frac{12}{32}$

2. $\frac{3}{12}$ 4. $\frac{4}{6}$ 6. $\frac{20}{24}$ 8. $\frac{2}{14}$ 10. $\frac{12}{9}$ 12. $\frac{12}{18}$ 14. $\frac{35}{14}$ 16. $\frac{10}{15}$ 18. $\frac{15}{27}$

Finding Missing Numbers in Equal Fractions

You can find a missing
numerator or denominator
in equal fractions.

A.

$$\frac{5}{6} = \frac{}{18}$$

6×3

6 was multiplied
by 3 to get 18.

5×3

$$\frac{5}{6} = \frac{15}{18}$$

Multiply 5 by 3
to get 15.

$$\frac{5}{6} = \frac{15}{18}$$

B.

$12 \div 4$

$$\frac{12}{16} = \frac{3}{}$$

12 was divided
by 4 to get 3.

$$\frac{12}{16} = \frac{3}{4}$$

$16 \div 4$

Divide 16 by 4
to get 4.

$$\frac{12}{16} = \frac{3}{4}$$

Find each missing
number.

1. $\frac{1}{2} = \frac{}{10}$ 13. $\frac{8}{24} = \frac{1}{}$

2. $\frac{2}{3} = \frac{}{18}$ 14. $\frac{1}{4} = \frac{5}{}$

3. $\frac{12}{32} = \frac{3}{}$ 15. $\frac{6}{11} = \frac{12}{}$

4. $\frac{5}{8} = \frac{10}{}$ 16. $\frac{1}{8} = \frac{6}{}$

5. $\frac{1}{2} = \frac{4}{}$ 17. $\frac{4}{5} = \frac{}{20}$

6. $\frac{3}{4} = \frac{9}{}$ 18. $\frac{8}{14} = \frac{}{7}$

7. $\frac{28}{8} = \frac{7}{}$ 19. $\frac{3}{2} = \frac{}{10}$

8. $\frac{14}{21} = \frac{}{3}$ 20. $\frac{32}{24} = \frac{8}{}$

9. $\frac{1}{6} = \frac{}{30}$ 21. $\frac{12}{30} = \frac{}{5}$

10. $\frac{3}{4} = \frac{6}{}$ 22. $\frac{7}{8} = \frac{}{24}$

11. $\frac{10}{12} = \frac{}{6}$ 23. $\frac{6}{5} = \frac{}{20}$

12. $\frac{6}{15} = \frac{2}{}$ 24. $\frac{6}{7} = \frac{}{21}$

More practice
Set A, page 190

134

Mixed Numbers

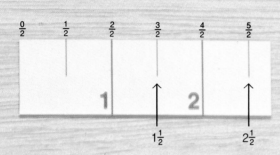

$$\frac{3}{2} = 1\frac{1}{2} \qquad \frac{5}{2} = 2\frac{1}{2}$$

$$\frac{5}{4} = 1\frac{1}{4} \qquad \frac{7}{4} = 1\frac{3}{4}$$

$$\frac{9}{4} = 2\frac{1}{4}$$

Numbers like $1\frac{3}{4}$, $2\frac{7}{8}$, and $4\frac{2}{3}$ are *mixed numbers*. A mixed number has a whole-number part and a fraction part.

Give the length of each object in inches. Use a mixed number.

1.

2. 3.

4.

5.

6.

7. 8.

9.

10.

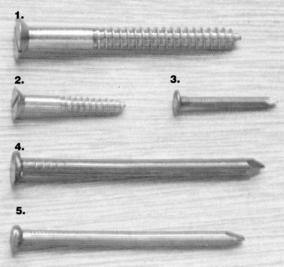

135

Fractions and Mixed Numbers

A. Change $\frac{58}{4}$ to a mixed number.

$$\frac{58}{4} = 58 \div 4$$

Divide and write the answer as a mixed number.

$$4\overline{)58}\;\;\;14\frac{2}{4},\text{ or }14\frac{1}{2}$$
$$\underline{-4}$$
$$18$$
$$\underline{-16}$$
$$2$$

$$\frac{58}{4} = 14\frac{1}{2}$$

B. Change $2\frac{3}{8}$ to a fraction.

$$2\frac{3}{8} = 2 + \frac{3}{8}$$

$$= \frac{16}{8} + \frac{3}{8}$$

$$= \frac{19}{8}$$

Here is a shortcut.

$$2\frac{3}{8} = \frac{19}{8}$$

Multiply 2 and 8. Then add 3.

Change each fraction to a mixed number or a whole number.

1. $\frac{5}{2}$ 7. $\frac{44}{2}$

2. $\frac{19}{6}$ 8. $\frac{87}{7}$

3. $\frac{12}{4}$ 9. $\frac{75}{4}$

4. $\frac{17}{3}$ 10. $\frac{122}{5}$

5. $\frac{23}{5}$ 11. $\frac{140}{8}$

6. $\frac{10}{9}$ 12. $\frac{173}{10}$

Change each mixed number to a fraction.

13. $1\frac{2}{3}$ 19. $9\frac{1}{3}$

14. $4\frac{1}{4}$ 20. $5\frac{7}{8}$

15. $2\frac{9}{10}$ 21. $8\frac{4}{5}$

16. $6\frac{2}{5}$ 22. $17\frac{1}{10}$

17. $7\frac{1}{6}$ 23. $10\frac{3}{4}$

18. $3\frac{3}{7}$ 24. $31\frac{1}{2}$

Express each quotient as a fraction or a mixed number. Rename in lowest terms.

Here's how

$$6 \div 4 \quad \frac{6}{4} = 1\frac{2}{4} = 1\frac{1}{2}$$

25. $4 \div 3$ 28. $1 \div 5$

26. $8 \div 5$ 29. $9 \div 6$

27. $16 \div 7$ 30. $2 \div 8$

Expressing Numbers as Fractions

Some numbers can be written as fractions in which both the numerator and the denominator are integers and the denominator is not zero. Such numbers are *rational numbers*.

The number line above shows examples of rational numbers. Here are other examples.

$$.7 = \frac{7}{10} \qquad\qquad 1\frac{7}{8} = \frac{15}{8}$$

$$1.4 = 1\frac{4}{10} = \frac{14}{10} = \frac{7}{5} \qquad 6\frac{2}{3} = \frac{20}{3}$$

$$3.89 = 3\frac{89}{100} = \frac{389}{100} \qquad 47\frac{1}{2} = \frac{95}{2}$$

$$4 = \frac{4}{1} \qquad\qquad ^-3 = \frac{^-3}{1}$$

$$0 = \frac{0}{2} \qquad\qquad ^-1\frac{1}{4} = \frac{^-5}{4}$$

$$10 = \frac{10}{1} \qquad\qquad ^-.9 = \frac{^-9}{10}$$

Write each rational number as a fraction in lowest terms.

1. $5\frac{1}{2}$ 6. 12 11. 1.19

2. $.4$ 7. $2\frac{9}{10}$ 12. $16\frac{1}{3}$

3. $3\frac{3}{4}$ 8. 1.6 13. $^-5$

4. 7 9. $.25$ 14. $^-1\frac{1}{2}$

5. 6.9 10. 3 15. $^-.8$

Write each rational number as a whole number.

16. $\frac{9}{3}$ 18. $\frac{22}{11}$ 20. $\frac{4}{1}$

17. $\frac{12}{2}$ 19. $\frac{25}{5}$ 21. $\frac{8}{8}$

22. Write three rational numbers that are greater than 1.

23. Write three rational numbers that are between 0 and 1.

24. Write three rational numbers that are less than 0.

Expressing Fractions as Decimals

A. You can find the decimal for a fraction by dividing the numerator by the denominator.

Change $\frac{3}{16}$ to a decimal.

$$\begin{array}{r} .1875 \\ 16\overline{)3.0000} \\ -16 \\ \hline 1\,40 \\ -1\,28 \\ \hline 120 \\ -112 \\ \hline 80 \\ -80 \\ \hline 0 \end{array}$$

$\frac{3}{16} = .1875$

B. Sometimes it is easy to find the decimal without dividing. See first whether you can change the fraction to a fraction with a denominator of 10, 100, or 1000.

Change $3\frac{4}{25}$ to a decimal.

$3\frac{4}{25} = 3\frac{16}{100} = 3.16$ $\quad\left(\frac{4}{25} = \frac{16}{100}\right)$

c. Change $2\frac{1}{8}$ to a decimal.

$$2\frac{1}{8} = \frac{17}{8}$$

$$\begin{array}{r} 2.125 \\ 8\overline{)17.000} \\ -16 \\ \hline 1\,0 \\ -\,8 \\ \hline 20 \\ -16 \\ \hline 40 \\ -40 \\ \hline 0 \end{array}$$

$$2\frac{1}{8} = 2.125$$

Examples A, B, and C show *terminating decimals*. When you divide, these decimals terminate, or end, with a remainder of 0.

Each of these rational numbers can be expressed as a terminating decimal. Find the decimal.

1. $\frac{1}{2}$ **5.** $\frac{2}{5}$ **9.** $2\frac{3}{50}$

2. $\frac{3}{4}$ **6.** $\frac{5}{8}$ **10.** $\frac{7}{16}$

3. $\frac{43}{100}$ **7.** $1\frac{1}{4}$ **11.** $1\frac{3}{80}$

4. $\frac{7}{10}$ **8.** $\frac{8}{25}$ **12.** $6\frac{7}{1000}$

D. Change $\frac{2}{11}$ to a decimal.

Study the division. Notice that a remainder of 0 does not appear. Instead, remainders begin to repeat, and repeating digits occur in the quotient.

```
      .1818
11)2.0000
   −11
     90
    −88
     20
    −11
     90
    −88
      2
```
If you continue to divide, you will continue to obtain 18's in the quotient.

The decimal for $\frac{2}{11}$ is a *repeating decimal*. The group of repeating digits is the *repetend*. When you write the decimal, put a bar over the repetend.

$$\frac{2}{11} = .\overline{18}$$

E. Change $3\frac{1}{6}$ to a decimal.

$$3\frac{1}{6} = \frac{19}{6}$$

```
      3.166
6)19.000
  −18
    1 0
    − 6
      40
     −36
      40
     −36
       4
```
If you continue to divide, you will continue to obtain 6's in the quotient.

$$3\frac{1}{6} = 3.1\overline{6}$$

■ *Any number that can be expressed as a terminating or a repeating decimal is a rational number.*

Write each number as a terminating or a repeating decimal.

13. $\frac{1}{3}$	**17.** $\frac{4}{15}$	**21.** $1\frac{2}{9}$
14. $\frac{5}{6}$	**18.** $\frac{1}{12}$	**22.** $5\frac{1}{7}$
15. $\frac{1}{4}$	**19.** $\frac{7}{8}$	**23.** $1\frac{1}{5}$
16. $\frac{3}{7}$	**20.** $4\frac{1}{11}$	**24.** $\frac{3}{23}$

Multiplying Fractions

A. Mr. Amos plowed $\frac{3}{4}$ of a field.

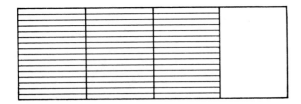

He planted $\frac{2}{3}$ of the plowed land in corn.

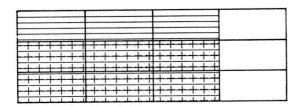

What fraction of the whole field did he plant in corn?

$\frac{2}{3}$ of $\frac{3}{4}$ is $\frac{6}{12}$.

$$\frac{2}{3} \times \frac{3}{4} = \frac{6}{12}$$

Mr. Amos planted $\frac{6}{12}$, or $\frac{1}{2}$, of his field in corn.

■ *To multiply fractions, first multiply the numerators. Then multiply the denominators.*

$$\frac{2}{3} \times \frac{4}{5} = \frac{8}{15} \quad \begin{array}{c} 2 \times 4 \\ 3 \times 5 \end{array}$$

B. Find $\frac{3}{4} \times \frac{6}{7}$.

$$\frac{3}{4} \times \frac{6}{7} = \frac{18}{28} = \frac{9}{14}$$

Sometimes you can use a shortcut when you multiply.

$$\frac{3}{\underset{2}{\cancel{4}}} \times \frac{\overset{3}{\cancel{6}}}{7} = \frac{9}{14}$$

A numerator, 6, and a denominator, 4, were divided by 2.

C. Find $\frac{9}{10} \times \frac{1}{6} \times \frac{5}{7}$.

$$\frac{\overset{3}{\cancel{9}}}{\underset{2}{\cancel{10}}} \times \frac{1}{\underset{2}{\cancel{6}}} \times \frac{\overset{1}{\cancel{5}}}{7} = \frac{3}{28}$$

Multiply.

1. $\frac{1}{3} \times \frac{3}{7}$

13. $\frac{5}{12} \times \frac{2}{5}$

2. $\frac{4}{5} \times \frac{1}{8}$

14. $\frac{5}{8} \times \frac{8}{25}$

3. $\frac{1}{4} \times \frac{8}{9}$

15. $\frac{8}{9} \times \frac{3}{4}$

4. $\frac{1}{6} \times \frac{4}{5}$

16. $\frac{9}{14} \times \frac{7}{12}$

5. $\frac{9}{10} \times \frac{2}{3}$

17. $\frac{2}{3} \times \frac{15}{16}$

6. $\frac{5}{6} \times \frac{7}{10}$

18. $\frac{7}{10} \times \frac{3}{7}$

7. $\frac{1}{2} \times \frac{6}{7}$

19. $\frac{5}{8} \times \frac{2}{5}$

8. $\frac{4}{5} \times \frac{15}{16}$

20. $\frac{2}{3} \times \frac{2}{3}$

9. $\frac{3}{4} \times \frac{4}{3}$

21. $\frac{2}{5} \times \frac{1}{2} \times \frac{1}{3}$

10. $\frac{7}{8} \times \frac{4}{7}$

22. $\frac{3}{4} \times \frac{2}{3} \times \frac{4}{5}$

11. $\frac{1}{4} \times \frac{1}{4}$

23. $\frac{7}{8} \times \frac{4}{5} \times \frac{3}{7}$

12. $\frac{8}{15} \times \frac{3}{4}$

24. $\frac{9}{10} \times \frac{5}{6} \times \frac{2}{3}$

25. The Wilson farm has an area of $\frac{2}{3}$ square mile. $\frac{3}{8}$ of the land is pasture. What fraction of a square mile is pasture?

$\frac{3}{8}$ of $\frac{2}{3}$

$\frac{3}{8} \times \frac{2}{3} = $ ▦

26. The Wilsons have a $\frac{1}{2}$-acre garden. They planted $\frac{1}{8}$ of the garden in squash. What fraction of an acre did they plant in squash?

27. Find the area of the shaded rectangle in square miles.

$A = lw$
$A = \frac{2}{3} \times \frac{1}{4}$
$A = $ ▦ sq. mi.

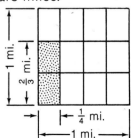

28. Find the area of a farm that is $\frac{3}{4}$ mile wide and $\frac{3}{4}$ mile long.

More practice
Set B, page 190

Multiplying Fractions and Whole Numbers

In Langara, British Columbia, precipitation is recorded on an average of $\frac{7}{10}$ of the days of a year. How many days is this?

Find $\frac{7}{10}$ of 365, or $\frac{7}{10} \times 365$.

$$\frac{7}{10} \times 365$$

$$\frac{7}{\underset{2}{\cancel{10}}} \times \frac{\overset{73}{\cancel{365}}}{1} = \frac{511}{2} = 255\frac{1}{2}$$

Precipitation is recorded on about 256 days of the year.

Multiply to find each answer.

1. $\frac{1}{2}$ of 15

2. $\frac{2}{3}$ of 21

3. $\frac{4}{9}$ of 24

4. $\frac{1}{6}$ of 50

5. $\frac{7}{10}$ of 45

6. $\frac{3}{5}$ of 100

7. $\frac{3}{4}$ of 125

8. $\frac{7}{8}$ of 96

9. $\frac{4}{7}$ of 245

10. $\frac{1}{3}$ of 568

The fraction refers to days of the year that have precipitation. Find about how many days have precipitation.

11. Milwaukee, Wisconsin: $\frac{1}{3}$

12. Phoenix, Arizona: $\frac{1}{10}$

13. Boise, Idaho: $\frac{1}{4}$

14. Charleston, West Virginia: $\frac{2}{5}$

15. Toronto, Ontario: $\frac{3}{8}$

The fraction refers to days of the year that are sunny. Find about how many days are sunny.

16. Reno, Nevada: $\frac{4}{5}$

17. Juneau, Alaska: $\frac{3}{10}$

18. Little Rock, Arkansas: $\frac{5}{8}$

19. El Paso, Texas: $\frac{5}{6}$

20. Mt. Waialeale in Hawaii has rain on more than $\frac{9}{10}$ of the days of the year. About how many days is this?

laboratory activity

To make a rain gauge, you will need:

a funnel and a can, each 4 inches in diameter;

a glass jar, 2 inches in diameter

a strip of tape marked in eighths of an inch.

Assemble your materials like this:

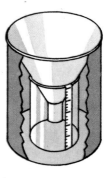

When it starts to rain, place your gauge outdoors in the open. When the rain stops, calculate the amount of rain that fell.

One inch of rain in the jar equals $\frac{1}{4}$ inch of rainfall. If, after the rain, there is $\frac{3}{4}$ inch of rain in your jar, the amount that fell is $\frac{3}{16}$ inch.

$$\frac{1}{4} \times \frac{3}{4} = \frac{3}{16}$$

Multiplying Mixed Numbers

Pictures in dictionaries often show things in reduced or enlarged size.

Bass

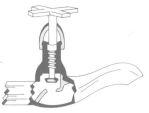

Faucet

Acuminate leaf

Mite

Thread (bolt)

ar ma dil lo (är′mə-dil′ō), *n., pl.* **-los.** any of several small burrowing mammals of South America and some parts of southern North America, with an armorlike shell of bony plates. Some kinds can roll up into a ball when attacked.

Armadillo

bun ting[2] (bun′ting), *n.* small bird with a stout bill. It is somewhat like a sparrow. [origin uncertain]

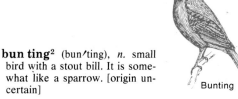

Bunting

A. In the picture the armadillo is $1\frac{1}{2}$ inches long. Actually, this animal is about 20 times as long. About how long is an armadillo?

Find $20 \times 1\frac{1}{2}$. First write 20 and $1\frac{1}{2}$ as fractions.

$$20 \times 1\frac{1}{2}$$

$$\overset{10}{\cancel{\frac{20}{1}}} \times \frac{3}{\underset{1}{\cancel{2}}} = \frac{30}{1} = 30$$

An armadillo is about 30 inches long.

B. In the picture the bunting is about $1\frac{1}{4}$ inches long. Actually, this bird is about $4\frac{1}{2}$ times as long. About how long is a bunting?

$$4\frac{1}{2} \times 1\frac{1}{4}$$

$$\frac{9}{2} \times \frac{5}{4} = \frac{45}{8} = 5\frac{5}{8}$$

A bunting is about $5\frac{5}{8}$ inches long.

Reciprocals

Multiply.

1. $6 \times 4\frac{1}{2}$ **10.** $15\frac{5}{6} \times 1\frac{1}{2}$

2. $3\frac{2}{3} \times 9$ **11.** $8\frac{3}{4} \times 2\frac{1}{7}$

3. $2\frac{1}{2} \times 2\frac{2}{3}$ **12.** $5\frac{1}{2} \times 3\frac{1}{2}$

4. $1\frac{7}{8} \times 1\frac{1}{3}$ **13.** $4\frac{1}{3} \times 24$

5. $1\frac{7}{10} \times 3\frac{1}{3}$ **14.** $1\frac{2}{3} \times 1\frac{2}{3}$

6. $5\frac{1}{2} \times 1\frac{1}{4}$ **15.** $2\frac{1}{7} \times 2\frac{1}{3}$

7. $2\frac{5}{8} \times 4$ **16.** $3\frac{1}{5} \times 1\frac{3}{4} \times \frac{1}{2}$

8. $7\frac{5}{8} \times 3\frac{1}{5}$ **17.** $2\frac{1}{2} \times \frac{7}{10} \times 1\frac{3}{7}$

9. $3\frac{3}{4} \times 1\frac{1}{3}$ **18.** $4\frac{1}{8} \times 1\frac{3}{5} \times 2\frac{1}{2}$

Find the actual length of each bird.

These birds are actually $2\frac{1}{2}$ times the lengths pictured in the dictionary.

19. Wren: pictured length, $1\frac{3}{4}$ in.

20. Finch: pictured length, $2\frac{1}{2}$ in.

These birds are actually $4\frac{1}{2}$ times the lengths pictured in the dictionary.

21. Robin: pictured length, 2 in.

22. Bluebird: pictured length, $1\frac{1}{2}$ in.

Two numbers whose product is 1 are *reciprocals*.

A. $\frac{2}{3}$ and $\frac{3}{2}$ are reciprocals.
$\frac{2}{3} \times \frac{3}{2} = \frac{6}{6} = 1$

B. 8 and $\frac{1}{8}$ are reciprocals.
$8 = \frac{8}{1}$
$\frac{8}{1} \times \frac{1}{8} = \frac{8}{8} = 1$

C. $11\frac{1}{4}$ and $\frac{4}{45}$ are reciprocals.
$11\frac{1}{4} = \frac{45}{4}$
$\frac{45}{4} \times \frac{4}{45} = \frac{180}{180} = 1$

D. What is the reciprocal of $4\frac{3}{5}$?

Give the reciprocal of each number.

1. $\frac{3}{4}$ **7.** 1   **13.** $\frac{3}{25}$

2. $\frac{5}{8}$ **8.** $2\frac{4}{5}$ **14.** $1\frac{3}{8}$

3. $\frac{7}{4}$ **9.** $12\frac{1}{2}$ **15.** $\frac{9}{10}$

4. 3   **10.** 17   **16.** $\frac{7}{16}$

5. $\frac{1}{4}$ **11.** $9\frac{2}{3}$ **17.** $\frac{8}{7}$

6. $\frac{3}{7}$ **12.** $\frac{11}{5}$ **18.** $1\frac{5}{6}$

● **Discuss**   Does zero have a reciprocal?

More practice
Set C, page 190

Dividing by Fractions

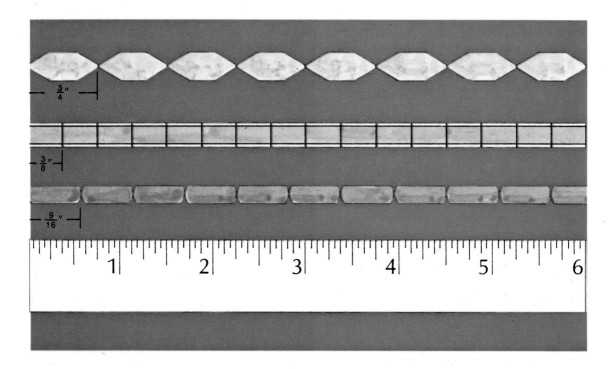

You can use reciprocals to help you divide by fractions.

A. $6 \div \frac{3}{4} = 8$ $\longleftarrow$ Number of $\frac{3}{4}$-inch links in a 6-inch watchband.

$6 \times \frac{4}{3} = 8$

B. $6 \div \frac{3}{8} = 16$ $\longleftarrow$ Number of $\frac{3}{8}$-inch links in a 6-inch watchband.

$6 \times \frac{8}{3} = 16$

C. $6 \div \frac{9}{16} = 10\frac{2}{3}$ $\longleftarrow$ Number of $\frac{9}{16}$-inch links in a 6-inch watchband.

$6 \times \frac{16}{9} = 10\frac{2}{3}$

■ *Dividing by a number is the same as multiplying by its reciprocal.*

$$2\frac{2}{3} \div \frac{5}{6}$$

$$2\frac{2}{3} \times \frac{6}{5} = \frac{8}{\underset{1}{\cancel{3}}} \times \frac{\overset{2}{\cancel{6}}}{5} = \frac{16}{5} = 3\frac{1}{5}$$

Divide.

1. $\frac{3}{4} \div \frac{1}{2}$ 9. $\frac{5}{12} \div \frac{2}{3}$ 17. $9 \div \frac{2}{3}$

2. $\frac{1}{4} \div \frac{2}{3}$ 10. $\frac{3}{4} \div \frac{9}{10}$ 18. $1\frac{1}{5} \div \frac{3}{5}$

3. $\frac{7}{8} \div \frac{1}{6}$ 11. $\frac{5}{8} \div \frac{5}{16}$ 19. $2\frac{1}{3} \div \frac{7}{8}$

4. $\frac{1}{5} \div \frac{1}{3}$ 12. $\frac{5}{7} \div \frac{5}{7}$ 20. $3\frac{1}{3} \div \frac{5}{8}$

5. $\frac{2}{3} \div \frac{5}{9}$ 13. $7\frac{1}{2} \div \frac{1}{2}$ 21. $1\frac{1}{2} \div \frac{3}{5}$

6. $\frac{9}{10} \div \frac{3}{5}$ 14. $2\frac{2}{3} \div \frac{5}{6}$ 22. $14\frac{2}{3} \div \frac{4}{5}$

7. $\frac{3}{8} \div \frac{3}{4}$ 15. $4 \div \frac{8}{9}$ 23. $8\frac{3}{4} \div \frac{5}{9}$

8. $\frac{4}{5} \div \frac{1}{3}$ 16. $3\frac{3}{4} \div \frac{3}{8}$ 24. $10\frac{1}{2} \div \frac{7}{8}$

**More practice
Set D, page 190**

How many beads are needed to make a 12-inch necklace?

25. $\frac{3}{4}$-inch beads

26. $\frac{1}{8}$-inch beads

27. $\frac{3}{8}$-inch beads

How many beads are needed to make a 30-inch necklace?

28. $\frac{3}{4}$-inch beads

29. $\frac{5}{8}$-inch beads

30. $\frac{3}{16}$-inch beads

How many silver rings can be made from $7\frac{1}{2}$ ounces of silver?

31. $\frac{3}{4}$-ounce rings

32. $\frac{5}{16}$-ounce rings

Time Out

Two volumes of an encyclopedia are standing side by side on a book shelf. Volume I is to the left of Volume II. A bookworm, starting at page 1 of Volume I, eats its way in a straight line to the last page of Volume II. If each cover is $\frac{1}{4}$ inch thick and each book, without the cover, is 1 inch thick, how far does the bookworm travel?

Dividing by Mixed Numbers

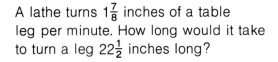

A lathe turns $1\frac{7}{8}$ inches of a table leg per minute. How long would it take to turn a leg $22\frac{1}{2}$ inches long?

Find $22\frac{1}{2} \div 1\frac{7}{8}$.

$$22\frac{1}{2} \div 1\frac{7}{8}$$

$$\frac{45}{2} \div \frac{15}{8} = \frac{\overset{3}{\cancel{45}}}{\underset{1}{\cancel{2}}} \times \frac{\overset{4}{\cancel{8}}}{\underset{1}{\cancel{15}}} = \frac{12}{1} = 12$$

It would take 12 minutes.

Divide.

1. $7\frac{1}{2} \div 1\frac{1}{2}$

2. $4 \div 1\frac{2}{3}$

3. $6\frac{1}{4} \div 2\frac{1}{2}$

4. $\frac{1}{2} \div 1\frac{1}{3}$

5. $\frac{3}{5} \div 1\frac{1}{5}$

6. $4\frac{5}{6} \div 4\frac{5}{6}$

7. $8\frac{3}{4} \div 14$

8. $1\frac{1}{4} \div 7\frac{1}{2}$

9. $2\frac{7}{8} \div 1\frac{5}{8}$

10. $4\frac{2}{3} \div 1\frac{1}{6}$

11. $3\frac{1}{8} \div 1\frac{1}{3}$

12. $\frac{5}{6} \div 2\frac{1}{2}$

13. $\frac{7}{8} \div 3\frac{5}{8}$

14. $10\frac{1}{2} \div 2\frac{1}{3}$

15. $13\frac{3}{4} \div 1\frac{2}{3}$

16. $6\frac{1}{2} \div 9\frac{1}{3}$

17. On each turn, a nut goes onto the bolt $\frac{3}{16}$ inch. How many turns are needed to make it go $1\frac{1}{2}$ inches?

18. To make a table, an oak board $6\frac{3}{4}$ feet long was cut into three pieces, each the same length. How long was each piece?

19. One sheet of wall paneling covers $2\frac{1}{4}$ feet of wall. How many sheets are needed to cover $24\frac{3}{4}$ feet of wall?

More practice
Set E, page 190

Pages 181

Poll-taking is big business. Some polls are used to predict the outcome of elections. The letters in these blocks can be used to show how a poll works.
Think of the space inside each block as a neighborhood. The letters in the block represent people living in that neighborhood. Vowels--a, e, i, o, and u--are too young to vote. No s or t is registered to vote. Among the remaining letters, all b through j plan to vote for Candidate X; and all k through z plan to vote for Candidate Y. A sample of people polled will likely show whether more people will vote for Candidate X or for Candidate Y.

For exercises 1–4, count only the letters in the three sample blocks.

1. How many people are too young to vote? (Count only the vowels.)

2. How many are not registered to vote? (Count only *s*'s and *t*'s.)

3. How many will vote for Candidate X? (Count only these letters: *b, c, d, f, g, h, j*.)

4. How many will vote for Candidate Y? (Count only these letters: *k, l, m, n, p, q, r, v, w, x, y, z*.)

There are 200 letters in the three blocks, representing 200 people in the sample.

5. What fraction of the people will vote for Candidate X?

$$\frac{\text{▦}}{200}$$ ←—Number for X
←—Number in sample

6. What fraction of the people will vote for Candidate Y?

7. Which candidate do you think will win the election?

8. How many votes would you predict for each candidate in a town of 50,000? Of 140,000? Of 600,000?

A. Tony would weigh $19\frac{1}{2}$ pounds on the moon. This is $\frac{1}{6}$ of his weight on Earth. What is his weight on Earth?

Write an equation. Use a letter for the number you want to find.

$$\frac{1}{6}n = 19\frac{1}{2}$$

Divide both sides of the equation by $\frac{1}{6}$. This is the same as multiplying both sides by $\frac{6}{1}$.

$$\left(\frac{6}{1}\right)\frac{1}{6}n = \left(\frac{6}{1}\right)19\frac{1}{2}$$

$$n = \left(\frac{6}{1}\right)\frac{39}{2}$$

$$n = 117$$

Tony's weight on Earth is 117 pounds.

B. Solve for m.

$$1\tfrac{3}{4}m = 4\tfrac{1}{2}$$

$$\tfrac{7}{4}m = 4\tfrac{1}{2}$$

$$\left(\tfrac{4}{7}\right)\tfrac{7}{4}m = \left(\tfrac{4}{7}\right)4\tfrac{1}{2}$$

$$m = \left(\tfrac{4}{7}\right)\tfrac{9}{2}$$

$$m = 2\tfrac{4}{7}$$

Solve each equation.

1. $\tfrac{1}{2}k = 5$

2. $\tfrac{2}{3}m = 12$

3. $\tfrac{4}{5}x = 6$

4. $\tfrac{7}{8}t = 14$

5. $1\tfrac{1}{2}n = 7$

6. $1\tfrac{3}{8}t = 11$

7. $\tfrac{5}{6}a = 400$

8. $\tfrac{3}{4}h = 1\tfrac{1}{2}$

9. $\tfrac{1}{2}t = \tfrac{7}{8}$

10. $2\tfrac{1}{2}s = 1\tfrac{3}{4}$

11. $1\tfrac{3}{4}n = 5$

12. $4\tfrac{2}{3}t = 12$

13. $\tfrac{3}{4}x = 342$

14. $1\tfrac{1}{6}n = 1\tfrac{1}{6}$

15. $3m = 4\tfrac{1}{3}$

Find each answer.

16. Felix would weigh 286 pounds on Jupiter. This is $2\tfrac{3}{5}$ times his weight on Earth. What is his weight on Earth?

$$2\tfrac{3}{5}n = 286$$

17. Sarah would weigh 69 pounds on Pluto. This is $\tfrac{7}{10}$ of her weight on Earth. What is her weight on Earth?

18. The crew of Apollo 16 brought back lunar rocks that weighed a total of $35\tfrac{1}{2}$ pounds on the moon. This is $\tfrac{1}{6}$ of the weight of these rocks on Earth. What is the weight of these rocks on Earth?

19. The picture of the first footprint on the moon is $\tfrac{1}{8}$ actual size. What are the actual length and width of the footprint?

20. Explorer XLI weighed 174 pounds. This is $9\tfrac{2}{3}$ times as much as Explorer I weighed. What was the weight of Explorer I?

A. The Bensons are paneling one end wall of an A-frame cottage. The area of this triangular wall is $22\frac{1}{2}$ square yards. The base of the triangle is $7\frac{1}{2}$ yards long. How high is the wall?

Use the formula for the area of a triangle.

Use $22\frac{1}{2}$ for A and $7\frac{1}{2}$ for b. Then solve for h.

$$A = \tfrac{1}{2}bh$$

$$22\tfrac{1}{2} = \tfrac{1}{2}(7\tfrac{1}{2})h$$

$$22\tfrac{1}{2} = \tfrac{15}{4}h$$

$$(\tfrac{4}{15})\, 22\tfrac{1}{2} = (\tfrac{4}{15})\tfrac{15}{4}h$$

$$(\tfrac{4}{15})\tfrac{45}{2} = h$$

$$6 = h$$

The wall is 6 yards high.

B. The Bensons paid $75 for the $7\frac{1}{2}$ sheets of paneling they used for the wall. What was the price per sheet? Use the cost formula.

$$C = np$$

$$75 = 7\tfrac{1}{2}p$$

$$75 = \tfrac{15}{2}p$$

$$(\tfrac{2}{15})\, 75 = (\tfrac{2}{15})\,\tfrac{15}{2}p$$

$$(\tfrac{2}{15})\,\tfrac{75}{1} = p$$

$$10 = p$$

The paneling cost $10 per sheet.

Find the answers.

1. The perimeter of a square room is $52\frac{1}{2}$ feet. Find the length of each side of the room. Use $P = 4s$.

2. A rectangular hallway has an area of $96\frac{1}{4}$ square feet. The hall is $3\frac{1}{2}$ feet wide. How long is it? Use $A = lw$.

3. A rectangular patio has an area of 190 square feet and is $12\frac{2}{3}$ feet long. Find the width of the patio. Use $A = lw$.

4. Astrid paid $11 for $5\frac{1}{2}$ sections of molding to go around a room. What was the price per section?

5. Mr. Willis paid 75¢ for $2\frac{1}{2}$ pounds of wallpaper paste. What was the price per pound?

6. Ms. Sawa paid $94 for 10 square yards of carpeting. What was the price per square yard?

7. Kay paid $66 for $8\frac{1}{4}$ yards of drapery material. What was the price per yard?

8. The perimeter of the equilateral triangle is $5\frac{1}{4}$ inches.

   Find s. Use $P = 3s$.

9. The area of the rectangle is 6 square feet.

   Find l. Use $A = lw$.

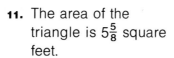

10. The area of the rectangle is $4\frac{3}{8}$ square inches.

    Find w. Use $A = lw$.

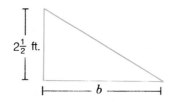

11. The area of the triangle is $5\frac{5}{8}$ square feet.

    Find b. Use $A = \frac{1}{2}bh$.

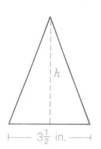

12. The area of the triangle is $7\frac{7}{8}$ square inches.

    Find h. Use $A = \frac{1}{2}bh$.

Chapter 7 Test
Multiplying and Dividing Fractions and Mixed Numbers, Pages 132-153

Fractions and mixed numbers, pages 132-139

Find each missing number.

1. $\frac{2}{3} = \frac{\text{▦}}{15}$

2. $\frac{3}{5} = \frac{18}{\text{▦}}$

Rename each fraction in lowest terms.

3. $\frac{9}{15}$ 4. $\frac{12}{8}$

Change each fraction to a mixed number.

5. $\frac{4}{3}$ 6. $\frac{19}{7}$

Give the fraction in lowest terms for each number.

7. $2\frac{1}{4}$ 8. $6\frac{3}{5}$

9. .5   10. 3

Find the decimal for each number.

11. $1\frac{1}{2}$ 12. $\frac{1}{3}$

Multiplying fractions and mixed numbers, pages 140-145

Multiply.

13. $\frac{7}{8} \times \frac{2}{3}$

14. $1\frac{1}{2} \times 1\frac{1}{3}$

15. $2\frac{5}{6} \times 12$

16. Find $\frac{3}{4}$ of 38.

Give the reciprocal of each number.

17. $\frac{5}{8}$ 18. $1\frac{3}{4}$

Dividing fractions and mixed numbers, pages 146-148

Divide.

19. $\frac{2}{3} \div \frac{5}{6}$

20. $2\frac{1}{3} \div \frac{2}{3}$

21. $5\frac{1}{2} \div 1\frac{3}{4}$

22. $6 \div 1\frac{7}{8}$

Solving equations, pages 150-151

Solve each equation.

23. $\frac{3}{4}k = 9$

24. $2\frac{1}{2}s = 15$

25. $1\frac{1}{5}n = 2$

Problem solving, pages 140-153

26. $\frac{3}{5}$ of the 245 students in Webster School voted for Rita for student council. How many students voted for Rita?

27. A toy piano keyboard is $22\frac{1}{2}$ inches long. Each key is $\frac{3}{4}$ inch wide. How many keys are there?

28. In a picture, a hawk is $1\frac{3}{4}$ inches long. Actually, this bird is about $6\frac{1}{2}$ times as long. About how long is the hawk?

29. It cost $6 to rent a boat for $1\frac{1}{2}$ hours. At this rate, what was the price per hour? Use $C = np$.

30. The area of this triangle is $6\frac{1}{8}$ square feet. Find h. Use $A = \frac{1}{2}bh$.

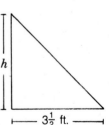

$3\frac{1}{2}$ ft.

$1\frac{1}{4}$ pounds

Finding Common Denominators

When you work with fractions, you often
need to find common denominators.

A. Write $\frac{3}{8}$ and $\frac{5}{6}$ with a common denominator.

A common denominator of $\frac{3}{8}$ and $\frac{5}{6}$
is a common multiple of 8 and 6.

List the multiples of 8 until you have
a common multiple of 8 and 6.

8, 16, 24   24 is a common denominator of $\frac{3}{8}$ and $\frac{5}{6}$.

Now find fractions equal to $\frac{3}{8}$ and to $\frac{5}{6}$ and
that have a denominator of 24.

$$\frac{3}{8} = \frac{9}{24} \qquad \frac{5}{6} = \frac{20}{24}$$

B. Write $\frac{2}{3}$, $\frac{3}{5}$, and $\frac{1}{6}$ with a common denominator.
First list the multiples of 6 until you have
a common multiple of 3, 5, and 6.

6, 12, 18, 24, 30   30 is a common denominator for the three fractions.

Now find equal fractions that have a denominator
of 30.

$$\frac{2}{3} = \frac{20}{30} \qquad \frac{3}{5} = \frac{18}{30} \qquad \frac{1}{6} = \frac{5}{30}$$

Write these
fractions with a
common denominator.

1. $\frac{1}{2}$, $\frac{3}{4}$

2. $\frac{5}{6}$, $\frac{5}{12}$

3. $\frac{2}{3}$, $\frac{1}{2}$

4. $\frac{1}{5}$, $\frac{7}{10}$

5. $\frac{3}{4}$, $\frac{1}{6}$

6. $\frac{5}{8}$, $\frac{2}{3}$

7. $\frac{1}{3}$, $\frac{3}{4}$

8. $\frac{2}{9}$, $\frac{5}{6}$

9. $\frac{7}{12}$, $\frac{1}{8}$

10. $\frac{7}{8}$, $\frac{1}{6}$

11. $\frac{2}{3}$, $\frac{4}{7}$

12. $\frac{4}{5}$, $\frac{1}{3}$

13. $\frac{2}{7}$, $\frac{3}{4}$

14. $\frac{2}{3}$, $\frac{1}{6}$, $\frac{1}{2}$

15. $\frac{1}{2}$, $\frac{1}{4}$, $\frac{1}{3}$

16. $\frac{3}{5}$, $\frac{5}{6}$, $\frac{2}{3}$

More practice
Set F, page 191

Comparing Numbers

A. Compare $\frac{5}{8}$ and $\frac{3}{8}$.

When fractions have the same denominators, the greater fraction has the greater numerator.

$$\frac{5}{8} > \frac{3}{8}, \text{ because } 5 > 3.$$

B. Compare $\frac{9}{16}$ and $\frac{5}{8}$.

Write $\frac{9}{16}$ and $\frac{5}{8}$ with a common denominator. Then compare the numerators.

$$\frac{9}{16} \qquad \frac{5}{8}$$

$$\frac{9}{16} < \frac{10}{16}, \text{ so } \frac{9}{16} < \frac{5}{8}.$$

C. Compare $2\frac{9}{16}$ and $2\frac{5}{8}$.

The whole numbers are the same. Compare the fractions.

$$\frac{9}{16} < \frac{5}{8}, \text{ so } 2\frac{9}{16} < 2\frac{5}{8}.$$

Compare. Use >, <, or =.

1. $\frac{3}{8}$ ⬤ $\frac{7}{8}$

2. $\frac{4}{9}$ ⬤ $\frac{2}{9}$

3. $\frac{2}{3}$ ⬤ $\frac{4}{5}$

4. $\frac{1}{2}$ ⬤ $\frac{5}{8}$

5. $\frac{1}{3}$ ⬤ $\frac{2}{9}$

6. $\frac{7}{8}$ ⬤ $\frac{5}{6}$

7. $\frac{8}{12}$ ⬤ $\frac{2}{3}$

8. $\frac{2}{5}$ ⬤ $\frac{3}{7}$

9. $\frac{5}{6}$ ⬤ $\frac{3}{4}$

10. $1\frac{4}{7}$ ⬤ $1\frac{5}{7}$

11. $2\frac{1}{2}$ ⬤ $3\frac{1}{2}$

12. $8\frac{3}{4}$ ⬤ $8\frac{7}{8}$

13. $17\frac{2}{5}$ ⬤ $16\frac{2}{3}$

14. $5\frac{1}{3}$ ⬤ $5\frac{1}{8}$

15. $12\frac{2}{7}$ ⬤ $12\frac{3}{8}$

16. $1\frac{3}{5}$ ⬤ $1\frac{6}{10}$

17. $14\frac{5}{8}$ ⬤ $14\frac{3}{5}$

18. $6\frac{1}{3}$ ⬤ $6\frac{2}{5}$

Write the numbers in order. Give the least number first.

19. $\frac{5}{6}, \frac{1}{6}, \frac{4}{6}$

20. $\frac{1}{5}, \frac{1}{2}, \frac{1}{3}$

21. $\frac{1}{4}, \frac{1}{6}, \frac{1}{7}$

22. $\frac{3}{5}, \frac{1}{2}, \frac{7}{10}$

23. $\frac{4}{5}, \frac{2}{3}, \frac{5}{6}$

24. $\frac{2}{3}, \frac{5}{6}, \frac{7}{12}$

157

Tues. $\frac{3}{8}$ in.

Mon. $\frac{3}{4}$ in.

Plant A

Tues. $\frac{15}{16}$ in.

Mon. $\frac{1}{2}$ in.

Plant B

Adding and Subtracting Fractions

A. How tall was plant A on Tuesday?

Find $\frac{3}{4} + \frac{3}{8}$.

To add fractions with different denominators first find equal fractions with a common denominator. Then add the numerators.

$$\frac{3}{4} = \frac{6}{8}$$
$$+ \frac{3}{8} = \frac{3}{8}$$
$$\overline{\phantom{+ \frac{3}{8} = }\,\frac{9}{8} = 1\frac{1}{8}}$$

The plant was $1\frac{1}{8}$ inches tall on Tuesday.

B. How much did plant B grow between Monday and Tuesday?

Find $\frac{15}{16} - \frac{1}{2}$.

To subtract fractions with different denominators, first find equal fractions with a common denominator. Then subtract the numerators.

$$\frac{15}{16} = \frac{15}{16}$$
$$- \frac{1}{2} = \frac{8}{16}$$
$$\overline{\phantom{- \frac{1}{2} = }\,\frac{7}{16}}$$

The plant grew $\frac{7}{16}$ of an inch.

Add.

1. $\dfrac{5}{6} = \dfrac{20}{24}$
$+\dfrac{3}{8} = \dfrac{9}{24}$

2. $\dfrac{1}{5} = \dfrac{}{10}$
$+\dfrac{3}{10} = \dfrac{}{10}$

3. $\dfrac{1}{3} = \dfrac{}{18}$
$\dfrac{5}{6} = \dfrac{}{18}$
$+\dfrac{4}{9} = \dfrac{}{18}$

4. $\dfrac{7}{8} + \dfrac{3}{4}$

5. $\dfrac{1}{5} + \dfrac{2}{3}$

6. $\dfrac{3}{4} + \dfrac{1}{5}$

7. $\dfrac{5}{9} + \dfrac{1}{2}$

8. $\dfrac{1}{4} + \dfrac{1}{6}$

9. $\dfrac{5}{6} + \dfrac{3}{10}$

10. $\dfrac{3}{4} + \dfrac{4}{7}$

11. $\dfrac{1}{4} + \dfrac{1}{9}$

12. $\dfrac{1}{8} + \dfrac{1}{4} + \dfrac{7}{16}$

13. $\dfrac{1}{2} + \dfrac{3}{5} + \dfrac{1}{4}$

Subtract.

14. $\dfrac{2}{3} = \dfrac{8}{12}$
$-\dfrac{5}{12} = \dfrac{5}{12}$

15. $\dfrac{9}{10} = \dfrac{}{30}$
$-\dfrac{5}{6} = \dfrac{}{30}$

16. $\dfrac{3}{7} = \dfrac{}{28}$
$-\dfrac{1}{4} = \dfrac{}{28}$

17. $\dfrac{1}{2} - \dfrac{1}{6}$

18. $\dfrac{7}{8} - \dfrac{3}{4}$

19. $\dfrac{7}{9} - \dfrac{1}{3}$

20. $\dfrac{4}{5} - \dfrac{2}{3}$

21. $\dfrac{1}{2} - \dfrac{2}{5}$

22. $\dfrac{3}{4} - \dfrac{3}{10}$

23. $\dfrac{5}{6} - \dfrac{1}{8}$

24. $\dfrac{3}{4} - \dfrac{2}{3}$

25. $\dfrac{11}{12} - \dfrac{1}{8}$

26. $\dfrac{6}{7} - \dfrac{1}{3}$

**More practice
Set G, page 191**

Some students are checking the weekly growth of seedlings. For each sample find the total height on Sunday.

	Sample	Height Monday	Growth	Height Sunday
27.	A	$\frac{1}{8}$ in.	$\frac{3}{4}$ in.	
28.	B	$\frac{3}{16}$ in.	$\frac{1}{2}$ in.	
29.	C	$\frac{1}{2}$ in.	$\frac{11}{16}$ in.	

Using only four 4's, write each of the whole numbers 0 through 10. You may use fractions or whole numbers and addition, subtraction, multiplication, or division.

Here are two ways to write the number 1.

$$1 = \dfrac{4}{4} \times \dfrac{4}{4}$$

$$1 = 4 - 4 + \dfrac{4}{4}$$

Adding Mixed Numbers

A. The boys' high-jump record at Wilson High School was $66\frac{1}{2}$ inches. Clem broke the record by $2\frac{7}{8}$ inches. How high did Clem jump?

Find $66\frac{1}{2} + 2\frac{7}{8}$.

8 is a common denominator.

$$66\frac{1}{2} = 66\frac{4}{8}$$
$$+\ 2\frac{7}{8} = \ \ 2\frac{7}{8}$$
$$\overline{\qquad\qquad 68\frac{11}{8} = 69\frac{3}{8}}$$

Clem jumped $69\frac{3}{8}$ inches.

B. Find $3\frac{1}{8} + 2\frac{5}{6}$.

24 is a common denominator.

$$3\frac{1}{8} = 3\frac{3}{24}$$
$$+\ 2\frac{5}{6} = 2\frac{20}{24}$$
$$\overline{\qquad\quad 5\frac{23}{24}}$$

C. Find $18\frac{3}{4} + 22\frac{1}{4}$.

$$18\frac{3}{4}$$
$$+\ 22\frac{1}{4}$$
$$\overline{\quad 40\frac{4}{4} = 41}$$

Add.

1. $3\frac{1}{6}$
   $+ 4\frac{1}{2}$

2. $6\frac{1}{4}$
   $+ 7\frac{2}{3}$

3. $2\frac{1}{6}$
   $+ 5\frac{5}{6}$

4. $1\frac{2}{3}$
   $+ 9\frac{2}{3}$

5. $3\frac{1}{2}$
   $+ 7\frac{7}{8}$

6. $5\frac{7}{16}$
   $+ 4\frac{3}{8}$

7. $25\frac{1}{4}$
   $+ 8\frac{5}{6}$

8. $12\frac{1}{5}$
   $+ 20\frac{3}{4}$

9. $15\frac{1}{3}$
   $+ 3\frac{2}{3}$

10. $9\frac{4}{5} + 3\frac{1}{2}$

11. $7\frac{2}{5} + 8\frac{1}{3}$

12. $11\frac{1}{2} + 38\frac{3}{7}$

13. $12\frac{7}{8} + 4\frac{3}{4}$

14. $8\frac{5}{6} + 15\frac{2}{3}$

15. $17\frac{1}{2} + 12\frac{1}{3}$

16. $46\frac{9}{10} + 9\frac{2}{5}$

17. $11\frac{3}{4} + 2\frac{1}{6}$

18. $16\frac{1}{2} + 10\frac{1}{2}$

19. $6\frac{1}{8} + 6\frac{1}{4}$

20. $1\frac{5}{8} + 2\frac{5}{8} + \frac{7}{8}$

21. $3\frac{5}{6} + 4\frac{2}{3} + 3\frac{1}{2}$

**More practice
Set H, page 191**

These problems involve other sports events at Wilson High School.

22. The boys' pole-vault record was 175 inches. Ernie broke the record by $3\frac{5}{8}$ inches. How high did Ernie pole vault?

23. The girls' record for the high jump was $56\frac{3}{4}$ inches. Sally broke the record by $1\frac{1}{2}$ inches. How high did Sally jump?

24. The boys' record for the long jump was $273\frac{1}{2}$ inches. Art broke the record by $1\frac{7}{8}$ inches. How far did Art jump?

25. Karen set a new record for the 100-yard dash. She ran 100 yards in $12\frac{1}{2}$ seconds. The previous record was $2\frac{7}{10}$ seconds longer. What was the previous record?

26. Diane set a new record for swimming 100 meters. She swam this distance in $73\frac{1}{10}$ seconds. The previous record was $1\frac{4}{5}$ seconds longer. What was the previous record?

Subtracting Mixed Numbers

A. In 1973 the women's world record for the 220-yard dash was $22\frac{3}{5}$ seconds. Fran ran 220 yards in $27\frac{1}{10}$ seconds. Fran's time was how much slower than the world record? Find $27\frac{3}{5} - 22\frac{1}{10}$.

10 is a common denominator.

$$27\frac{3}{5} = 27\frac{6}{10}$$
$$- 22\frac{1}{10} = 22\frac{1}{10}$$
$$\overline{\phantom{-22\frac{1}{10} = } 5\frac{5}{10} = 5\frac{1}{2}}$$

Fran's time was $5\frac{1}{2}$ seconds slower than the world record.

B. Find $5 - 3\frac{1}{4}$.

$$5 = 4\frac{4}{4}$$
$$- 3\frac{1}{4} = 3\frac{1}{4}$$
$$\overline{\phantom{-3\frac{1}{4} = } 1\frac{3}{4}}$$

Rename 5 to show a fraction in fourths.

c. Find $4\frac{1}{2} - 2\frac{2}{3}$.

6 is a common denominator.

Rename $4\frac{3}{6}$ to show more sixths.

$$4\frac{1}{2} = 4\frac{3}{6} = 3\frac{9}{6}$$
$$- 2\frac{2}{3} = 2\frac{4}{6} = 2\frac{4}{6}$$
$$\overline{\phantom{-2\frac{2}{3}=2\frac{4}{6}=}\,1\frac{5}{6}}$$

Subtract.

1. $\quad 7 \quad\; = 6\frac{10}{10}$
$\quad\; - 1\frac{3}{10} = 1\frac{3}{10}$

2. $\quad 4\frac{1}{2} = 4\frac{\boxed{}}{6} = 3\frac{\boxed{}}{6}$
$\quad\; - 2\frac{5}{6} = 2\frac{5}{6} = 2\frac{5}{6}$

3. $\quad 1\frac{1}{5} = 1\frac{\boxed{}}{20} = \frac{\boxed{}}{20}$
$\quad\; - \frac{3}{4} = \frac{\boxed{}}{20} = \frac{\boxed{}}{20}$

4. $\quad 24\frac{5}{8} = 24\frac{\boxed{}}{24} = 23\frac{\boxed{}}{24}$
$\quad\; - 11\frac{2}{3} = 11\frac{\boxed{}}{24} = 11\frac{\boxed{}}{24}$

5. $\quad 7\frac{5}{6}$
$\quad\; - 4\frac{1}{3}$

6. $\quad 5\frac{3}{8}$
$\quad\; - 1\frac{5}{8}$

7. $\quad 8$
$\quad\; - 6\frac{1}{3}$

8. $\quad 3\frac{2}{3}$
$\quad\; - 1\frac{1}{4}$

9. $6\frac{2}{3} - 2\frac{5}{6}$

10. $9\frac{4}{5} - 4\frac{1}{10}$

11. $10 - 6\frac{3}{4}$

12. $3\frac{1}{2} - 3\frac{1}{6}$

13. $2 - 1\frac{3}{8}$

14. $2\frac{8}{9} - 1\frac{1}{2}$

15. $4\frac{7}{10} - 2\frac{9}{10}$

16. $14\frac{3}{4} - 9\frac{1}{5}$

17. $36\frac{3}{8} - 24\frac{1}{4}$

18. $18 - \frac{7}{12}$

19. $1\frac{5}{8} - \frac{3}{4}$

20. $15 - 6\frac{5}{7}$

Each student's time is how much slower than the 1973 world record?

21. 100 yards—Women
Record: 10 seconds
Lillian: $14\frac{3}{4}$ seconds

22. 100 yards—Men
Record: $9\frac{1}{10}$ seconds
Tim: $11\frac{1}{2}$ seconds

23. 220 yards—Men
Record: $19\frac{1}{2}$ seconds
Melvin: 24 seconds

24. 440 yards—Women
Record: $52\frac{2}{5}$ seconds
Maria: $58\frac{7}{10}$ seconds

25. 440 yards—Men
Record: $44\frac{9}{10}$ seconds
Sam: $51\frac{4}{5}$ seconds

★ **26.** 1 mile—Women
Record: 4 minutes and $34\frac{9}{10}$ seconds
Alice: 9 minutes and $14\frac{3}{5}$ seconds

**More practice
Set I, page 191**

Equations Involving Fractions

A. Shelly grew $3\frac{1}{2}$ inches since last May and is now $51\frac{3}{4}$ inches tall. How tall was Shelly last May?

Write an equation. Use n for the number you want to find.

$$n + 3\frac{1}{2} = 51\frac{3}{4}$$

Solve for n. $3\frac{1}{2}$ was added to n so subtract $3\frac{1}{2}$ from both sides.

$$n + 3\frac{1}{2} - 3\frac{1}{2} = 51\frac{3}{4} - 3\frac{1}{2}$$

$$n = 51\frac{3}{4} - 3\frac{1}{2}$$

$$n = 48\frac{1}{4}$$

Answer the question.

Shelly was $48\frac{1}{4}$ inches tall last May.

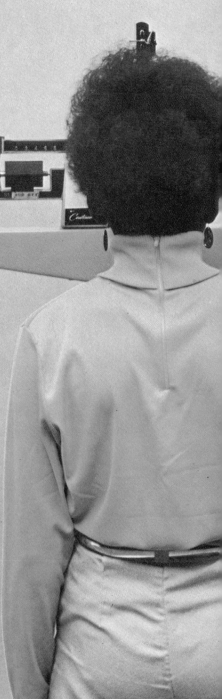

B. Shelly lost $1\frac{1}{4}$ pounds, and now she weighs $94\frac{1}{2}$ pounds. How much did Shelly weigh before she lost the weight?

Write an equation.

$$k - 1\frac{1}{4} = 94\frac{1}{2}$$

Solve for k.

$1\frac{1}{4}$ was subtracted from k, so add $1\frac{1}{4}$ to both sides.

$$k - 1\frac{1}{4} + 1\frac{1}{4} = 94\frac{1}{2} + 1\frac{1}{4}$$

$$k = 94\frac{1}{2} + 1\frac{1}{4}$$

$$k = 95\frac{3}{4}$$

Answer the question.

Shelly weighed $95\frac{3}{4}$ pounds before she lost the weight.

Solve the equations.

1. $k + \frac{1}{6} = \frac{5}{6}$

2. $m - \frac{3}{4} = \frac{3}{4}$

3. $x - \frac{2}{3} = 6$

4. $1\frac{3}{8} + n = 2$

5. $\frac{1}{2} + h = \frac{3}{4}$

6. $4\frac{1}{6} + z = 8\frac{2}{3}$

7. $n - \frac{1}{5} = 2\frac{3}{10}$

8. $n - 5\frac{2}{3} = 7\frac{1}{2}$

9. $25\frac{1}{3} + s = 28$

10. $d + 37\frac{1}{2} = 42\frac{3}{4}$

11. $m - 12\frac{9}{10} = 14\frac{1}{5}$

12. $10\frac{1}{2} + n = 47\frac{4}{5}$

Find the answers.

13. The normal body temperature is $98\frac{6}{10}$ degrees F. When Ruth was ill, her temperature rose to 101 degrees. This is how many degrees above normal?

14. Rosa rode $4\frac{3}{4}$ miles. Then she rested and rode on. If she rode $10\frac{7}{8}$ miles in all, how far did she ride after resting?

15. After Mr. Gordon sold $12\frac{1}{2}$ yards of material, there were $5\frac{3}{4}$ yards left on the bolt. How much material was on the bolt before the sale?

16. After Phyllis poured $2\frac{1}{4}$ cups of milk from a pitcher, there were $5\frac{1}{8}$ cups left. How much milk had been in the pitcher?

Laboratory Activity

Plant popcorn seeds as shown in the picture. Set the glass in a sunny place and keep the towel moist with water.

When the green stems appear, select one plant to measure. Each day for a week, measure the length of the stem to the nearest sixteenth of an inch. Then find how much the stem grew each day.

Your popcorn plants should continue growing if you transplant them in soil out-of-doors.

Chapter 8 Test
Adding and Subtracting Fractions and Mixed Numbers, Pages 156-165

Finding common denominators; comparing numbers, pages 156-157

Write with a common denominator.

1. $\frac{1}{2}, \frac{2}{3}$

2. $\frac{5}{8}, \frac{5}{6}$

Compare the numbers.

3. $\frac{2}{3}$ ⬤ $\frac{5}{6}$

4. $1\frac{3}{4}$ ⬤ $1\frac{7}{8}$

5. $4\frac{5}{6}$ ⬤ $4\frac{3}{4}$

Adding fractions and mixed numbers, pages 158-161

Add.

6. $\frac{3}{10} + \frac{1}{5}$

7. $5 + 1\frac{4}{7}$

8. $6\frac{1}{3} + 3\frac{2}{3}$

9. $1\frac{1}{6} + 2\frac{5}{12}$

10. $9\frac{5}{8} + \frac{2}{3}$

Subtracting fractions and mixed numbers, pages 158-159, 162-163

Subtract.

11. $\frac{5}{6} - \frac{1}{9}$

12. $5\frac{1}{2} - 1\frac{1}{4}$

13. $3 - \frac{1}{8}$

14. $6\frac{5}{6} - 3\frac{3}{4}$

15. $4\frac{1}{3} - 2\frac{5}{9}$

16. $8 - 3\frac{2}{3}$

Solving equations, pages 164-165

Solve each equation.

17. $m + \frac{1}{3} = 2$

18. $1\frac{1}{2} + h = 4\frac{1}{2}$

19. $k - \frac{3}{4} = 5$

20. $n - 3\frac{5}{6} = 1\frac{1}{3}$

Problem solving, pages 158-165

21. Marilyn ran the 100-yard dash in $15\frac{2}{5}$ seconds. Diane ran the same distance in $16\frac{7}{10}$ seconds. Find the difference between Marilyn's time and Diane's time.

22. After a carpenter cut $4\frac{7}{8}$ feet from a board, there was a $5\frac{3}{4}$ foot piece of board left. How long was the board before it was cut?

23. Carole's dog weighed $7\frac{1}{4}$ pounds in June. Since then the dog has gained $3\frac{1}{2}$ pounds. How much does the dog weigh now?

24. Ann's sunflower plant grew $1\frac{2}{3}$ feet since last Saturday and is now $5\frac{1}{2}$ feet tall. How tall was the plant last Saturday?

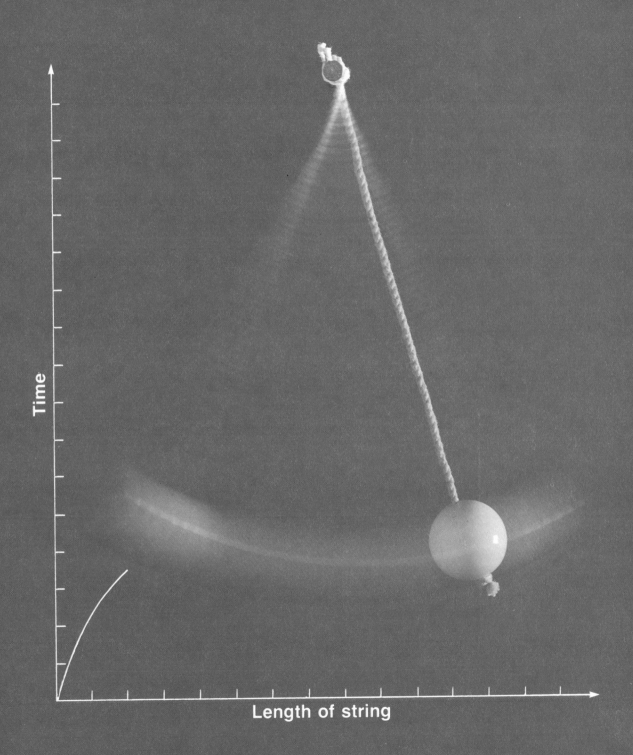

Time

Length of string

Locating Points for Ordered Pairs

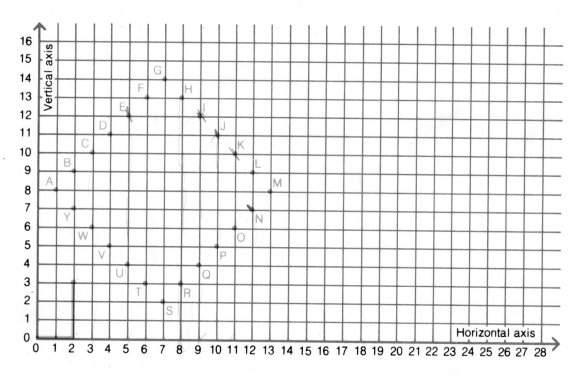

You can use ordered pairs of numbers to locate points on a grid. Start at point (0, 0).

(2,3)

Move 2 units to the right. ⌐ ⌐ Then move 3 units up.

Here is a social studies puzzle. To find the answers, locate the point for each ordered pair. Then write the letter for the point.

1. World's longest river

(12, 7) (9, 12) (12, 9) (5, 12)

2. World's oldest city

(10, 11) (5, 12) (8, 3) (9, 12)
(3, 10) (8, 13) (11, 6)

3. World city with the greatest population

(6, 3) (11, 6) (11, 10) (2, 7)
(11, 6)

4. Country that produces the most tea.

(9, 12) (12, 7) (4, 11) (9, 12)
(1, 8)

5. Country with the most tourists

(9, 12) (6, 3) (1, 8) (12, 9) (2, 7)

6. U.S. state with the fewest telephones

(1, 8) (12, 9) (1, 8) (7, 2) (11, 10)
(1, 8)

7. Southernmost U.S. city

(8, 13) (9, 12) (12, 9) (11, 6)

Moving Figures on a Grid

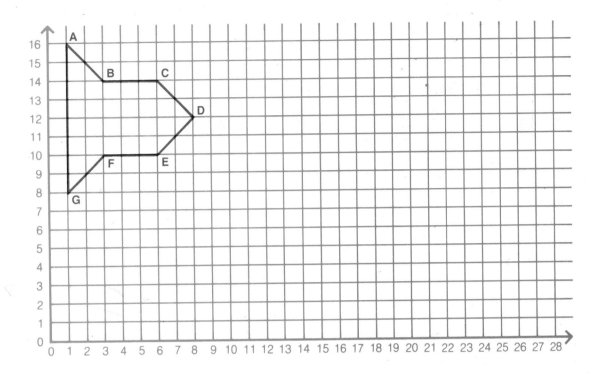

1. Copy the outline of the space capsule on a grid. Write ordered pairs for points A through G.

For each of these exercises, start with the ordered pairs from exercise 1. Change the ordered pairs as described. Then use the new pairs to draw another picture on the same grid.

2. Add 7 to the first number in each pair.

3. Add 14 to the first number in each pair.

4. Subtract 8 from the second number in each pair.

5. Add 7 to the first number in each pair and subtract 8 from the second number.

6. Add 14 to the first number in each pair and subtract 8 from the second number.

● **Discuss** How do the new pictures compare with the original picture?

7. Do you see more than six space capsules on your grid?

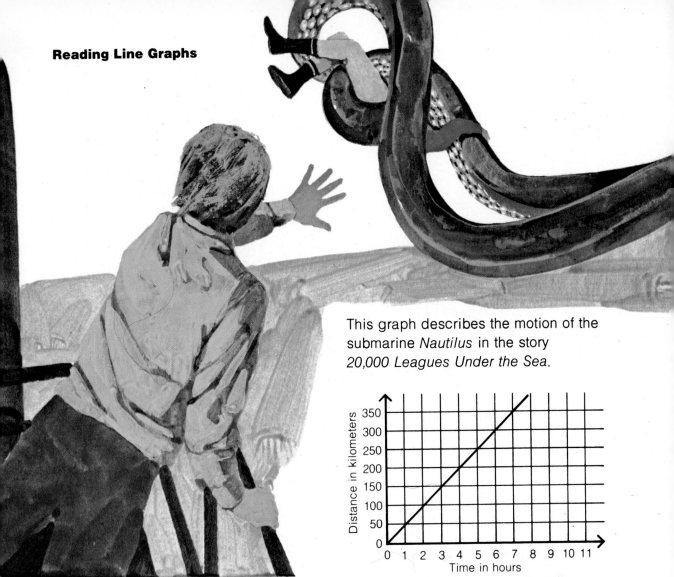

This graph describes the motion of the submarine *Nautilus* in the story *20,000 Leagues Under the Sea.*

1. How far did the *Nautilus* travel in

   a. 2 hours?

   b. 3 hours?

   c. 5 hours?

2. How long did it take to travel

   a. 50 kilometers?

   b. 200 kilometers?

   c. 350 kilometers?

"Just as we were pressing one on the other to reach the platform, two other arms, lashing the air, came down on the seaman placed before Captain Nemo, and lifted him up with irresistible power. Captain Nemo uttered a cry, and rushed out."

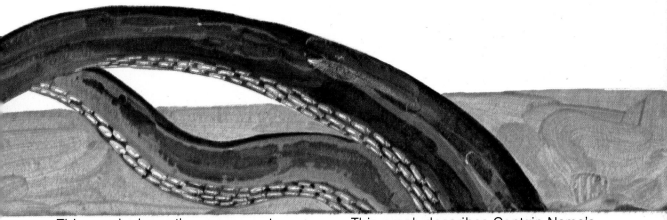

This graph shows the pressure at various depths in the ocean. There is 1 atmosphere of pressure at sea level.

This graph describes Captain Nemo's heartbeats while the *Nautilus* was being attacked by a giant squid.

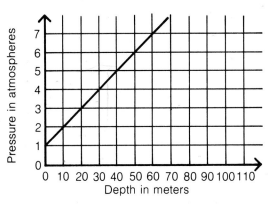

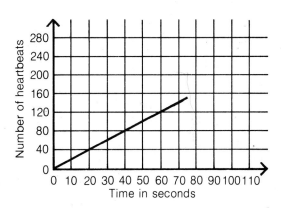

3. Give the approximate pressure at

  a. a depth of 10 meters.

  b. a depth of 50 meters.

  ★ **c.** a depth of 25 meters.

4. At what depth is the pressure about

  a. 3 atmospheres?

  b. 6 atmospheres?

  ★ **c.** 5.5 atmospheres?

5. About how many heartbeats occurred

  a. in 20 seconds?

  b. in 60 seconds?

  c. in 80 seconds?

6. About how many seconds did it take

  a. for 80 heartbeats?

  b. for 60 heartbeats?

  c. for 200 heartbeats?

Making Line Graphs for Equations

1. The bowling ball is traveling 4 meters per second. Use this formula to complete the table.

Distance in meters ⟶ Time in seconds ⟶

$$d = 4t$$

t	d
0	0
1	4
2	
3	
4	

2. Make a graph on a grid like the one below. Locate points for ordered pairs obtained from your table. Connect the points.

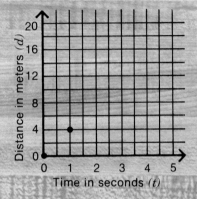

Use your graph to answer these questions.

3. About how far does the ball travel

   a. in .5 second?

   b. in 3.5 seconds?

   c. in 5.0 seconds?

4. About how much time does it take the ball to travel

   a. 6 meters?

   b. 10 meters?

   c. the length of the bowling alley (about 18 meters)?

Pat's bowling handicap is 50. She adds her handicap to her scratch score (actual score) to get her final score.

To compute a bowler's handicap, subtract the average scratch score from 200 and then multiply by .8.

5. Use this formula to complete the table.

Final score ↓   Scratch score ↓

$$f = s + 50$$

s	f
0	50
75	125
100	
175	

8. Use this formula to complete the table.

Handicap ↓   Average scratch score ↓

$$h = .8\,(200 - a)$$

a	h	
0	160	.8(200 − 0)
75	100	.8(200 − 75)
100		.8(200 − 100)
175		.8(200 − 175)

6. Make a graph for the formula. Write "Scratch score s" along the horizontal axis. Write "Final score f" along the vertical axis. Use these labels on each axis: 0, 25, 50, and so on, up to 300.

7. Use your graph to find Pat's scratch score when her final score is 175.

9. Make a graph for the formula. Write "Average scratch score (a)" along the horizontal axis. Use these labels: 0, 25, 50, and so on, up to 200. Write "Handicap h" along the vertical axis. Use these labels: 0, 20, 40, and so on, up to 200.

10. Ted's handicap is 60. Use your graph to find his scratch score.

Using Graphs to Solve Problems

In the latest episode of *Alaska Four-Nine*, police chief Steve McCarrot was chasing the archcriminal known as the Nome Gnome.

The Gnome left town at noon by dog sled, traveling 40 kilometers per hour.

McCarrot left town at 1:30 P.M. in a helicopter with Sandusky, his trusty husky. McCarrot traveled 60 kilometers per hour.

1. Complete the tables. Draw both graphs on one grid.

Use your graph to answer these questions.

2. When McCarrot left at 1:30, how far had the Gnome already traveled?

3. When McCarrot caught up to the Gnome, what time was it and how far were they from town?

Nome Gnome	
Time	Distance in kilometers
Noon	0
1:00	40
2:00	80
3:00	
4:00	
5:00	
6:00	

Steve McCarrot	
Time	Distance in kilometers
1:30	0
2:30	60
3:30	120
4:30	
5:30	

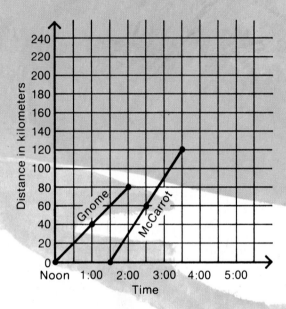

Meanwhile, back at the Snow Bank, police detective Felicia Fairbanks was chasing the Gnome's accomplice, Ken Ketchikan.

Ken left the bank at noon and traveled 60 kilometers per hour.

Felicia left the bank at 1:00 P.M. and traveled 100 kilometers per hour.

4. Complete the tables below. Draw both graphs on one grid.

5. When Felicia caught up to Ken, what time was it and how far were they from the bank?

Ken Ketchikan		Felicia Fairbanks	
Time	Distance in kilometers	Time	Distance in kilometers
Noon	0		
1:00	60	1:00	0
2:00		2:00	100
3:00		3:00	
4:00		4:00	

175

Writing Equations for Tables and Graphs

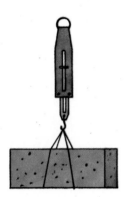

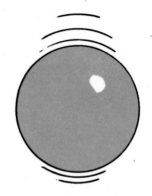

A.

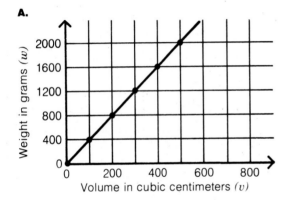

B.

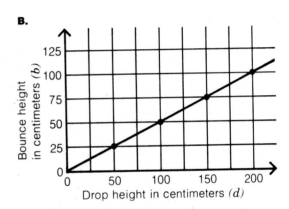

Graph A gives the weight and the volume for different-sized samples of bricks.

1. Write ordered pairs for four points on the graph.

2. Which equation fits the data?

   $w = 3v$ $w = 4v$ $w = v + 4$

3. Write an equation for the table.

r	1	2	3	4
t	3	6	9	12

$t = \text{⬛}r$

Graph B gives the height from which a ball is dropped and the height to which it bounces.

4. Write ordered pairs for four points on the graph.

5. Which equation fits the data?

   $b = \dfrac{d}{2}$ $b = d + 2$ $b = \dfrac{d}{25}$

6. Write an equation for the table.

k	3	12	21	27
m	1	4	7	9

$m = \dfrac{k}{\text{⬛}}$

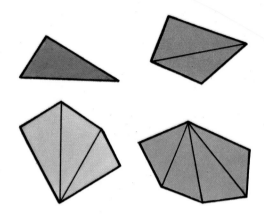

C.

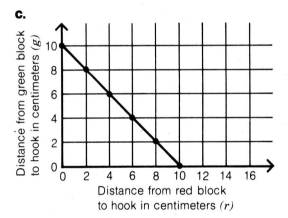

Distance from green block to hook in centimeters (g) [vertical axis, marked 0, 2, 4, 6, 8, 10]

Distance from red block to hook in centimeters (r) [horizontal axis, marked 0, 2, 4, 6, 8, 10, 12, 14, 16]

D.

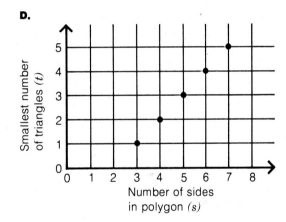

Smallest number of triangles (t) [vertical axis, marked 0, 1, 2, 3, 4, 5]

Number of sides in polygon (s) [horizontal axis, marked 0, 1, 2, 3, 4, 5, 6, 7, 8]

Graph C gives distances for the blocks as the string is moved over the hook.

7. Write ordered pairs for four points on the graph.

8. Which equation fits the data?

$$g = 10r \qquad g = r + 4 \qquad g = 10 - r$$

9. Write an equation for the table.

w	1	2	3	4
z	4	3	2	1

$z = \text{▦} - w$

Graph D shows the relationship of polygons and the triangles determined by the diagonals.

10. Write ordered pairs for four points on the graph.

11. Which equation fits the data?

$$t = s - 2 \qquad t = 2s \qquad t = s + 5$$

12. Write an equation for the table.

g	4	6	7	9
h	1	3	4	6

$h = g - \text{▦}$

177

Laboratory Activity

Use string, tape, and marbles to make pendulums as shown below.

With the second hand on a clock or a stopwatch, time 20 full swings of each pendulum. A full swing means back and forth. The size of the swing does not matter.

Record your results in a table and make a graph.

Length of pendulum in centimeters	Time for 20 full swings in seconds
0	0
10	
15	
20	
25	
30	
35	
40	

As the length increases, does the time for 20 swings increase or decrease?

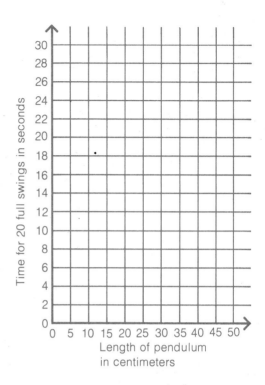

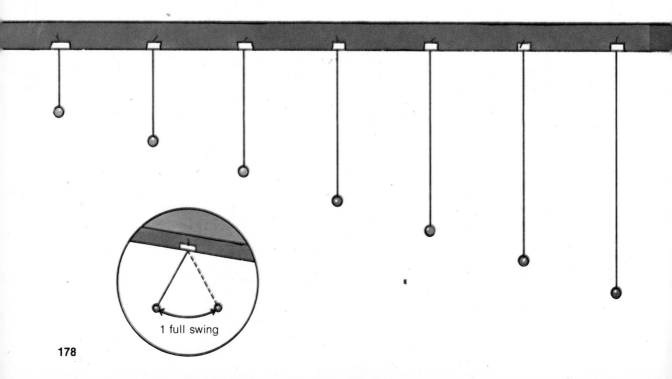

1 full swing

Side Trip

1. Follow these directions to make the first design at the right.

   Draw a circle with a compass. Using the same compass setting, mark six points on the circle.

   With the point of the compass on each of the six marks, draw six more circles.

   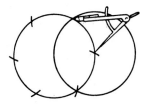

2. Use a compass and a straightedge to copy the design at the right, or make up your own design.

179

Locating Points in Four Quadrants

You can use ordered pairs of integers to locate points on a grid.
Start at the *origin*, point (0, 0). The first number in a pair tells you to move to the right (if positive) or to the left (if negative). The second number tells you to move up (if positive) or down (if negative).

For each exercise, write ordered pairs for the labeled points and copy the figure. Change the sign of the first number in each ordered pair. Draw the resulting figure. Then go back to the original set of pairs and change the sign of the second number in each pair. Draw the resulting figure.

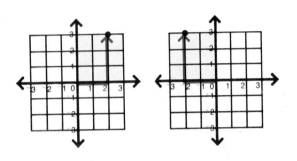

Point (2, 3) is in the first *quadrant*.

Point (⁻2, 3) is in the second quadrant.

1.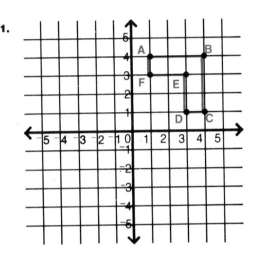

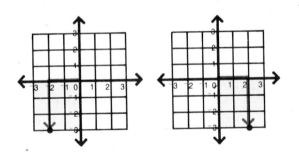

Point (⁻2, ⁻3) is in the third quadrant.

Point (2, ⁻3) is in the fourth quadrant.

2.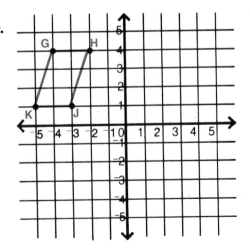

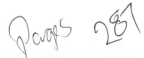

180

Four-in-a-Row

This is a game for two players. Place a blank sheet of paper over the game board. Players take turns marking points on the grid. One player marks X's. The other marks O's. Each time a point is marked, that player must say the ordered pair for the point. Any player who says the wrong ordered pair loses a turn.

The winner is the first person to make four marks in a row horizontally, vertically, or diagonally.

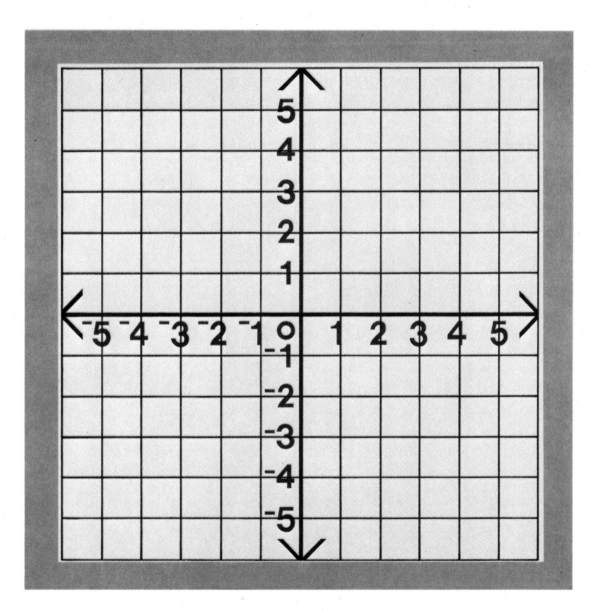

Making Line Graphs for Equations in Four Quadrants

A.

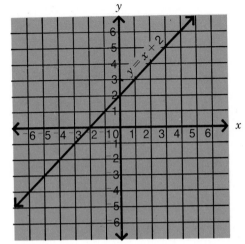

B.

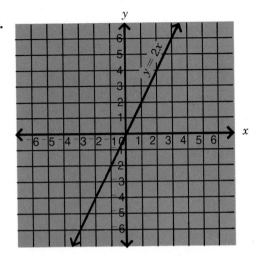

Draw the graph for $y = x + 2$ as shown in diagram A. Complete the tables. Draw all the graphs on the same grid.

Draw the graph for $y = 2x$ as shown in diagram B. Complete the tables. Draw all the graphs on the same grid.

1. $y = x + 1$

x	y
4	5
2	3
⁻1	
⁻5	
⁻6	

3. $y = x - 2$

x	y
5	
2	
0	
⁻1	
⁻4	

5. $y = 3x$

x	y
2	6
1	3
0	
⁻1	
⁻2	

7. $y = {}^-1x$

x	y
6	⁻6
3	
0	
⁻2	
⁻5	

2. $y = x - 1$

x	y
6	5
0	⁻1
⁻2	
⁻3	
⁻5	

4. $y = x + 4$

x	y
2	6
0	
⁻1	
⁻2	
⁻6	

6. $y = {}^-2x$

x	y
3	
2	
0	
⁻1	
⁻2	

8. $y = {}^-3x$

x	y
2	⁻6
1	
0	
⁻1	
⁻2	

c.

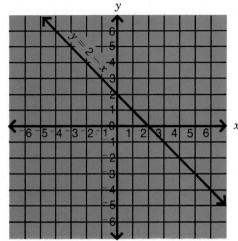

Draw the graph for $y = 2 - x$ as shown in diagram C. Complete the tables. Draw all the graphs on the same grid.

How many different ways can you wrap a rubber band around the nails to form a square?

9. $y = 4 - x$

x	y
6	⁻2
4	0
3	
2	
⁻2	

11. $y = {}^{-}2 - x$

x	y
4	⁻6
3	
1	
0	
⁻4	

10. $y = 1 - x$

x	y
5	⁻4
3	⁻2
1	
0	
⁻4	

12. $y = {}^{-}1 - x$

x	y
5	⁻6
3	
1	
0	
⁻5	

Reading and Making Curved Graphs

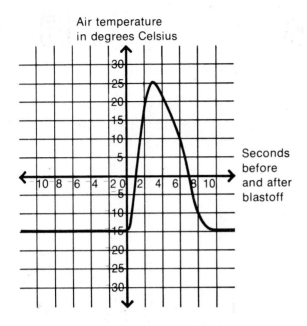

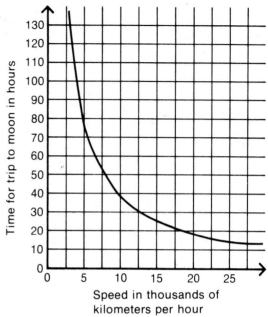

This graph shows the air temperature recorded by an observer of a space launch on a cold winter day.

1. What was the temperature before blastoff?

2. What was the temperature

   a. 1 second after blastoff?

   b. 6 seconds after blastoff?

   c. 8 seconds after blastoff?

3. When was the temperature highest?

4. What was the highest temperature?

5. When did the temperature return to ⁻15°C?

The graph shown above tells how long it takes to travel from the earth to the moon at different speeds.

6. As speed increases, does the time increase or decrease?

7. About how many hours does a trip to the moon take if you travel

   a. 5000 kilometers per hour?

   b. 10,000 kilometers per hour?

   c. 25,000 kilometers per hour?

8. About what speed is needed to make the trip in one 24-hour day?

★9. Apollo 11 averaged 6400 kilometers per hour coming back from the moon. The trip was about how many hours?

10. Here is a formula for a falling object on the moon. Complete the table. Draw the graph on a grid like the one shown at the right.

Distance in meters → Time in seconds →

$$d = .8\, t^2$$

Remember:
t^2 means t times t.

t	d
0	0
5	20
10	80
15	
20	
25	

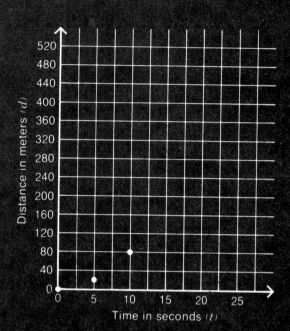

11. On the earth, an object dropped from a height of 500 meters takes about 10 seconds to reach the ground. How long would it take the object to drop on the moon?

185

CAREERS   Automobile Mechanic

A skilled automobile mechanic is interested in the performance of various kinds of cars. A mechanic often studies graphs to get a picture of a car's performance.

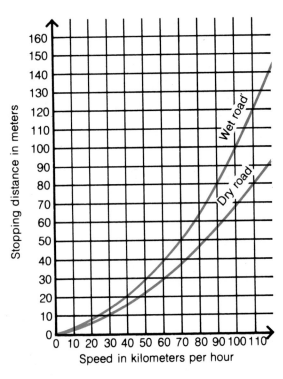

This graph gives the stopping distance for a car at different speeds on a wet road and a dry road.

1. What is the stopping distance on a dry road when the car is going

   a. 60 kilometers per hour?

   b. 110 kilometers per hour?

2. What is the car's speed on a wet road when the stopping distance is

   a. 30 meters?

   b. 110 meters?

3. At 100 kilometers per hour on a dry road, can the car stop in 60 meters?

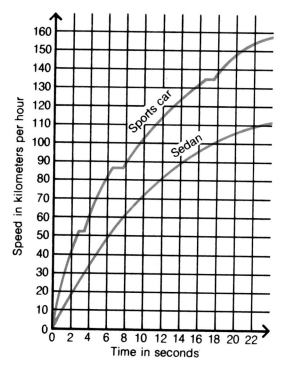

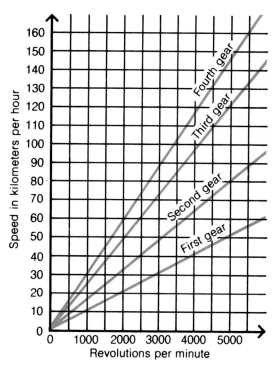

This graph gives the speed for two cars accelerating from a standing stop.

4. What was the sedan's speed after

   a. 6 seconds?

   b. 14 seconds?

5. How many seconds did it take the sports car to reach a speed of

   a. 80 kilometers per hour?

   b. 140 kilometers per hour?

6. After 10 seconds, what was the difference of the speeds of the two cars?

This graph shows how a car's speed in a certain gear depends on the number of engine revolutions per minute.

7. What is the car's speed at

   a. 2000 revolutions per minute in first gear?

   b. 5000 revolutions per minute in third gear?

8. How many revolutions per minute occur when the car is traveling

   a. 40 kilometers per hour in second gear?

   b. 145 kilometers per hour in fourth gear?

Graphing in one quadrant, pages 168–178, 184–185

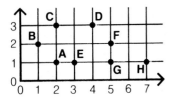

Give the ordered pair for each point.

1. A   **2.** C   **3.** E

Name the point for each ordered pair.

4. (5, 2)   **5.** (1, 2)

The graph below shows how far Marie drove on an interstate highway.

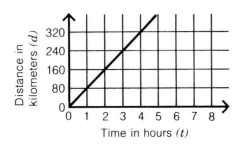

6. How far did she drive in 3 hours?

7. How long did it take her to drive 160 kilometers?

8. Which is the equation for the graph?

$$d = 80t \qquad d = t + 80 \qquad d = t - 8$$

The graph below gives the speed of a boat in a race.

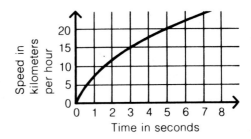

9. What was the boat's speed after 3 seconds?

10. How long did it take the boat to reach a speed of 20 kilometers per hour?

Graphing in four quadrants, pages 180–185

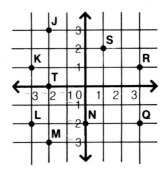

Give the ordered pair for each point.

11. J   **12.** M   **13.** N

Name the point for each ordered pair.

14. ($^-$3, $^-$2)   **15.** (3, $^-$2)

Unit 3 Test

Multiplying and dividing fractions and mixed numbers, pages 132–153

1. Rename $\frac{9}{30}$ in lowest terms.

2. Give a mixed number for $\frac{26}{7}$.

3. Express $8\frac{3}{5}$ as a fraction.

4. Express $\frac{2}{3}$ as a repeating decimal.

5. Give the reciprocal of $2\frac{1}{2}$.

6. Find $\frac{3}{4}$ of 41.

7. Solve $1\frac{3}{8}x = 33$.

Find each answer.

8. $\frac{7}{8} \times \frac{4}{9}$

9. $3\frac{1}{3} \times 1\frac{1}{5}$

10. $\frac{3}{4} \div \frac{7}{8}$

11. $2\frac{2}{3} \div 5\frac{1}{3}$

12. $\frac{2}{5}$ of the 485 students at Stanford School eat lunch in the cafeteria. How many students eat in the cafeteria?

13. A baker has $17\frac{1}{2}$ dozen cookies. How many $1\frac{1}{4}$-dozen packages can he make?

Adding and subtracting fractions and mixed numbers, pages 156–165

14. Replace ⬤ with >, <, or =.

    $6\frac{7}{8}$ ⬤ $6\frac{2}{3}$

15. Solve $\frac{2}{7} + m = 5$.

16. Solve $h - 1\frac{1}{2} = 6\frac{1}{2}$.

Find each answer.

17. $\frac{7}{8} + \frac{1}{3}$

18. $5\frac{3}{4} + 8\frac{5}{6}$

19. $\frac{9}{10} - \frac{3}{4}$

20. $7\frac{1}{3} - 2\frac{1}{2}$

21. Diane swam 200 meters in $145\frac{3}{5}$ seconds. Her previous record was $2\frac{7}{10}$ seconds longer. What was her previous record?

22. Ralph spent $3\frac{1}{2}$ hours reading and writing a book report. He spent $1\frac{3}{4}$ hours of the time reading. How long did he spend writing the report?

Graphing, pages 168–187

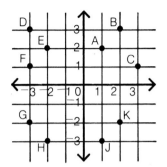

Give the ordered pair for each point.

23. A   25. F

24. C   26. H

Name the point for each ordered pair.

27. (2, 3)   29. (1, ⁻3)

28. (⁻3, ⁻2)   30. (⁻3, 3)

The graph below tells how far a train traveled.

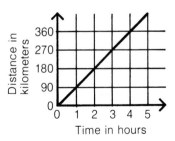

31. How far did the train travel in 2 hours?

32. How long did it take to go 270 kilometers?

More Practice

Set A

Find each missing number.

1. $\frac{4}{9} = \frac{12}{\text{□}}$

2. $\frac{9}{15} = \frac{\text{□}}{5}$

3. $\frac{3}{7} = \frac{18}{\text{□}}$

4. $\frac{15}{20} = \frac{3}{\text{□}}$

5. $\frac{7}{5} = \frac{\text{□}}{35}$

6. $\frac{3}{8} = \frac{24}{\text{□}}$

Set B

1. $\frac{10}{11} \times \frac{4}{5}$

2. $\frac{3}{4} \times \frac{5}{6}$

3. $\frac{8}{9} \times \frac{9}{16}$

4. $\frac{5}{6} \times \frac{9}{10}$

5. $\frac{3}{5} \times \frac{5}{9}$

6. $\frac{2}{3} \times \frac{6}{7}$

7. $\frac{3}{4} \times \frac{5}{6} \times \frac{8}{9}$

8. $\frac{2}{7} \times \frac{14}{15} \times \frac{5}{8}$

Set C

1. $2\frac{1}{2} \times 9\frac{1}{5}$

2. $5\frac{1}{6} \times 4$

3. $8\frac{2}{5} \times 6\frac{2}{3}$

4. $9 \times 1\frac{5}{6}$

5. $1\frac{1}{2} \times 4\frac{2}{3}$

6. $7\frac{1}{7} \times 1\frac{4}{5}$

7. $5\frac{1}{7} \times 6\frac{1}{8}$

8. $6\frac{3}{7} \times 9\frac{1}{3}$

9. $3\frac{3}{4} \times 5\frac{1}{7}$

10. $2\frac{5}{8} \times 7\frac{6}{7}$

11. $1\frac{5}{7} \times 8\frac{4}{7}$

12. $1\frac{7}{8} \times 2\frac{1}{4}$

13. $3\frac{1}{9} \times 4\frac{2}{7}$

14. $5\frac{3}{5} \times 8\frac{2}{9}$

15. $1\frac{1}{8} \times 12$

16. $9\frac{4}{9} \times 7\frac{7}{8}$

17. $3\frac{3}{7} \times 8\frac{2}{5} \times 3\frac{3}{4}$

18. $7\frac{1}{5} \times 6\frac{3}{8} \times 4\frac{4}{9}$

Set D

1. $\frac{9}{14} \div \frac{3}{4}$

2. $\frac{9}{16} \div \frac{3}{8}$

3. $\frac{2}{3} \div \frac{4}{9}$

4. $\frac{4}{7} \div \frac{2}{3}$

5. $\frac{2}{5} \div \frac{4}{5}$

6. $\frac{1}{3} \div \frac{5}{6}$

7. $\frac{7}{9} \div \frac{5}{18}$

8. $\frac{5}{8} \div \frac{15}{16}$

9. $\frac{21}{30} \div \frac{7}{12}$

10. $4\frac{2}{3} \div \frac{7}{9}$

11. $11\frac{2}{5} \div \frac{5}{12}$

12. $3\frac{1}{2} \div \frac{1}{4}$

13. $7\frac{1}{5} \div \frac{9}{20}$

14. $12\frac{1}{4} \div \frac{7}{8}$

15. $1\frac{3}{5} \div \frac{16}{25}$

16. $5\frac{1}{3} \div \frac{4}{15}$

17. $9\frac{3}{4} \div \frac{13}{16}$

18. $2\frac{1}{7} \div \frac{5}{14}$

Set E

1. $6\frac{3}{4} \div 3\frac{3}{8}$

2. $11\frac{3}{7} \div 1\frac{2}{7}$

3. $9 \div 4\frac{1}{5}$

4. $3\frac{1}{5} \div 2\frac{2}{3}$

5. $8\frac{5}{9} \div 4\frac{1}{6}$

6. $4\frac{1}{2} \div 1\frac{1}{2}$

7. $1\frac{5}{7} \div 5\frac{1}{4}$

8. $7\frac{2}{9} \div 8\frac{1}{3}$

9. $\frac{4}{5} \div 2\frac{4}{7}$

10. $5\frac{1}{3} \div 1\frac{5}{9}$

11. $12\frac{5}{6} \div 4\frac{13}{16}$

12. $10\frac{2}{5} \div 3\frac{9}{10}$

13. $2\frac{4}{7} \div 1\frac{1}{14}$

14. $5\frac{1}{4} \div 2\frac{5}{8}$

15. $8\frac{1}{6} \div 3\frac{1}{9}$

16. $9\frac{3}{5} \div 2\frac{7}{10}$

17. $4\frac{2}{3} \div 6\frac{8}{9}$

18. $6\frac{3}{7} \div 1\frac{7}{8}$

More Practice

191

Set F

For each exercise, write the fractions with a common denominator.

1. $\frac{3}{4}, \frac{2}{3}$

2. $\frac{5}{9}, \frac{15}{24}$

3. $\frac{4}{5}, \frac{12}{25}$

4. $\frac{4}{7}, \frac{1}{3}$

5. $\frac{1}{2}, \frac{3}{5}$

6. $\frac{2}{5}, \frac{1}{3}$

7. $\frac{3}{8}, \frac{5}{6}$

8. $\frac{5}{6}, \frac{5}{9}$

9. $\frac{4}{9}, \frac{1}{3}$

10. $\frac{1}{3}, \frac{5}{8}$

11. $\frac{5}{8}, \frac{4}{5}$

12. $\frac{3}{7}, \frac{3}{4}$

13. $\frac{2}{3}, \frac{3}{5}$

14. $\frac{1}{5}, \frac{2}{3}, \frac{5}{6}$

15. $\frac{3}{7}, \frac{1}{2}, \frac{5}{8}$

Set G

1. $\frac{4}{5} + \frac{1}{2}$

2. $\frac{3}{4} + \frac{2}{3}$

3. $\frac{3}{7} + \frac{5}{6}$

4. $\frac{1}{2} + \frac{3}{5}$

5. $\frac{5}{8} + \frac{4}{9}$

6. $\frac{1}{4} + \frac{5}{6}$

7. $\frac{2}{5} + \frac{1}{4}$

8. $\frac{1}{3} + \frac{3}{7}$

9. $\frac{3}{4} - \frac{1}{6}$

10. $\frac{7}{10} - \frac{3}{8}$

11. $\frac{1}{3} - \frac{2}{9}$

12. $\frac{2}{5} - \frac{1}{7}$

13. $\frac{7}{9} - \frac{7}{15}$

14. $\frac{2}{3} - \frac{1}{4}$

15. $\frac{7}{10} - \frac{1}{6}$

16. $\frac{5}{6} - \frac{1}{2}$

17. $\frac{7}{12} - \frac{7}{15}$

18. $\frac{5}{8} - \frac{2}{9}$

Set H

1. $5\frac{3}{10} + 20\frac{1}{5}$

2. $7\frac{5}{6} + 3\frac{5}{8}$

3. $18\frac{3}{4} + 6\frac{1}{6}$

4. $1\frac{3}{7} + 11\frac{3}{5}$

5. $3\frac{4}{7} + 40\frac{2}{3}$

6. $9\frac{1}{2} + 2\frac{3}{5}$

7. $35\frac{4}{5} + 5\frac{7}{8}$

8. $4\frac{1}{2} + 17\frac{1}{3}$

9. $25\frac{1}{6} + 3\frac{5}{9}$

10. $6\frac{5}{9} + 9\frac{2}{5}$

11. $4\frac{2}{3} + 8\frac{3}{8}$

12. $12\frac{1}{2} + 2\frac{2}{7}$

13. $7\frac{5}{7} + 15\frac{3}{4}$

14. $3\frac{5}{6} + 30\frac{1}{4}$

15. $16\frac{3}{4} + 4\frac{6}{7}$

16. $3\frac{3}{7} + 10\frac{4}{7}$

17. $4\frac{2}{3} + 1\frac{3}{4} + 7\frac{2}{5}$

18. $8\frac{1}{2} + 6\frac{2}{5} + 2\frac{5}{6}$

Set I

1. $4\frac{1}{5} - 2\frac{1}{6}$

2. $23\frac{4}{5} - 8\frac{3}{4}$

3. $7\frac{5}{7} - 4\frac{5}{8}$

4. $42\frac{1}{3} - 13\frac{2}{5}$

5. $1\frac{3}{4} - \frac{5}{6}$

6. $31 - 17\frac{1}{3}$

7. $8\frac{1}{2} - 4\frac{1}{7}$

8. $15\frac{2}{5} - 12\frac{1}{2}$

9. $5\frac{1}{6} - 3\frac{3}{5}$

10. $60\frac{1}{4} - 25\frac{4}{9}$

11. $2\frac{3}{8} - 1\frac{1}{4}$

12. $37\frac{3}{5} - 15\frac{1}{2}$

13. $9\frac{2}{3} - 5\frac{1}{5}$

14. $54 - 32\frac{5}{7}$

15. $6\frac{5}{8} - 3\frac{2}{3}$

16. $29\frac{5}{6} - 21\frac{4}{5}$

17. $3 - 2\frac{2}{7}$

18. $11\frac{2}{7} - 6\frac{3}{8}$

Individualized Skills Maintenance

Diagnosis

A. $15.85 + 6.7$

$.372 + .518$

$27 + 3.631$

B. $4.72 - 3.87$

$5 - 1.13$

$.5816 - .43$

C. $.6 \times 5.3$

$.48 \times 2.7$

6.05×9.13

D. $.03 \times .051$

$.007 \times .39$

$.028 \times .836$

Practice

Set A (pp. 86–87)

1. $4.83 + 86.7$
2. $24.41 + 2.9$
3. $.93 + 4.97$
4. $72.4 + .94$
5. $2.7 + 3.47$
6. $388.6 + 7.7$
7. $.365 + 5.55$
8. $.8934 + .291$
9. $4.943 + 22.9$
10. $76 + 4.83$

Set B (pp. 86–87)

1. $5.7 - 4.87$
2. $8.07 - 6.49$
3. $9 - 3.7$
4. $65.2 - 13.67$
5. $9.794 - 5.9$
6. $.6 - .364$
7. $.395 - .14$
8. $.98 - .868$
9. $80.83 - 7.22$
10. $482.1 - 1.62$

Set C (p. 92)

1. $2.6 \times .864$
2. $.6 \times .77$
3. 9.39×1.6
4. $2.15 \times .19$
5. 3.5×2.69
6. $.565 \times 6.68$
7. 8×4.6
8. 6.1×48.6
9. $.19 \times 5.21$
10. 6.75×2.18
11. $39.3 \times .687$
12. 5.3×1.9
13. $.9 \times .95$
14. $.487 \times 91.2$
15. 43×2.2
16. $4.8 \times .77$
17. 83.3×3.33
18. 3.51×65.7
19. $.7 \times 1.22$
20. $.89 \times 37.8$
21. 87.1×63.3
22. $.77 \times .491$
23. $21.6 \times .36$

Set D (p. 92)

1. $.05 \times .23$
2. $.19 \times .177$
3. $.006 \times 4.7$
4. $.146 \times .68$
5. $.057 \times .98$
6. $.06 \times .546$
7. $.157 \times .35$
8. $.081 \times .91$
9. $.24 \times .11$
10. $.009 \times 5.36$
11. $.217 \times .22$
12. $.08 \times .386$
13. $.235 \times .12$
14. $.025 \times .262$
15. $.04 \times .647$
16. $.17 \times .31$
17. $.045 \times .92$
18. $.198 \times .48$
19. $.07 \times .724$
20. $.29 \times .251$
21. $.008 \times 8.53$
22. $.226 \times .17$
23. $.09 \times .251$

Unit 4

Geometry and Measurement

$$360 \div 12 = 30$$

Parallel Lines and Transversals

Parallel lines lie in the same plane (flat surface) and do not intersect.

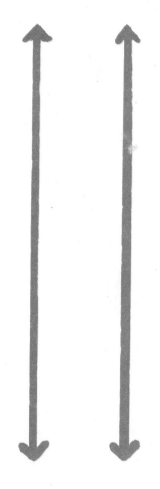

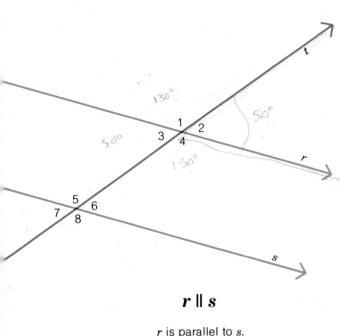

r ‖ s

r is parallel to *s*.

Lines *r* and *s* are parallel. No matter how long you make them, they will never meet.

Line *t* is a ***transversal*** of lines *r* and *s*.

1. Use your protractor to measure each angle. Complete the table.

Angle	1	2	3	4	5	6	7	8
Measure		50°						

2. Which angles have the same measure as angle 1?

3. Which angles have the same measure as angle 2?

Lines *x* and *y* are *not* parallel.

Line *z* is a transversal of lines *x* and *y*.

4. Use your protractor to measure each angle. Complete the table.

Angle	9	10	11	12	13	14	15	16
Measure					35°			

5. Do any angles have the same measure? If so, which ones?

Parallelograms

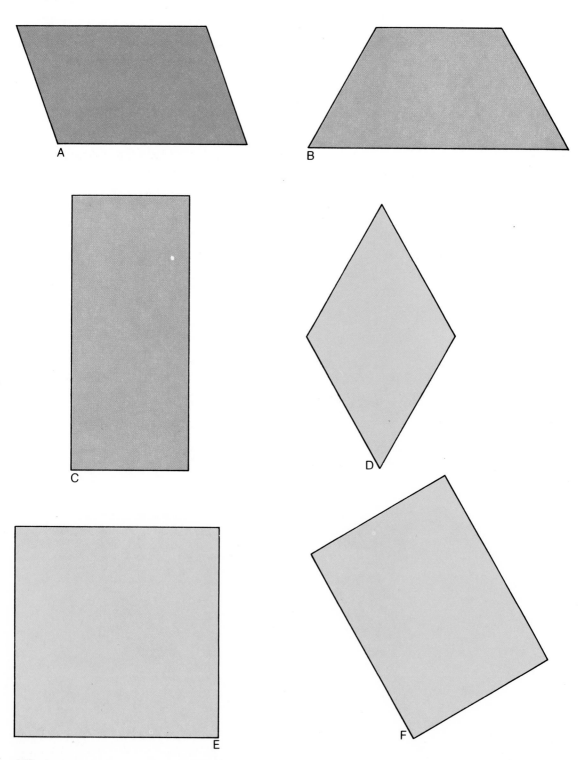

A

B

C

D

E

F

A *parallelogram* is a quadrilateral (four-sided figure) whose opposite sides are parallel.

A *rhombus* is a parallelogram whose sides are all the same length.

A *rectangle* is a parallelogram with four right angles. (A right angle measures 90°.)

A *square* is a parallelogram whose sides are all the same length and whose angles are all right angles.

This regular dodecagon has been divided into six regions by connecting vertices. Trace the drawing and cut apart regions A through F. Rearrange the six pieces to form a square.

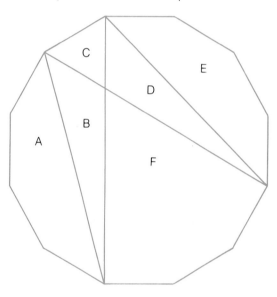

1. Decide which of figures A through F fit each definition. Complete the table.

Figures	A	B	C	D	E	F
Parallelogram			yes			
Rhombus						
Rectangle						
Square		no				

2. Is every square a rectangle?

3. Is every rectangle a square?

4. Is every square a rhombus?

5. Is every rhombus a square?

Angles of a Parallelogram

A.

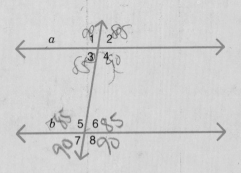

$$a \parallel b$$

The measures of the angles are given in the table. The symbol m∠1 means "the measure of angle 1."

m∠1	m∠2	m∠3	m∠4	m∠5	m∠6	m∠7	m∠8
100°	80°	80°	100°	100°	80°	80°	100°

B. You can use transversals to find relationships among angles of a parallelogram.

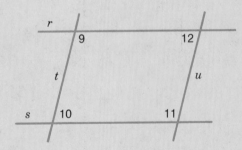

$$r \parallel s \text{ and } t \parallel u$$

The quadrilateral formed is a parallelogram.

angle	∠9	∠10	∠11	∠12
measure	105°	75°	105°	75°

1. m∠1 = m∠4 =
   m∠▦ = m∠▦

2. m∠2 = m∠▦ =
   m∠▦ = m∠▦

3. Angles 3 and 6 are *alternate interior angles.* The measures are equal. Name the other pair of alternate interior angles.

4. m∠4 + m∠6 = ▦ degrees

5. m∠3 + m∠5 = ▦ degrees

6. *m∠1 + m∠2 = 180°.* This is because ∠1 and ∠2 form a straight line. Name four other pairs of angles that form a straight line.

7. m∠9 + m∠10 = ▦ degrees

8. m∠11 + m∠12 = ▦ degrees

9. m∠12 + m∠9 = ▦ degrees

10. m∠9 = m∠▦

11. m∠10 = m∠▦

12.

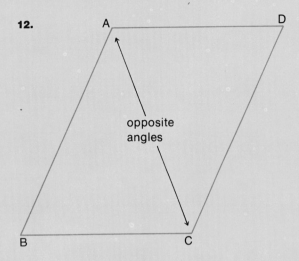

opposite angles

Angles A and C are *opposite angles*.
Name another pair of opposite angles.

13.

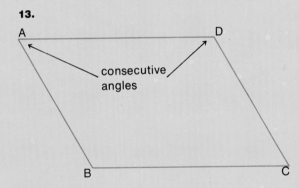

consecutive angles

Angles A and D are *consecutive angles*.
Name three other pairs of consecutive angles.

14. Use the parallelograms in exercises 12 and 13. Measure the angles and complete the table.

	Exercise 12 parallelogram	Exercise 13 parallelogram
m∠A		
m∠B		
m∠C		
m∠D		
m∠A + m∠B		
m∠B + m∠C		
m∠C + m∠D		
m∠D + m∠A		

15. How do the measures of opposite angles of a parallelogram compare?

16. What is the sum of the measures of any two consecutive angles of a parallelogram?

17. What is the sum of the measures of all the angles of a parallelogram?

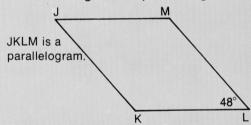

JKLM is a parallelogram.

48°

18. m∠J = ▦ degrees

19. m∠K = ▦ degrees

20. m∠M = ▦ degrees

21. m∠J + m∠K + m∠L + m∠M = ▦ degrees

More practice
Set A, page 254

Sum of the Measures of the Angles of a Triangle

In every triangle, the sum of the measures of the angles is the same.

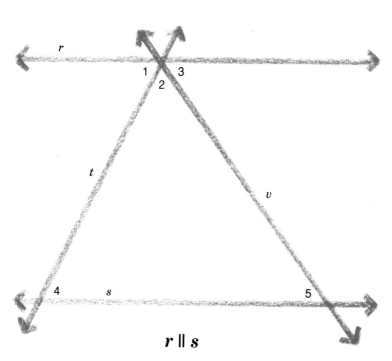

r ∥ s

Line *t* is a transversal, so m∠1 = m∠4.

Line *v* is a transversal, so m∠3 = m∠5.

Angles 1, 2, and 3 make up a straight line, so

m∠1 + m∠2 + m∠3 = 180°.

m∠1 = m∠4
m∠3 = m∠5

m∠4 + m∠2 + m∠5 = 180°

Angles 4, 2, and 5 are the angles of the triangle. The sum of their measures is 180°.

■ *In any triangle, the sum of the measures of the angles is 180°.*

Find each missing angle measure. Do not use a protractor.

1.
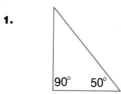
90°   50°

2.
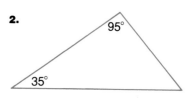
95°
35°

3.
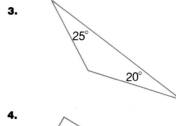
25°
20°

4.
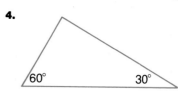
60°   30°

5.

125°
35°

6.
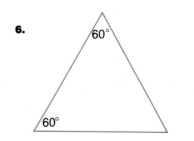
60°
60°

Sum of the Measures of the Angles of a Polygon

Choose one vertex of a hexagon and draw all the
diagonals from this vertex. The diagonals separate
the hexagon into four triangles. The sum of the
measures of the angles of a hexagon is
$4 \times 180°$, or $720°$.

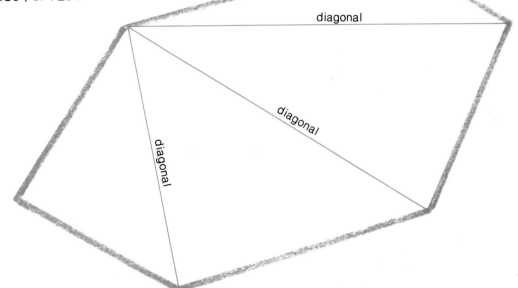

Complete the table for each polygon.

	Polygon	Number of sides	Number of diagonals from one vertex	Number of triangles	Sum of measures of all angles
	Triangle	3	0	1	$1 \times 180° = 180°$
1.	Quadrilateral	4	1		
2.	Pentagon	5			
3.	Hexagon	6			
4.	Heptagon	7			
5.	Octagon	8			
6.	Nonagon	9	6		
7.	Decagon	10			
★ 8.	n-gon	n			

★ 9. What is the sum of the measures of the angles of a polygon with 102 sides?

Circles

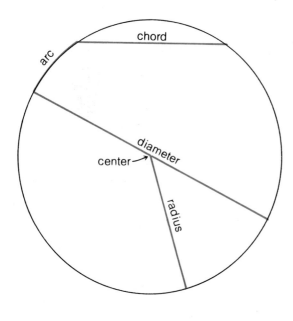

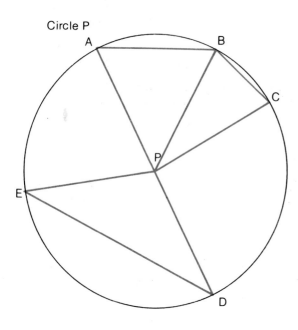

Circle P

1. A *chord* is a segment with endpoints on the circle.
   Is a diameter also a chord?

2. Name four chords of circle P.

3. Name four radii of circle P.

4. An *arc* is part of a circle.
   In circle P, the arc from A to C, moving clockwise, is arc ABC.
   For arc ABC you write $\overarc{ABC}$.
   Name four other arcs of circle P.

5. a. Draw a circle with center Q and radius QR of 3 cm.

   b. Draw a diameter RS.

   c. Draw a chord XY.

   d. Label an arc JK.

6. If the diameter of a circle is 8 cm, how long is the radius?

7. If the radius of a circle is 50 cm, how long is the diameter?

8. Circles that have the same center but different radii are called *concentric circles*. Draw three concentric circles.

9. Draw two concentric circles. Make the diameter of one circle equal to the radius of the other circle.

Inscribed Polygons

A *regular polygon* has all sides the same length and all angles the same size. You can use a circle to construct a regular polygon.

Steps 1–4 show how to *inscribe* a square in a circle.

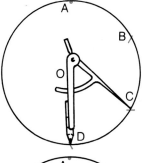

Step 1
Draw a circle. Mark a point A. Using the same radius and starting at A, mark three more points on the circle.

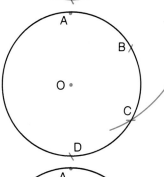

Step 2
Adjust the compass so that the point is on A and the pencil on C. Draw an arc.

Step 3
Put the point of the compass on D and pencil on B. Draw an arc. Label the point where the arcs cross E. The distance between O and E is the length of a side of a square.

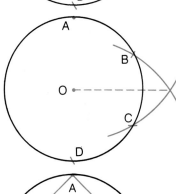

Step 4
Set your compass to the length of $\overline{OE}$. Starting at A, mark three more points around the circle. Connect the points.

1. Inscribe a square in a circle.

2. Find the midpoint of each side of the inscribed square. Draw a radius through each of the midpoints to bisect the four arcs of the circle. Connect the eight points on the circle to form a regular octagon.

3. Draw a circle. Keeping your compass set at the same radius, divide the circle into six arcs of equal length. Connect the points to form a regular hexagon.

4. Draw a circle. Divide it into six arcs of equal length. Connect every other point. What have you constructed?

Central Angles and Inscribed Angles

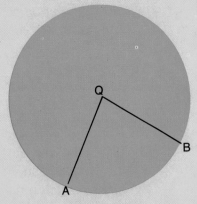

Angle AQB is a *central angle*.
Its vertex is the center of circle Q.
It has arc AB.

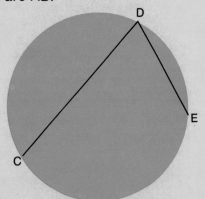

Angle CDE is an *inscribed angle*.
Its vertex is on the circle. It has arc CE.

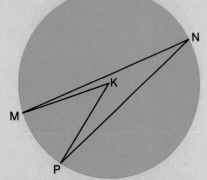

Central angle MKP and inscribed
angle MNP have the same arc, $\overset{\frown}{MP}$.

1. Draw four circles, A, B, C, and D.
In each circle, draw a central angle
and an inscribed angle that have
the same arc. Measure the angles
and complete the table.

Circle	Measure of central angle	Measure of inscribed angle
K	40°	20°
A		
B		
C		
D		

2. What is the measure of inscribed angle RTS?

This symbol shows that the radii are *perpendicular*. RMS is a right angle.

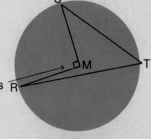

3. What is the measure of central angle AOB?

4. What is the measure of central angle MPN?

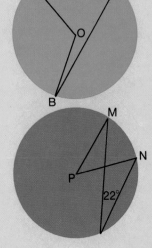

206

5.

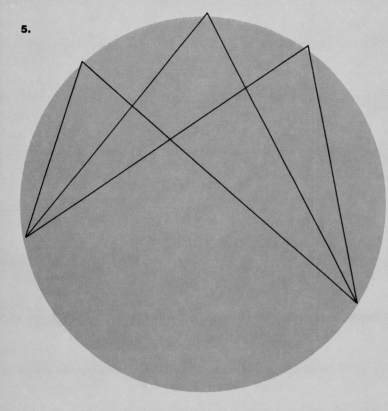

a. All three inscribed angles have the same arc. Measure the angles. How do they compare?

b. Draw a circle and four inscribed angles with the same arc. Measure the angles. How do they compare?

6. Give each measure.

   a. ∠XWZ

   b. ∠YXW

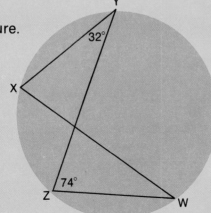

7.

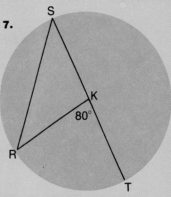

a. Which two angles have arc RT?

b. What is m∠RST?

c. What is the sum of the measures of angles RKT and RKS?

d. What is m∠RKS?

e. What is m∠SRK? (Use the sum of the measures of the angles of a triangle.)

★8.

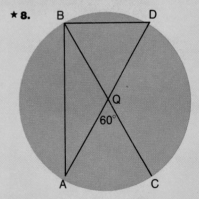

Give each measure.

   a. ∠ABC   **d.** ∠BQD

   b. ∠AQB   **e.** ∠BDA

   c. ∠BAQ   **f.** ∠DBQ

Measuring Arcs

The measure of an arc is equal to
the measure of its central angle.

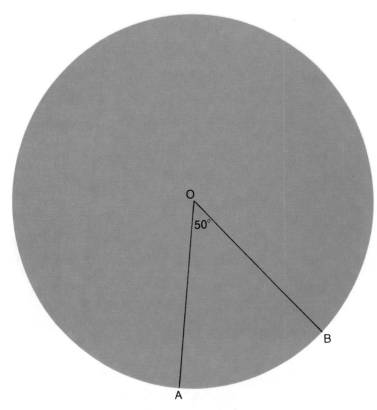

m∠AOB = 50°   m $\widehat{AB}$ = 50°

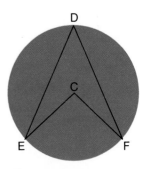

2. For circle C,
m∠EDF = 48°.

    a. What is m∠ECF?

    b. What is m $\widehat{EF}$?

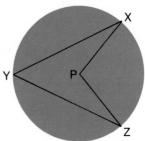

3. For circle P, m $\widehat{XZ}$ = 100°.

    a. What is m∠XPZ?

    b. What is m∠XYZ?

4. a. Draw a circle with
center Q and
diameter XY.

    b. Draw and measure
three inscribed angles
that have arc XY.

    c. What is the measure
of arc XY?

    d. What kind of angles
are inscribed in a
semicircle?

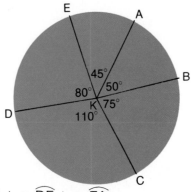

1. Give each measure.
    a. ∠AKC
    b. $\widehat{ABC}$
    c. $\widehat{AE}$
    d. $\widehat{ED}$
    e. $\widehat{AED}$
    f. $\widehat{EAC}$
    g. m $\widehat{AB}$ + m $\widehat{BC}$ + m $\widehat{CD}$ + m $\widehat{DE}$ + m $\widehat{EA}$

More practice
Set B, page 254

Laboratory Activity

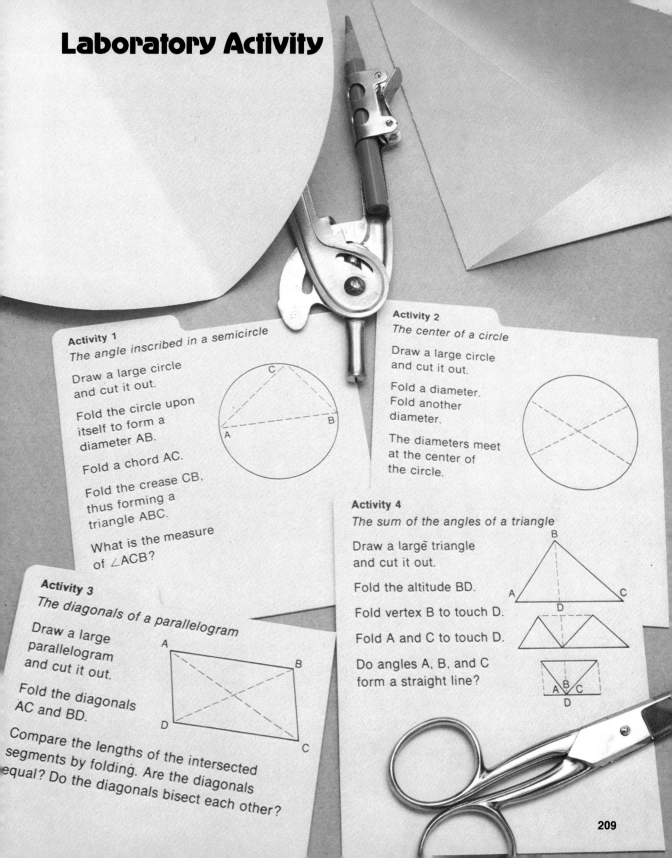

Activity 1
The angle inscribed in a semicircle

Draw a large circle and cut it out.

Fold the circle upon itself to form a diameter AB.

Fold a chord AC.

Fold the crease CB, thus forming a triangle ABC.

What is the measure of ∠ACB?

Activity 2
The center of a circle

Draw a large circle and cut it out.

Fold a diameter. Fold another diameter.

The diameters meet at the center of the circle.

Activity 3
The diagonals of a parallelogram

Draw a large parallelogram and cut it out.

Fold the diagonals AC and BD.

Compare the lengths of the intersected segments by folding. Are the diagonals equal? Do the diagonals bisect each other?

Activity 4
The sum of the angles of a triangle

Draw a large triangle and cut it out.

Fold the altitude BD.

Fold vertex B to touch D.

Fold A and C to touch D.

Do angles A, B, and C form a straight line?

Congruent Figures

Figures that have the same size and shape are *congruent*.

A. Segments AB and CD are congruent because m $\overline{AB}$ = m $\overline{CD}$.

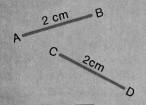

$$\overline{AB} \cong \overline{CD}$$

Segment AB is congruent to segment CD.

B. Angles PQR and XYZ are congruent because m∠PQR = m∠XYZ.

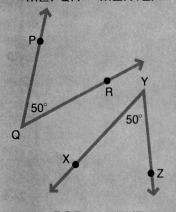

$$\angle PQR \cong \angle XYZ$$

Angle PQR is congruent to angle XYZ.

c. Triangles ABC and DEF are congruent. Imagine fitting triangle ABC exactly onto triangle DEF. Put vertex A on vertex D, vertex B on vertex E, and vertex C on vertex F.

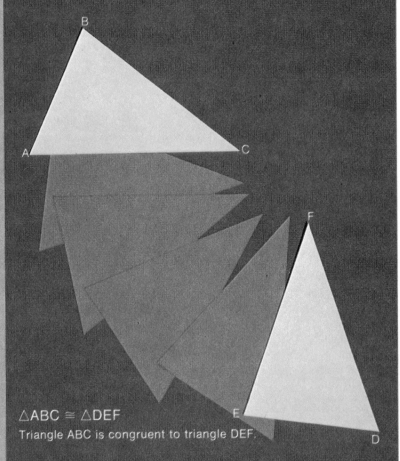

$$\triangle ABC \cong \triangle DEF$$

Triangle ABC is congruent to triangle DEF.

When the vertices are paired to show congruence, the sides and angles also are paired.

Corresponding vertices	Corresponding sides	Corresponding angles
A and D	$\overline{AB}$ and $\overline{DE}$	∠ABC and ∠DEF
B and E	$\overline{BC}$ and $\overline{EF}$	∠BCA and ∠EFD
C and F	$\overline{CA}$ and $\overline{FD}$	∠CAB and ∠FDE

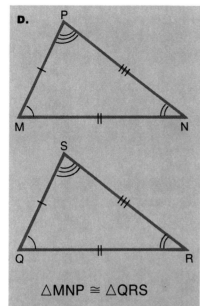

D.

△MNP ≅ △QRS

Use the markings to tell which sides and angles are congruent.

$\overline{MN}$ ≅ ▦

$\overline{NP}$ ≅ ▦

$\overline{PM}$ ≅ ▦

∠M ≅ ▦

∠N ≅ ▦

∠P ≅ ▦

1. These two quadrilaterals are congruent. Name all pairs of corresponding sides and corresponding angles.

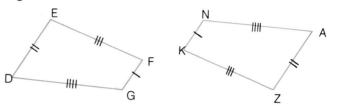

2. Diagonal HK divides parallelogram GHJK into two congruent triangles.

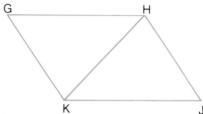

a. Name the congruent triangles.

b. Name all pairs of corresponding sides and angles.

★ **3.** Hexagon ABCDEF is inscribed in circle K. Each chord connecting two vertices is the same length as the radius of the circle.

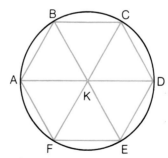

a. Name six congruent triangles.

b. CKED is a parallelogram. Name five other parallelograms congruent to CKED.

c. BCDE is a trapezoid. Name two other trapezoids congruent to BCDE.

Congruent Triangles: Three Sides

You can construct a triangle that is congruent to triangle ABC.

Step 1
Draw a segment. Copy side AB.

Step 2
Open your compass to the length of side AC and draw an arc.

Step 3
Open your compass to the length of side BC and draw another arc.

Step 4
Draw the triangle.

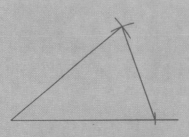

■ *If the three sides of one triangle are congruent to the three sides of another triangle, then the triangles are congruent.*

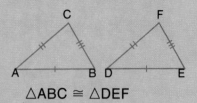

$\triangle ABC \cong \triangle DEF$

Triangle ABC is congruent to triangle DEF.

1. Draw a triangle. Construct a triangle congruent to it by copying the three sides.

2. In parallelogram FGHJ, $\overline{FH}$ is one side of two triangles.

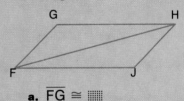

   a. $\overline{FG} \cong$ ▦

   b. $\overline{GH} \cong$ ▦

   c. $\triangle FGH \cong$ ▦

★ 3. Are two quadrilaterals congruent if their corresponding sides are congruent? Draw pictures to help you decide.

Congruent Triangles: Two Sides and an Angle

Here is another way to construct a triangle congruent to △ABC.

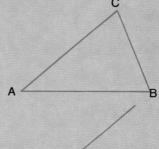

Step 1
Copy ∠A.

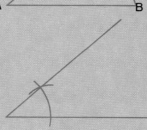

Step 2
Copy side AC and side AB.

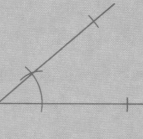

Step 3
Draw the triangle.

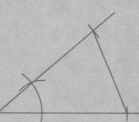

■ *If two sides and the angle between them in a triangle are congruent to two sides and the angle between them in another triangle, then the triangles are congruent.*

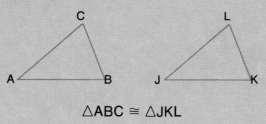

△ABC ≅ △JKL

1. Draw a triangle. Construct a triangle that is congruent to it by copying two sides and the angle between them.

In exercises 2, 3, and 4, give enough information about the second triangle to show that the triangles are congruent.

2.

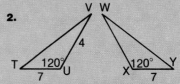

3.

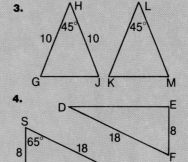

4.

5. Which triangles are congruent?

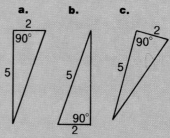

213

Congruent Triangles: Two Angles and a Side

Here is another way
to construct a triangle
that is congruent to △ABC.

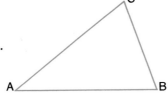

Step 1
Copy side AB.

Step 2
Copy ∠A.

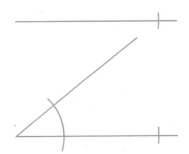

Step 3
Copy ∠B and draw the triangle.

■ *If two angles and the side between them in one
triangle are congruent to two angles and the side
between them in another triangle, then the
triangles are congruent.*

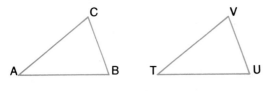

△ABC ≅ △TUV

1. Draw a triangle.
Construct a triangle
that is congruent to it
by copying two angles
and the side between
them.

In exercises 2, 3, and 4,
give enough information
about the second triangle
to show that the triangles
are congruent.

2.

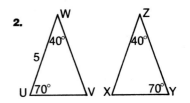

3.

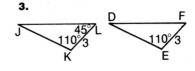

4.

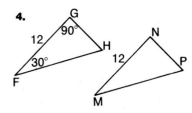

★ **5. a.** If two triangles have
the same angle
measures, can they
be congruent?

b. Do such triangles
have to be
congruent? Draw
pictures to help
you decide.

Side Trip: Number-Letter Codes

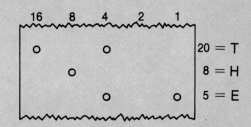

16	8	4	2	1	
o		o			20 = T
		o			8 = H
		o		o	5 = E

If you assign the numbers 1 through 26 to the letters of the alphabet, you can "write" and "read" words in code by using powers of 2.

A B C D E F G H I J K L M N O P Q R S T U V W X Y Z
1 2 3 4 5 6 7 8 9 10 11 12 13 14 15 16 17 18 19 20 21 22 23 24 25 26

Read these coded answers.

1. First President to live in the White House

16	8	4	2	1
	o		o	
	o	o	o	o
	o			
	o	o	o	
				o
		o		
				o
	o	o		o
o			o	o

2. First President to have automobiles at the White House

16	8	4	2	1
	o		o	o
		o		o
		o	o	
		o	o	
		o		o
				o
				o
	o	o		o
				o
		o		
	o	o	o	
	o		o	

Write these words in code.

3. MISSISSIPPI

4. UTAH

5. VERMONT

6. AARDVARK

7. Your name

215

Angle measures of polygons,
pages 196–203

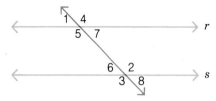

Lines *r* and *s* are parallel.
The measure of ∠7 is 45°.

1. m∠1 = ▓▓ degrees

2. m∠6 = ▓▓ degrees

3. m∠2 = ▓▓ degrees

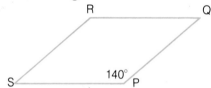

PQRS is a parallelogram.

4. m∠R = ▓▓ degrees

5. m∠Q = ▓▓ degrees

6. m∠S = ▓▓ degrees

7. m∠P + m∠Q + m∠R + m∠S =
▓▓ degrees

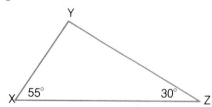

8. In triangle XYZ,
m∠X + m∠Y + m∠Z = ▓▓ degrees

9. m∠Y = ▓▓ degrees

Angle measures in a circle,
pages 204–208

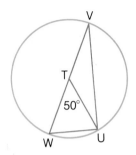

10. Name a diameter of circle T.

11. Name three radii.

12. m∠WVU = ▓▓ degrees

13. m $\overset{\frown}{WU}$ = ▓▓ degrees

14. m∠VUW = ▓▓ degrees

Congruent polygons, pages 210–214

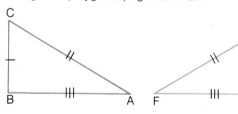

15. Side DE ≅ ▓▓

16. Side EF ≅ ▓▓

17. Side FD ≅ ▓▓

18. Angle D ≅ ▓▓

19. Angle E ≅ ▓▓

20. Angle F ≅ ▓▓

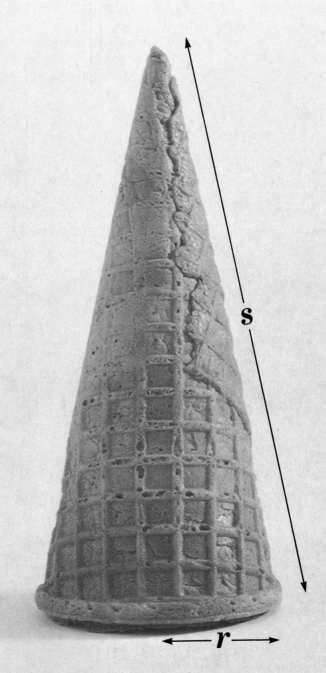

$$A = \pi rs$$

Areas of Rectangles and Parallelograms

A. Rectangle

Imagine a segment with the same length as b that starts at b, and sweeps over the inside of a rectangle.

When it meets the opposite side, it will have swept the area of the rectangle.

You can find the area of the rectangle by multiplying the length of the sweeping segment and the vertical distance traveled.

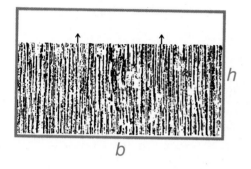

$$A = b\,h$$

Area of rectangle   Length of sweeping segment   Height of rectangle

B. Parallelogram

Imagine a segment sweeping over the inside of a parallelogram.

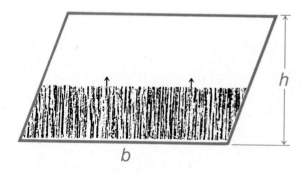

$$A = b\,h$$

Area of parallelogram   Length of sweeping segment   Height of parallelogram

Find each area in square units

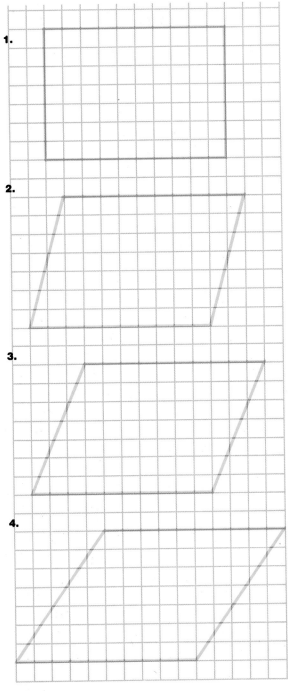

1.

2.

3.

4.

5.

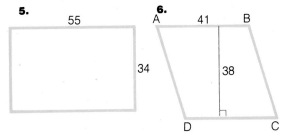

55

34

6.

A   41   B

38

D   C

7. A baseball diamond is a 90-foot square. What is its area?

8. A football field is 120 yards long and 160 feet wide. What is its area in square yards?

9. The area of a rectangular desk top is 2562 square centimeters. If the width is 42 centimeters, what is the length?

10. An adult guppy requires 3 square inches of air surface to live in an aquarium. How many adult guppies can live in a rectangular aquarium that is 18 inches long and 12 inches wide?

219

Areas of Trapezoids and Triangles

A. Trapezoid

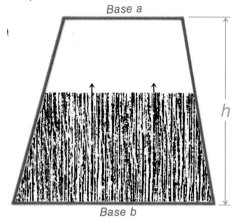

Base a

h

Base b

A *trapezoid* is a quadrilateral with one pair of parallel sides called *bases*.

Imagine a segment sweeping over the inside of a trapezoid. During the sweep, it changes length from b to a.

To find the area of the trapezoid, use the average length of the sweeping segment.

$$A = h\left(\frac{a + b}{2}\right)$$

Area of trapezoid

Height of trapezoid

Average length of sweeping segment

B. Triangle

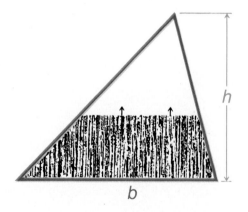

h

b

Imagine a segment sweeping over the inside of a triangle. During the sweep, it changes length from b to 0.

The average length of the sweeping segment is

$$\frac{b + 0}{2} \text{ or } \tfrac{1}{2}b.$$

$$A = \tfrac{1}{2}bh$$

Area of triangle

Average length of sweeping segment

Height of triangle

Find each area in square units.

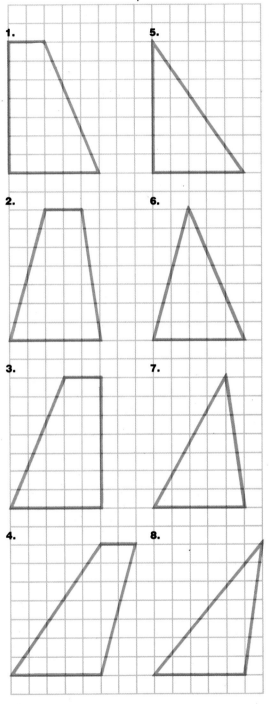

1.

5.

2.

6.

3.

7.

4.

8.

9.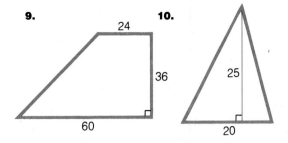
24
36
60

10.
25
20

11. How much material was used to make the sail?

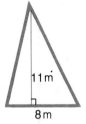
11 m
8 m

12. St. Mark's Square in Venice, Italy, actually has the shape of a trapezoid. The bases are about 82 meters and 57 meters long. They are about 175 meters apart. What is the approximate area of St. Mark's Square?

**More practice
Set C, page 254**

Surface Area of Polyhedrons

A. *Polyhedrons* are space figures with faces that are polygons.

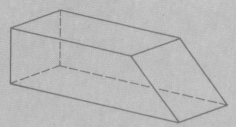

A *right prism* is a polyhedron with two parallel bases that are congruent polygons. Its other faces are rectangles.

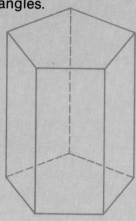

Pentagonal prism

A *pyramid* is a polyhedron with one base. Its other faces are triangles.

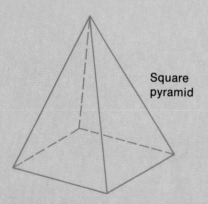

Square pyramid

B. The total *surface area* of a polyhedron is the sum of the areas of all the faces.

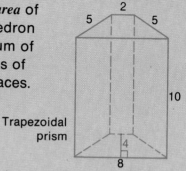

Trapezoidal prism

Sometimes it is helpful to draw a pattern of the polyhedron.

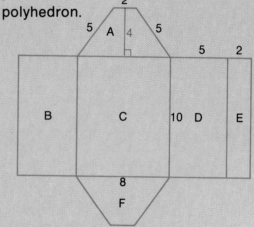

Complete the table to find the total surface area.

Face	Finding area of face	Area of face (square units)
A	$\frac{1}{2}(4)(2 + 8)$	20
B	5(10)	
C		
D		
E		
F		
	Total surface area in square units	

Find the surface area.

1. Cube

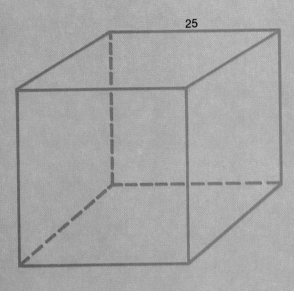

25

2. Rectangular prism

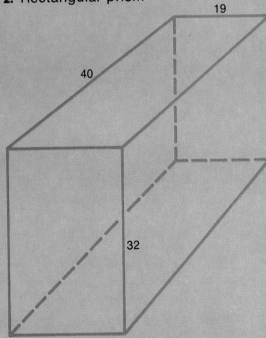

19

40

32

3. Square pyramid

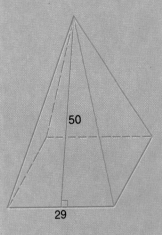

50

29

4. How many square feet of tile are needed to tile the sides and bottom of the swimming pool?

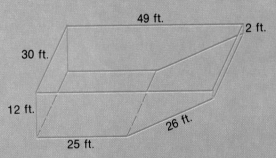

49 ft.

2 ft.

30 ft.

12 ft.

26 ft.

25 ft.

5. If one gallon of paint covers 300 square feet of surface, how many gallons of red paint are needed to paint the barn?

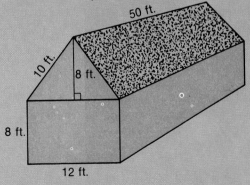

50 ft.

10 ft.

8 ft.

8 ft.

12 ft.

Volume of a Prism

A. Rectangular prism

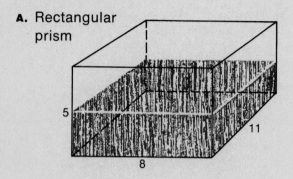

Imagine the bottom base sweeping upward inside the prism. When it meets the top base, it will have swept the volume of the prism.

You can find the volume of the prism by multiplying the area of the sweeping base and the vertical distance traveled.

$V = (88)(5)$

The volume is 440 cubic units.

B. Triangular prism

$V = (24)(10)$
The volume is 240 cubic units.

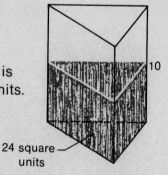

24 square units

For any prism,

$$V = Bh$$

Volume of prism   Area of a base   Height of prism

1. Find the volume of the rectangular prism.

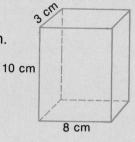

2. The first three steps in a 20-step staircase are shown. Find the amount of concrete used to make the staircase.

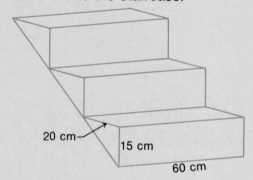

3. Find the volume of the figure.

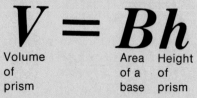

4. The area of each base of a hexagonal prism is 24 square centimeters. The volume is 168 cubic centimeters. What is the height of the prism?

5. A classroom is 15 feet high. Its floor has an area of 642 square feet. How many students can be assigned to the room if each student needs 300 cubic feet of air?

Volume of a Pyramid

The volume of a pyramid is one-third the volume of a prism with the same base and height.

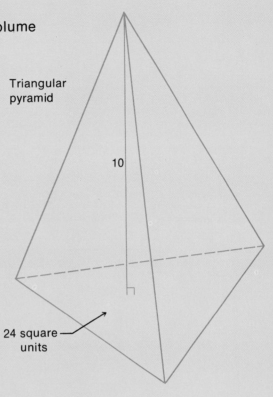

Triangular pyramid

$V = \frac{1}{3}(24)(10)$

The volume is 80 cubic units.

For any pyramid,

$$V = \frac{1}{3}Bh$$

Volume of pyramid   Area of base   Height of pyramid

10

24 square units

Find the volume of each pyramid described in the table.

	Base	Area of base	Height
1.	Square	16 cm²	12 cm
2.	Rectangle	35 cm²	27 cm
3.	Pentagon	7.65 cm²	1.77 cm
4.	Triangle	15 cm²	8 cm
5.	Hexagon	37.8 cm²	16.3 cm

6. The Pyramid of Cheops has a square base 240 yards on a side. Its height is 160 yards. What is its volume?

More practice
Set D, page 254

Circumference of a Circle

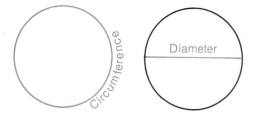

Students in a mathematics class used a graph to measure some circular objects.

They marked off the diameter of each object along the horizontal axis of the graph. They then rolled the object upwards one complete turn and marked off the circumference.

Notice that the points seem to lie on a straight line that is close to the line for $C = 3d$.

They used the graph to find the circumference for each diameter. In dividing C by d, they obtained either 3.1 or 3.2.

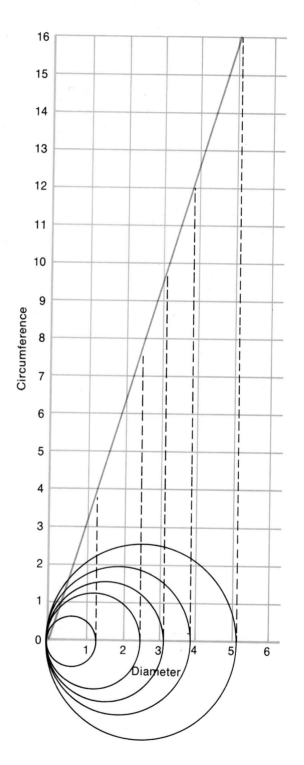

Diameter	Circumference	$C \div d$
1.2	3.8	3.2
2.4	7.5	3.1
3.1	9.7	3.1
3.8	12.0	3.2
5.1	16.0	3.1

The quotient $C \div d$ is the same for any circle. Its exact value is denoted by the Greek letter π (pi). The value of π correct to two decimal places is 3.14.

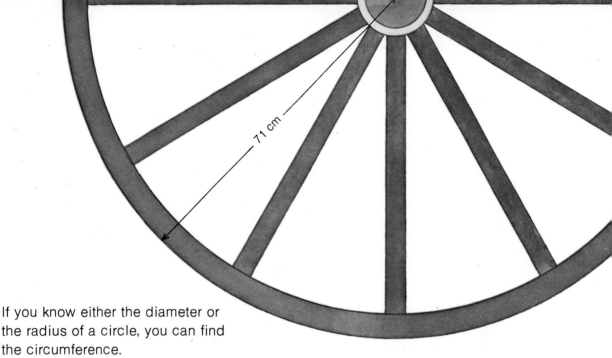

71 cm

If you know either the diameter or the radius of a circle, you can find the circumference.

$$C = \pi d$$

$$C = 2\pi r$$

In the exercises, use 3.14 for π.

1. A circular garden has a 3.5-meter radius. How long is the fence that encloses it? Give your answer to the nearest tenth.

2. The circumference of the earth is about 25,000 miles. Find the diameter to the nearest mile.

3. The diameter of the sun is about 110 times as great as the diameter of the earth. How many times as great is the circumference?

4. How many revolutions will the wheel above make in going one kilometer? Give your answer to the nearest tenth.

5. How much farther will you ride in one turn of a merry-go-round if your horse is 6 meters from the center than if it is 4 meters from the center?

6. Jenny rides her bicycle around a circular field that has a diameter of 10 meters. If she rides around the field 8 times, will she have gone more than 1 kilometer or less than 1 kilometer?

● Discuss If the radius of a circle is doubled, what happens to the circumference? If the diameter is doubled, what happens to the circumference?

227

Area of a Circle

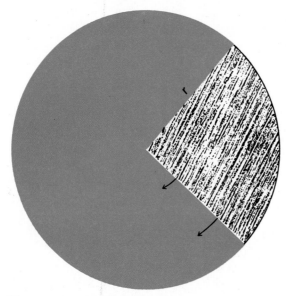

The area of a circle is swept by a radius that rotates until it reaches its original position.

The distance the radius travels varies from $2\pi r$ at the circumference to 0 at the center.

The average distance traveled is:

$$\frac{2\pi r + 0}{2} \text{ or } \pi r.$$

To find the area of the circle, multiply the length of the sweeping segment, r, by the average distance traveled.

$$A = \pi r(r)$$

| Area of circle | Average distance traveled | Length of sweeping segment |

$$A = \pi r^2$$

In the exercises, use 3.14 for π. Give your answers to the nearest tenth.

1. Find the area of each circle.

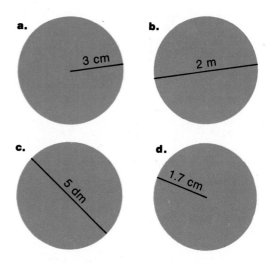

a. 3 cm

b. 2 m

c. 5 dm

d. 1.7 cm

2. Which has a greater area, a circle whose diameter is 6 centimeters or a square whose side is 6 centimeters? How much greater?

3. A dog is tied to a stake by a rope that is 5.7 meters long. What is the area of the ground available for it to play on?

4. A revolving lawn sprinkler sprays water for a distance of 9 meters from the sprinkler. What is the area of the lawn watered by the sprinkler?

5. The diameter of a metal washer is 4 centimeters. The diameter of the hole is 2 centimeters. How many square centimeters of metal are in ten washers?

6. Pietro's pizzas come in three sizes. Which size is the best buy? (Hint: Find the area of each. Then find the number of square inches of pizza per dollar.)

7. This dartboard has five regions. Find the area of each region.

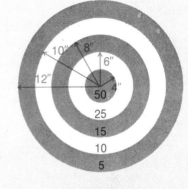

inch diameter
$2.00

12 inch diameter
$3.00

14 inch diameter
$4.00

8. What is the area of the largest circle that can be cut out of a 4-centimeter square?

9. Find the area of a circle whose circumference is 62.8 millimeters.

● **Discuss** If the radius of a circle is doubled, what happens to the area? If the diameter is doubled, what happens to the area?

**More practice
Set E, page 254**

Volume of a Cylinder

A circular *cylinder* has one curved face and two parallel bases that are congruent circles.

Suppose that you open both ends of a can of bread. To remove the bread, you push the lid down to where the bottom originally was. The lid has swept the volume of the can.

To find the volume of a cylinder, multiply the area of the sweeping base and the vertical distance traveled.

$$V = \pi r^2 h$$

Volume   Area   Height
of a   of a   of
cylinder   base   cylinder

Find each volume in cubic units. Use 3.14 for π and give your answers to the nearest tenth.

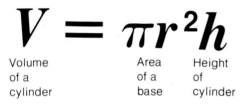

1. 1 cm   2 cm

2. 1.2 cm   2.2 cm

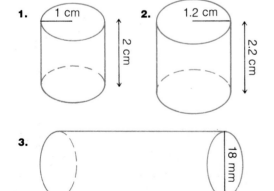

3. 18 mm   45 mm

4. Which can is the better buy?

3.7 cm   10.6 cm   36¢

3.2 cm   7 cm   18¢

Volume of a Cone

A *cone* has one circular base and one curved face.

The volume of a cone is one-third the volume of a cylinder with the same base and height.

$$V = \frac{1}{3}\pi r^2 h$$

Volume of a cone   Area of base   Height of cone

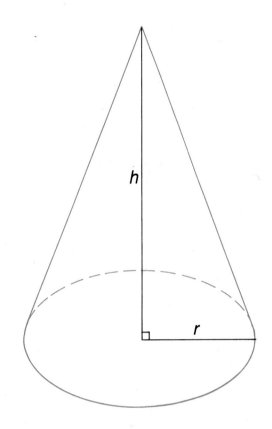

Find each volume.

For each exercise, use 3.14 for π.
Give your answers to the nearest tenth.

1.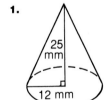

25 mm

12 mm

2.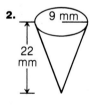

9 mm

22 mm

3. There are two sizes of soft drinks in cone-shaped paper cups. Which is the better buy?

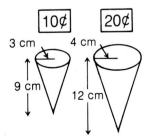

10¢   20¢

3 cm   4 cm

9 cm   12 cm

4. The cones in this hourglass are congruent. What is the volume of the two cones?

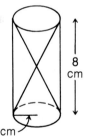

8 cm

2 cm

5. What is the volume of this cone?

6. How does the volume of one cone in a cylinder compare to the volume of two cones in a cylinder the same size?

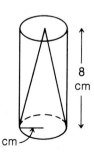

8 cm

2 cm

231

Surface Areas of Cylinders and Cones

A. The total surface area of a cylinder is the sum of the areas of the bases and the area of the curved surface.

The bases are congruent circles. Each has area πr^2.

To find the area of the curved surface, imagine segment h sweeping around the cylinder.

B. The total surface area of a cone is the sum of the area of the base and the area of the curved surface.

The area of the base is πr^2.

To find the area of the curved surface, imagine segment s sweeping around the cone. The distance traveled varies from $2\pi r$ to 0. To find the area, use the average distance.

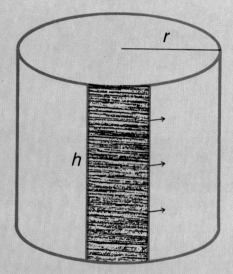

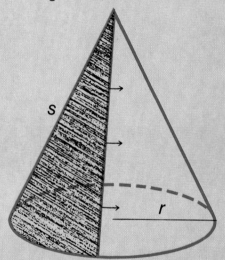

The length of the sweeping segment is h.

The distance traveled is $2\pi r$.

The area of the curved surface is $2\pi rh$.

The total surface area is the sum of πr^2, πr^2, and $2\pi rh$.

$$A = 2\pi rh + 2\pi r^2$$

The length of the sweeping segment is s.

The average distance traveled is πr.

The area of the curved surface is πrs.

The total surface area is the sum of πr^2 and πrs.

$$A = \pi r^2 + \pi rs$$

Find the total surface area. Use 3.14 for π and give your answers to the nearest tenth.

1.

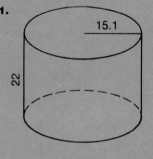

15.1

22

2.

12

33

3.

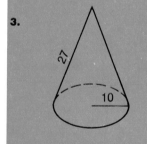

27

10

4.

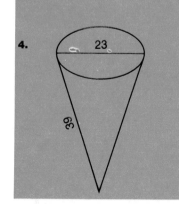

23

39

For exercises 5–7, use 3.14 for π and give your answers to the nearest square centimeter.

5. a. About how many square centimeters of metal are needed to make this can?

b. About how much paper is needed to make the label?

11 cm

8 cm

6. About how much cardboard is needed to make the party hat?

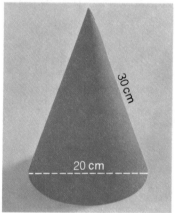

30 cm

20 cm

7. About how many square centimeters of paper are needed to make 100 drinking cups?

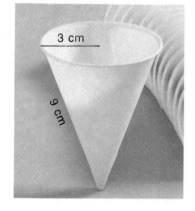

3 cm

9 cm

More practice
Set F, page 254

Laboratory Activity

You can make a rotating ring of pyramids.

Draw this pattern of equilateral triangles with tabs.

Cut out the pattern. Score all solid lines on the front and the dotted lines on the back. Fold along the lines and join tabs with the same letter.

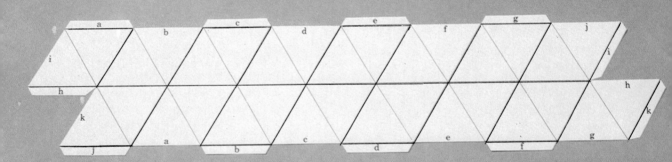

The finished model is composed of eight triangular pyramids that are joined together by their edges. The model will turn round and round as you twist it.

You can make the pattern longer by drawing more triangles.

The faces of the pyramids can be painted in different colors to create attractive patterns.

Side Trip Pyramids

◦ Trace the pattern three
times. Cut out each
pattern and fold it to
form a pyramid. Tape the
three pyramids together
to form a cube.

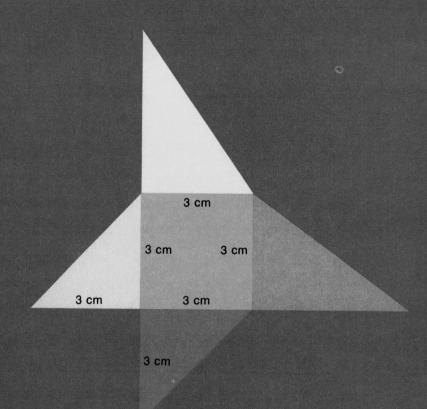

3 cm

3 cm   3 cm

3 cm   3 cm

3 cm

3 cm

1. The length of a side of the cube
   is three centimeters. What is the
   volume of the cube?

2. The volume of the cube is how
   many times as great as the volume
   of each pyramid?

3. What is the volume of each
   pyramid?

Chapter 11 Test
Area and Volume, Pages 218–235

Areas of polygons, pages 218–223

Find each area.

1. Rectangle

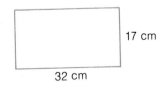

17 cm

32 cm

2. Parallelogram

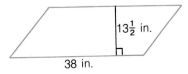

$13\frac{1}{2}$ in.

38 in.

3. Trapezoid

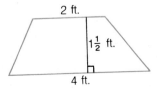

2 ft.

$1\frac{1}{2}$ ft.

4 ft.

4. Triangle

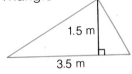

1.5 m

3.5 m

Surface area of polyhedrons, pages 222–224

5. Find the total surface area of a 3-centimeter cube.

Volume of polyhedrons, pages 224–225

Find each volume.

6. Square prism

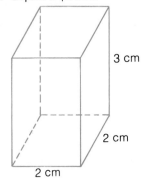

3 cm

2 cm

2 cm

7. Square pyramid

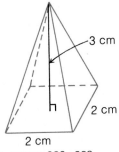

3 cm

2 cm

2 cm

Circles, pages 226–229

Use 3.14 for π and give answers to the nearest tenth.

8. Find the circumference.

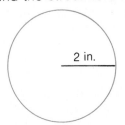

2 in.

9. Find the area.

Cylinders and cones, pages 230–233

Use 3.14 for π and give answers to the nearest tenth.

Find each volume.

10. Cylinder

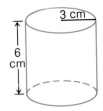

3 cm

6 cm

11. Cone

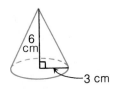

6 cm

3 cm

Find the total surface area of each figure.

12. Cylinder

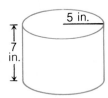

5 in.

7 in.

13. Cone

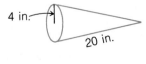

4 in.

20 in.

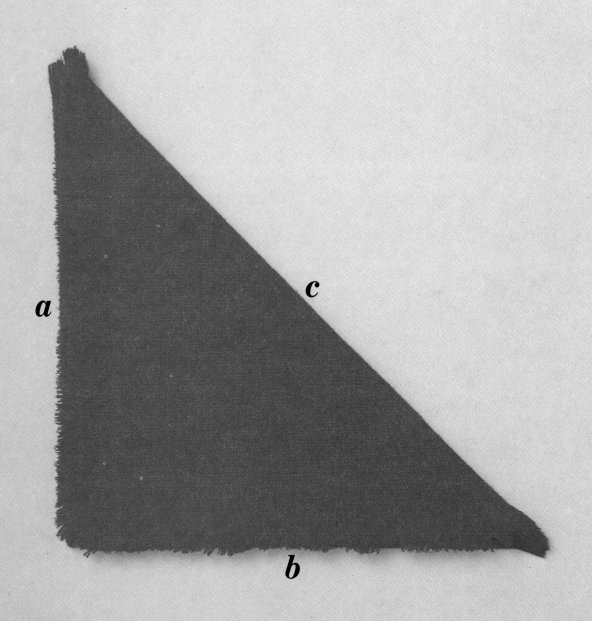

$$a^2 + b^2 = c^2$$

s

s

s

s

Squares and Their Areas

A square has four sides of equal length and four right angles.

Perimeter:

$$P = s + s + s + s = 4s$$

Area: $A = s \times s = s^2$

1.5 cm

Find the perimeter (P) and area (A) of the square.

$$P = 4(1.5)\text{cm} = 6 \text{ cm}$$

$$A = (1.5)^2 \text{ cm}^2 = 2.25 \text{ cm}^2$$

For each square, find the perimeter and the area.

1.

3.2 cm

2.
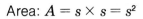

2.5 cm

3.

1.25 cm

4.

1.7 cm

5. For this square, what is the length of a side and what is the perimeter?

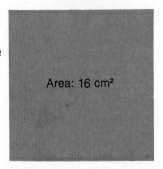

Area: 16 cm²

6. For this square, what is the length of a side and what is the perimeter?

Area: 144 mm²

7. For this square, what is the length of a side and what is the area?

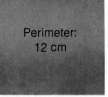

Perimeter: 12 cm

★ 8. Find the area of both squares.

3 cm   2 cm

2 cm

3 cm   3 cm

3 cm

2 cm

2 cm   3 cm

Drawing Squares and Finding Areas on Dot Paper

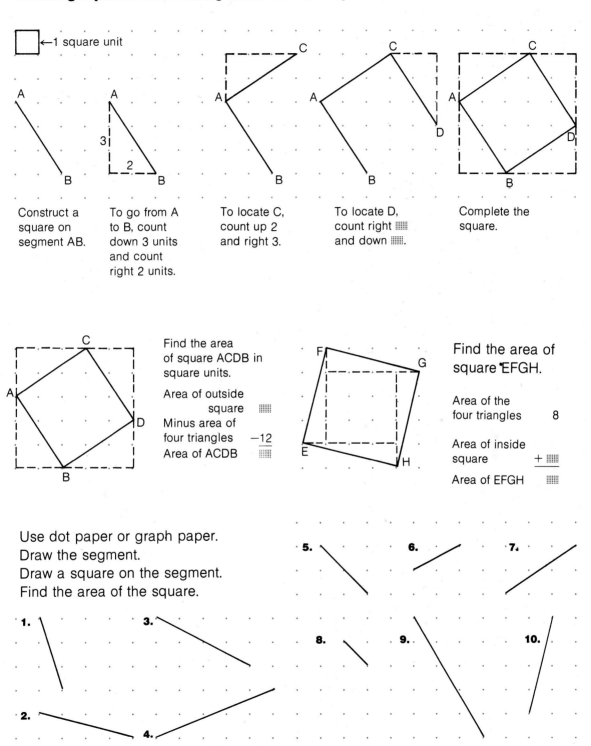

☐ ←1 square unit

Construct a square on segment AB.

To go from A to B, count down 3 units and count right 2 units.

To locate C, count up 2 and right 3.

To locate D, count right ▦ and down ▦.

Complete the square.

Find the area of square ACDB in square units.

Area of outside square ▦
Minus area of four triangles −12
Area of ACDB ▦

Find the area of square EFGH.

Area of the four triangles   8

Area of inside square   + ▦

Area of EFGH   ▦

Use dot paper or graph paper.
Draw the segment.
Draw a square on the segment.
Find the area of the square.

1.

2.

3.

4.

5.

6.

7.

8.

9.

10.

Square and Square Root

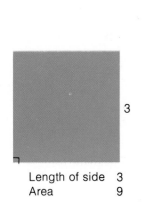

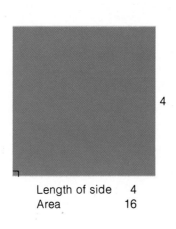

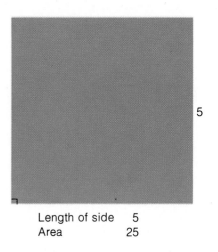

Length of side 3
Area   9

Length of side 4
Area   16

Length of side 5
Area   25

The area of a square is the square of the length of a side.

$3^2 = 3 \times 3 = 9$ $4^2 = 4 \times 4 = 16$ $5^2 = 5 \times 5 = 25$

The length of a side of a square is the *square root* ($\sqrt{}$) of the area.

$\sqrt{9} = 3$ $\sqrt{16} = 4$ $\sqrt{25} = 5$

$9^2 = 9 \times 9 = 81$ 81 is the square of 9.

$\sqrt{81} = \sqrt{9^2} = 9$ 9 is the square root of 81.

$(\sqrt{81})^2 = \sqrt{81} \times \sqrt{81} = 9 \times 9 = 81$

$\sqrt{81}$ is the length of a side of a square whose area is 81.

Area   2
Length of a side $\sqrt{2}$

$\sqrt{2}$ is the length of a side of a square with an area of 2 square units.

$(\sqrt{2})^2 = \sqrt{2} \times \sqrt{2} = 2$

Find the squares.
Use the table.

1. 13^2

2. 29^2

3. 35^2

4. 14^2

5. $(1.4)^2$

6. 27^2

7. $(2.7)^2$

8. 22^2

9. $(2.2)^2$

10. $(3.1)^2$

Find the
square roots.

11. $\sqrt{36}$

12. $\sqrt{49}$

13. $\sqrt{64}$

14. $\sqrt{1}$

15. $\sqrt{361}$

16. $\sqrt{576}$

17. $\sqrt{121}$

18. $\sqrt{1024}$

19. $\sqrt{225}$

20. $\sqrt{144}$

21. $\sqrt{12^2}$

22. $\sqrt{784}$

Squares are drawn on each
side of right triangle ABC.

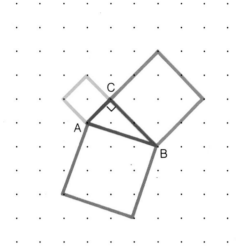

23. Find the area of the square
on $\overline{AC}$.

24. Find the length of $\overline{AC}$.

25. Find the area of the square
on $\overline{AB}$.

26. Find the length of $\overline{AB}$.

27. Find the area of the square
on $\overline{BC}$.

28. Find the length of $\overline{BC}$.

n	n^2
1	1
2	4
3	9
4	16
5	25
6	36
7	49
8	64
9	81
10	100
11	121
12	144
13	169
14	196
15	225
16	256
17	289
18	324
19	361
20	400
21	441
22	484
23	529
24	576
25	625
26	676
27	729
28	784
29	841
30	900
31	961
32	1024
33	1089
34	1156
35	1225
36	1296

Measuring to Find Square Roots

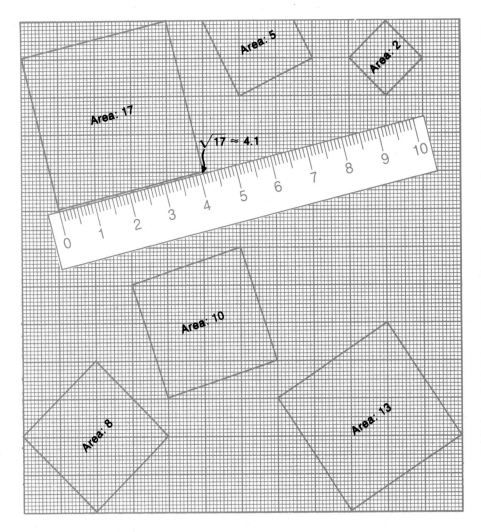

n	√n (nearest tenth)
1	1.0
2	
3	1.7
4	2.0
5	
6	2.4
7	2.6
8	
9	3.0
10	
11	3.3
12	3.5
13	
14	3.7
15	3.9
16	4.0
17	
18	4.2
19	4.4
20	4.5
21	4.6
22	4.7
23	4.8
24	4.9
25	5.0
26	5.1
27	5.2
28	5.3
29	5.4
30	5.5
31	5.6
32	5.7

Find the square roots (nearest tenth). Use squares on the centimeter grid and your metric ruler.

1. $\sqrt{17}$ **4.** $\sqrt{13}$

2. $\sqrt{2}$ **5.** $\sqrt{8}$

3. $\sqrt{5}$ **6.** $\sqrt{10}$

Find the approximate square roots (nearest tenth). Use the table.

7. $\sqrt{3}$ **10.** $\sqrt{30}$

8. $\sqrt{15}$ **11.** $\sqrt{21}$

9. $\sqrt{6}$ **12.** $\sqrt{27}$

Dividing and Averaging to Find Square Roots

The divide-and-average method of finding
a square root uses the following idea.

$25 = 5^2$ and $25 \div 5 = 5$

$268 \approx 16.4^2$ and $268 \div 16.4 \approx 16.4$

Find $\sqrt{1789}$. (nearest tenth)
Think: $40^2 = 1600$
$\qquad 50^2 = 2500$
$\sqrt{1789}$ is between 40 and 50.
It is closer to 40 than 50.
Try 41.

$$\begin{array}{r} 43.63 \approx 43.6 \\ 41\overline{)1789.00} \end{array}$$

$\qquad$ ← Divide.

$$\frac{41 + 43.6}{2} = \frac{84.6}{2} = 42.3$$

← Find the average of the divisor and the quotient.

$$\begin{array}{r} 42.29 \approx 42.3 \\ 42.3\overline{)1789.00} \end{array}$$

← Divide.

$$\sqrt{1789} \approx 42.3$$

Check: $42.3 \times 42.3 = 1789.29$
$\qquad\qquad\qquad\quad \approx 1789$

Continue to divide and average
until the divisor and quotient
are the same.

Estimate the
square root.

Find the
approximate
square roots
(nearest tenth). Use
the divide and
average method.

1. $\sqrt{66}$

2. $\sqrt{89}$

3. $\sqrt{164}$

4. $\sqrt{188}$

5. $\sqrt{750}$

6. $\sqrt{440}$

7. $\sqrt{985}$

8. $\sqrt{1225}$

9. $\sqrt{883.6}$

10. $\sqrt{130.2}$

11. $\sqrt{174.5}$

12. $\sqrt{1883.6}$

13. $\sqrt{342.7}$

14. $\sqrt{1212}$

15. $\sqrt{121.2}$

**More practice
Set G, page 254**

Right-Triangle Relation

A triangle that has a right angle
is called a *right triangle*.

In a right triangle, the side opposite
the right angle (usually labeled c) is
called the *hypotenuse*. The other two
sides (usually labeled a and b) are
called legs.

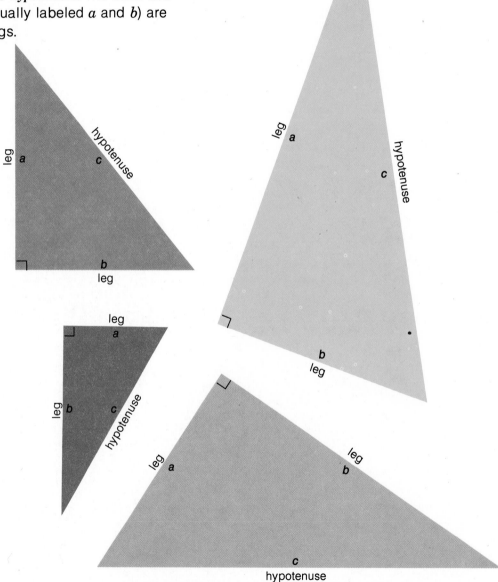

Draw the right triangles on dot paper or graph paper. Construct squares on the three sides.

Here's how

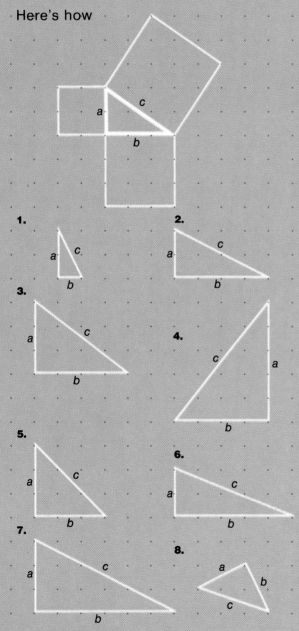

1.

2.

3.

4.

5.

6.

7.

8.

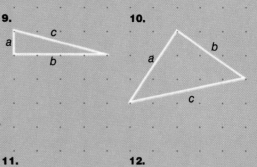

9.

10.

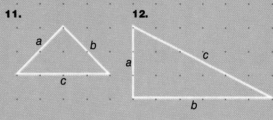

11.

12.

Find the areas of the squares on the sides of the triangles in exercises 1–12. Make a copy of the table below. Then complete the table. Use your answers to exercises 1–12 to help you. See if you can find the relationship among the sides of a right triangle.

	Area of square		
	on leg a	on leg b	on hypotenuse c
	4	9	13
13.	4	1	
14.		16	20
15.	9	16	
16.	25	16	
17.	9		18
18.	4	25	
19.		36	
20.		5	
21.			17
22.	13	13	
23.		8	
24.	9		

Using the Right-Triangle Relation

■ *The sum of the areas of the squares on the legs of a right triangle is equal to the area of the square on the hypotenuse.*

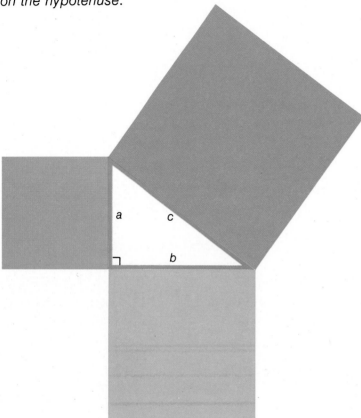

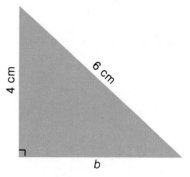

B. Find b.

$$4^2 + b^2 = 6^2$$
$$16 + b^2 = 36$$
$$b^2 = 36 - 16$$
$$b^2 = 20$$

$$b = \sqrt{20}$$
$$b \approx 4.5$$

Another way to state the relationship is $a^2 + b^2 = c^2$.

Using this formula, if the lengths of two sides of a right triangle are known, you can find the length of the third side.

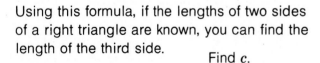

C. Find a.

$$a^2 + 4^2 = 5^2$$
$$a^2 + 16 = 25$$
$$a^2 = 25 - 16$$
$$a^2 = 9$$

$$a = \sqrt{9}$$
$$a = 3$$

A.

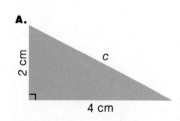

Find c.

$$4^2 + 2^2 = c^2$$
$$16 + 4 = c^2$$
$$20 = c^2$$

$$\sqrt{20} = c$$
$$4.5 \approx c$$

Find the length of the side that is not given.

1.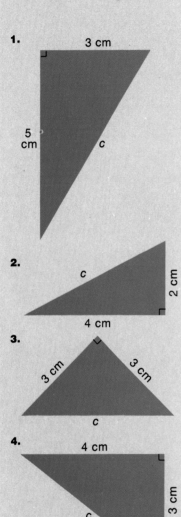

3 cm

5 cm

c

2.

c

4 cm

2 cm

3.

3 cm

3 cm

c

4.

4 cm

3 cm

c

5.

3 cm

5 cm

b

6. What is the height of the chair seat?

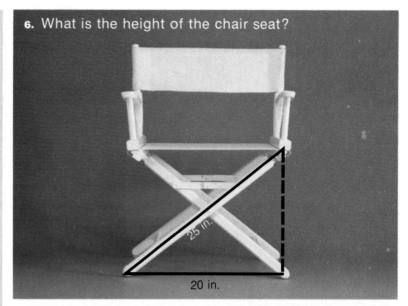

25 in.

20 in.

7. How long is the ladder?

4 m

2 m

Find the length

8. of d.
9. of e.
10. of f.

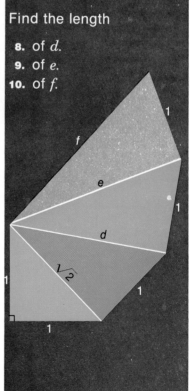

f

e

d

$\sqrt{2}$

1

1

1

1

1

1

Similar Figures

These two maps of Texas have the same shape. They are *similar*.

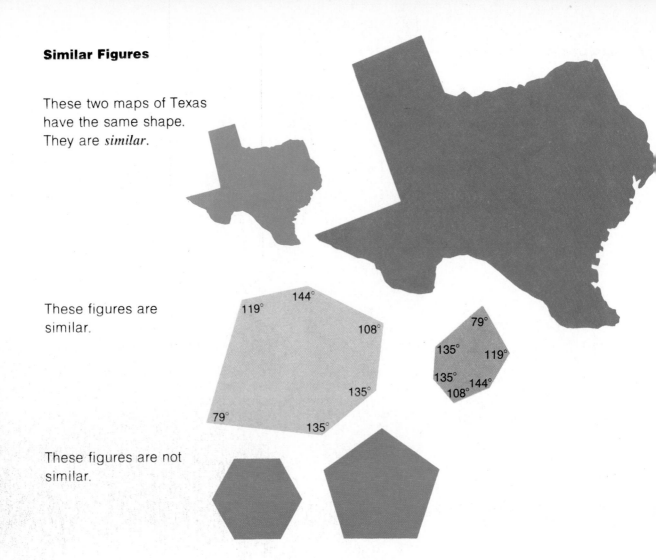

These figures are similar.

These figures are not similar.

Which pairs of figures are similar?

Figures C and ▦
Figures ▦ and ▦
Figures ▦ and ▦

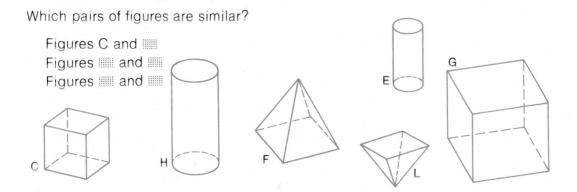

Photographs are enlarged by shining light through a negative onto a light-sensitive paper. The pictures are similar.

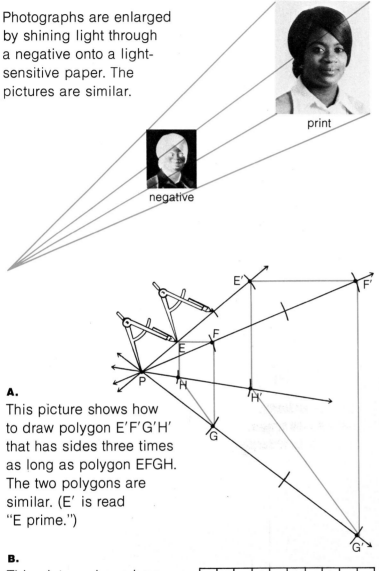

print

negative

Use a point and lines to make these enlargements.

1. Draw a triangle. Then construct a similar triangle with sides twice as long.

2. Draw a parallelogram. Then construct a similar parallelogram four times as large.

Use graph paper with large squares to make enlargements of these pictures.

3.

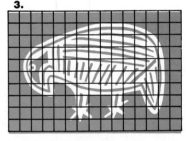

4.

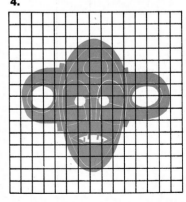

A.
This picture shows how to draw polygon E′F′G′H′ that has sides three times as long as polygon EFGH. The two polygons are similar. (E′ is read "E prime.")

B.
This picture shows how to use graph paper with different sized squares to make enlargements of pictures.

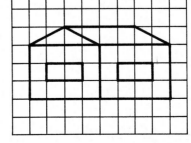

★ 5. Make an enlargement of your favorite cartoon character.

Corresponding Parts of Similar Figures

A.

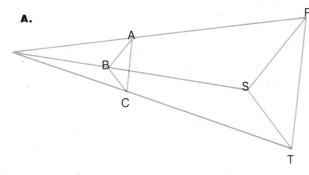

△ABC is similar to △RST.
You can write

        △ABC ~ △RST

Corresponding angles are:
∠A and ∠R, ∠B and ∠S, ∠C and ∠T
Corresponding sides are:
$\overline{AB}$ and $\overline{RS}$, $\overline{BC}$ and $\overline{ST}$, $\overline{CA}$ and $\overline{TR}$

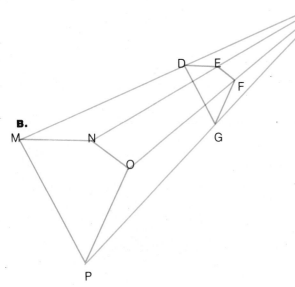

        DEFG ~ MNOP

Corresponding angles are:
∠D and ∠M, ∠E and ∠N,
∠F and ∠O, ∠G and ∠P
Corresponding sides are:
$\overline{DE}$ and $\overline{MN}$, $\overline{EF}$ and $\overline{NO}$,
$\overline{FG}$ and $\overline{OP}$, $\overline{DG}$ and $\overline{MP}$

B.

List the corresponding angles and
the corresponding sides for each
pair of similar figures.

Here's how

 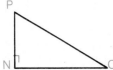

Corresponding angles:
∠H and ∠O, ∠L and ∠N, ∠M and ∠P
Corresponding sides:
$\overline{HL}$ and $\overline{NO}$, $\overline{LM}$ and $\overline{NP}$, $\overline{HM}$ and $\overline{PO}$

1.

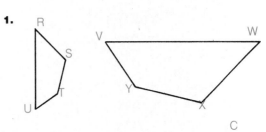

2.

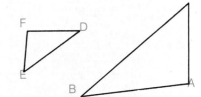

3.

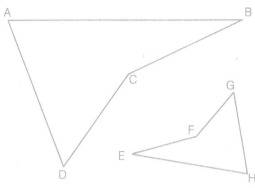

4.

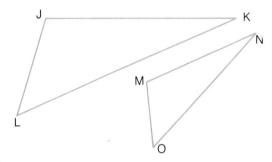

5.

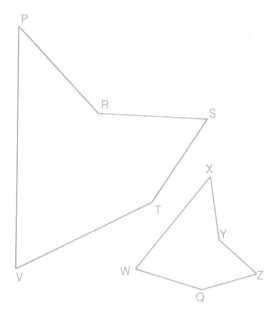

CAREERS Designer

Geometric figures are the bases of many beautiful designs.

Make up your own designs based on geometric patterns.

Squares and square roots,
pages 238–243

Use the table to find the squares.

1. 9^2 **3.** 15^2 **5.** 19^2

2. 13^2 **4.** $(1.5)^2$ **6.** $(1.9)^2$

Use the table to find the square roots.

7. $\sqrt{1}$ **9.** $\sqrt{289}$ **11.** $\sqrt{400}$

8. $\sqrt{256}$ **10.** $\sqrt{121}$ **12.** $\sqrt{19^2}$

Use the table to approximate each square root to the nearest tenth.

13. $\sqrt{7}$ **15.** $\sqrt{20}$ **17.** $\sqrt{19}$

14. $\sqrt{2}$ **16.** $\sqrt{12}$ **18.** $\sqrt{10}$

n	n^2	$\sqrt{n}$ (nearest tenth)
1	1	1.0
2	4	1.4
3	9	1.7
4	16	2.0
5	25	2.2
6	36	2.4
7	49	2.6
8	64	2.8
9	81	3.0
10	100	3.2
11	121	3.3
12	144	3.5
13	169	3.6
14	196	3.7
15	225	3.9
16	256	4.0
17	289	4.1
18	324	4.2
19	361	4.4
20	400	4.5

19. What is the area of a square that measures 1.7 centimeters on a side?

20. A square has an area of 196 square millimeters. What is the measure of each side?

Right-triangle relation, pages 244–247

Find the length of the side that is not given.

21.

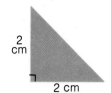

2 cm

2 cm

22.

2 cm

1 cm

Similar figures, pages 248–251

23. Which triangles are similar?

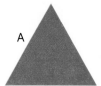

A   B   C

24. List the corresponding angles and the corresponding sides for these similar triangles.

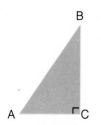

B

A   C

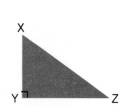

X

Y   Z

Unit 4 Test

ABCD is a parallelogram.

1. Angle A ≅ Angle ▨

2. Angle B ≅ Angle ▨

3. The sum of the measures of the angles of a parallelogram is ▨.

4. Give the measure of angle F.

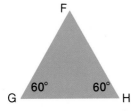

5. Angle STU ≅ Angle ▨

6. Angle TSV ≅ Angle ▨

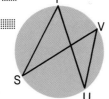

Area and volume, pages 218–235

7. Find the area of the triangle.

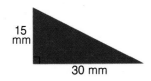

8. Find the volume of a triangular prism that has a base of 39 square centimeters and a height of 7 centimeters.

9. Find the volume of a pyramid with the same base and height as the prism in exercise 8.

In exercises 10–13, use 3.14 for π. Give your answers to the nearest tenth.

10. Find the circumference of the circle.

11. Find the area.

12. Find the volume of a cylinder that is 5 centimeters high and that has a circular base with a 2-centimeter radius.

13. Find the volume of a cone with the same base and height as the cylinder in exercise 12.

Squares, square roots, and the right-triangle relation, pages 238–251

Give the square roots.

14. $\sqrt{81}$ **15.** $\sqrt{9}$ **16.** $\sqrt{17^2}$

17. Find the length of side AC.

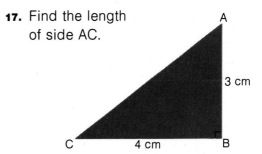

More Practice

Set A

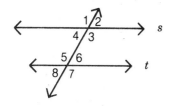

line s ∥ line t
m ∠1 = 120°

1. m ∠2 = ▦

2. m ∠3 = ▦

3. m ∠4 = ▦

4. m ∠6 = ▦

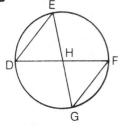

ABCD is a parallelogram.

5. m ∠B = ▦

6. m ∠C = ▦

Set B

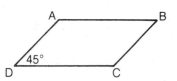

m ∠DEG = 50°

1. m $\widehat{DG}$ = ▦

2. m ∠DHG = ▦

3. m ∠DFG = ▦

Set C

Find the area of each figure.

1.

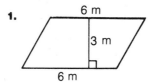

6 m · 3 m · 6 m

2.

10 m · 4 m · 8 m

3.

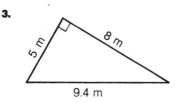

5 m · 8 m · 9.4 m

Set D

Find the volume of each figure.

1.

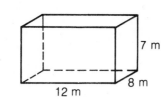

7 m · 12 m · 8 m

2.

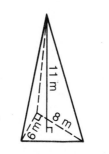

11 m · 8 m · 6 m

Set E

Find the circumference and area of each circle.

1.

5 m · 28 m

2.

7 m · 10 m

Set F

Find the volume and the total surface area of each figure.

1.

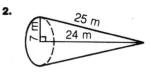

3 m · 7.2 m

2.

7 m · 25 m · 24 m

Set G

Give each square root to the nearest tenth.

1. $\sqrt{35}$ **3.** $\sqrt{73}$

2. $\sqrt{51}$ **4.** $\sqrt{94}$

Individualized Skills Maintenance

Diagnosis	Practice		
	Set A (p. 96)	**Set B** (p. 97)	**Set C** (p. 97)

A. $8\overline{)3.424}$

    $31\overline{)2092.5}$

B. $.5\overline{)365.5}$

    $.9\overline{)7.5924}$

C. $5.5\overline{)1.265}$

    $.78\overline{)4.4928}$

D. $.403\overline{)1.6523}$

    $81.7\overline{)50.654}$

E. Round each quotient to the nearest tenth.

    $.8\overline{)376.7}$

    $5.9\overline{)25.012}$

F. Round each quotient to the nearest hundredth.

    $1.7\overline{)83}$

    $.356\overline{).214}$

Set A (p. 96)

1. $8\overline{)37.84}$
2. $7\overline{)49.119}$
3. $6\overline{)220.2}$
4. $8\overline{)1.6936}$
5. $7\overline{)198.1}$
6. $6\overline{)21.834}$
7. $9\overline{)6.579}$
8. $32\overline{)279.36}$
9. $89\overline{)2394.1}$
10. $72\overline{)315.36}$
11. $92\overline{)908.96}$
12. $49\overline{)62.23}$
13. $29\overline{)2064.8}$
14. $16\overline{)140.48}$
15. $68\overline{)1944.8}$
16. $59\overline{)192.34}$
17. $75\overline{)66.825}$

Set B (p. 97)

1. $.7\overline{)7.714}$
2. $.9\overline{)461.07}$
3. $.5\overline{)9.055}$
4. $.6\overline{)1227.6}$
5. $.9\overline{)80.064}$
6. $.8\overline{)269.6}$
7. $.7\overline{)4.865}$
8. $.4\overline{)195.28}$
9. $.7\overline{).77035}$
10. $.6\overline{)2155.2}$
11. $.7\overline{)3.5147}$
12. $.8\overline{).21616}$
13. $.9\overline{)393.3}$
14. $.6\overline{)56.574}$
15. $.8\overline{).4872}$
16. $.5\overline{)305.85}$
17. $.8\overline{)1.8944}$

Set C (p. 97)

1. $3.2\overline{)302.08}$
2. $.13\overline{)4.511}$
3. $8.4\overline{)6.4932}$
4. $.68\overline{)3.774}$
5. $5.9\overline{)135.11}$
6. $.82\overline{)3.9606}$
7. $3.4\overline{)109.14}$
8. $.28\overline{)2.0272}$
9. $5.5\overline{)2.0075}$
10. $.73\overline{)17.812}$
11. $6.5\overline{)25.220}$
12. $.71\overline{)3.5074}$
13. $5.7\overline{)532.95}$
14. $.84\overline{)2.2932}$
15. $2.8\overline{)2.5004}$
16. $1.7\overline{)129.71}$
17. $.89\overline{)2.2339}$

Individualized Skills Maintenance

Practice *(continued)*

Set D (p. 97)

1. $81.6\overline{)39.168}$

2. $.253\overline{)8096}$

3. $4.54\overline{)3.2688}$

4. $9.04\overline{)32.544}$

5. $78.7\overline{)188.88}$

6. $9.47\overline{)35.986}$

7. $.466\overline{)2.2834}$

8. $57.6\overline{)53.568}$

9. $19.8\overline{)53.46}$

10. $8.07\overline{)7.1823}$

11. $6.52\overline{)4.9552}$

12. $39.2\overline{)199.92}$

13. $.979\overline{)94963}$

14. $.808\overline{)2.3432}$

15. $48.2\overline{)33.258}$

16. $3.71\overline{)3.1906}$

17. $83.6\overline{)51.832}$

Set E (p. 98)

Round each quotient
to the nearest tenth.

1. $.8\overline{)19.39}$

2. $.19\overline{)21.509}$

3. $.7\overline{)31.74}$

4. $2.1\overline{)9046.84}$

5. $.31\overline{)2.874}$

6. $.9\overline{)8231.3}$

7. $9.4\overline{)51.67}$

8. $.28\overline{)54.536}$

9. $.9\overline{)865.83}$

10. $8.2\overline{)451.97}$

11. $.7\overline{)29.85}$

12. $5.1\overline{)775.37}$

13. $.8\overline{)80.33}$

14. $.86\overline{)31.425}$

15. $4.7\overline{)57.24}$

16. $.6\overline{)816.77}$

Set F (p. 98)

Round each quotient to
the nearest hundredth.

1. $3.1\overline{)31.2}$

2. $21.6\overline{)7.53}$

3. $.39\overline{)113}$

4. $5.67\overline{)7.62}$

5. $4.8\overline{)6.913}$

6. $.308\overline{)761}$

7. $.18\overline{)952}$

8. $8.71\overline{)15.63}$

9. $9.3\overline{)29.3}$

10. $61.8\overline{)92.24}$

11. $.98\overline{)2.668}$

12. $6.73\overline{)9.912}$

13. $5.3\overline{)87.66}$

14. $4.36\overline{)3.337}$

15. $.83\overline{)63.74}$

16. $86.7\overline{)136.28}$

Unit 5

Proportion, Percent, and Applications

$$\frac{16}{30} = \frac{n}{75}$$

Ratio and Proportion

A.

Pro Hockey Record		
Team	Games won	Games lost
Boston	52	17
Montreal	45	24
New York Rangers	40	24
Toronto	35	27
Buffalo	32	34
Detroit	29	39
Vancouver	24	44

Boston's *ratio* of games won to games lost is 52 to 17.

$$\frac{52}{17}$$ ← Games won

← Games lost

Bill Mosienko set a record by scoring 3 goals in 21 seconds. This ratio is "3 in 21."

$$\frac{3}{21}$$ ← Goals

← Seconds

Use the data from the table. For each team, write the ratio of games won to games lost.

1. Montreal

2. New York Rangers

3. Toronto

4. Buffalo

5. Detroit

6. Vancouver

B. Two ratios are equal and form a *proportion* if their cross-products are equal.

$$3 \times 42 \qquad 21 \times 6$$

$$126 \qquad\qquad 126$$

The cross-products are equal.

$\frac{3}{21} = \frac{6}{42}$ is a proportion.

Tell whether the ratios would form a proportion. Find cross-products to help you decide.

7. $\frac{5}{20}$ $\frac{7}{28}$

8. $\frac{4}{10}$ $\frac{9}{25}$

9. $\frac{13}{39}$ $\frac{6}{18}$

10. $\frac{6}{16}$ $\frac{15}{40}$

11. $\frac{8}{12}$ $\frac{24}{32}$

12. $\frac{19}{57}$ $\frac{7}{21}$

13. $\frac{.6}{15}$ $\frac{1.8}{45}$

14. $\frac{1.4}{2.1}$ $\frac{8}{12}$

15. $\frac{14}{11}$ $\frac{91}{88}$

16. $\frac{75}{12}$ $\frac{90}{15}$

17. $\frac{1.8}{27}$ $\frac{4.2}{63}$

18. $\frac{25}{30}$ $\frac{3.5}{4.6}$

Solving Proportions

Chris can skate the length of the hockey rink, about 61 meters, in 10 seconds. At this rate, how far could Chris skate in 60 seconds?

Write a proportion. Use a letter for the number you want to find.

$$\frac{61}{10} = \frac{n}{60}$$ ←— Meters ←— Seconds

Write the cross-products.

$$61 \times 60 = 10 \times n$$

$$3660 = 10n$$

Find n.

$$366 = n$$

Answer the question.

Chris could skate 366 meters in 60 seconds.

Use cross-products to find the missing numbers.

1. $\dfrac{21}{6} = \dfrac{n}{4}$

8. $\dfrac{6}{a} = \dfrac{15}{25}$

2. $\dfrac{7}{c} = \dfrac{28}{8}$

9. $\dfrac{25}{n} = \dfrac{10}{14}$

3. $\dfrac{9}{3} = \dfrac{z}{7}$

10. $\dfrac{9}{12} = \dfrac{a}{32}$

4. $\dfrac{c}{25} = \dfrac{4}{5}$

11. $\dfrac{.18}{m} = \dfrac{24}{28}$

5. $\dfrac{36}{54} = \dfrac{r}{15}$

12. $\dfrac{21}{63} = \dfrac{s}{7.8}$

6. $\dfrac{57}{95} = \dfrac{18}{v}$

13. $\dfrac{u}{.9} = \dfrac{35}{21}$

7. $\dfrac{r}{68} = \dfrac{16}{17}$

14. $\dfrac{21}{12} = \dfrac{4.9}{v}$

**More practice
Set A, page 318**

Using Proportions: Estimation of Fish Population

At Green Lake, a fisheries research team tagged 120 fish for identification. Later they took a sample of 308 fish and found 8 tagged fish. Estimate the number of fish in the lake.

Number of tagged fish

Total number of fish

Write a proportion. Use a letter for the number you want to find.

$$\frac{120}{a} = \frac{8}{308}$$

Write the cross-products.

$$120 \times 308 = a \times 8$$

$$36{,}960 = 8a$$

Find a.

$$4620 = a$$

Answer the question.

The researchers estimated that there were about 4620 fish in Green Lake.

Use proportions to find each answer.

1. Researchers tagged 150 fish in Fox Lake. In a later sample, they found that 6 out of 480 fish were tagged. About how many fish were in Fox Lake?

2. In Cedar Lake, 275 fish were tagged. In a later sample, 12 out of the 600 fish netted had been tagged. About how many fish were in Cedar Lake?

3. A research team tagged 758 fish in 2 days. At this rate, how many fish could they tag in 15 days?

4. Researchers tagged 250 trout in Franks Lake. Later they took a sample and found 3 out of 48 trout were tagged. About how many trout were in Franks Lake?

5. A stream is being stocked with fish in a ratio of 2 largemouth bass to 15 bluegills. If 70 largemouth bass are put into the stream, how many bluegills should be put in?

6. In Lake LaHache, 325 bass were tagged. In a sample taken later, 12 out of 96 bass were tagged. About how many bass were in Lake LaHache?

7. A research team traveled 23.7 kilometers in 3 hours. At this rate, how far could they travel in 8 hours?

8. A pike swam 5.5 meters in 2 seconds. At this rate, how far could it travel in 60 seconds?

9. A sailfish swam 66 meters in 5 seconds. At this rate, how long would it take the sailfish to swim 330 meters?

10. On a certain map, the length of Lake Ida is 0.8 centimeters. On this map 2 centimeters represents 35 kilometers. What is the actual length of Lake Ida?

Using Proportions: Bicycle Gears

Pat's 5-speed bicycle has a chain attached to the pedal sprocket and to the gears on the rear wheel. The ratio of pedal turns to rear-wheel turns for each gear is given below.

	1st gear	2nd gear	3rd gear	4th gear	5th gear
Number of pedal turns →	$\dfrac{9}{14}$	$\dfrac{4}{7}$	$\dfrac{1}{2}$	$\dfrac{3}{7}$	$\dfrac{5}{14}$
Number of rear-wheel turns →					

In first gear, how many times does the rear wheel turn if the pedals turn 180 times? (Use the ratio for first gear: 9 to 14.)

$$\frac{9}{14} = \frac{180}{n}$$

← Number of pedal turns
← Number of rear-wheel turns

$$n = 280$$

The rear wheel turns 280 times.

Use the ratios given on page 264 to help you complete these tables.

	Gear	Number of pedal turns	Number of rear-wheel turns
	1st	180	280
1.	2nd	180	
2.	3rd	180	
3.	4th	180	
4.	5th	180	

	Gear	Number of pedal turns	Number of rear-wheel turns
5.	1st		14
6.	2nd		14
7.	3rd		14
8.	4th		14
9.	5th		14

	Gear	Number of pedal turns	Number of rear-wheel turns
10.	1st		42
11.	1st	63	
12.	1st		112
13.	2nd	72	
14.	2nd		70
15.	2nd		56
16.	3rd	100	
17.	3rd		300
18.	3rd	500	
19.	4th		35
20.	4th	150	
21.	4th	75	
22.	5th		140
23.	5th	100	
24.	5th	1000	

25. One day, Pat counted 166 turns of her pedals while she traveled one kilometer. If she was riding in third gear, how many times did the rear wheel turn as she traveled one kilometer?

Using Proportions: Automobile Supplies

Floor mats	2 for $4.69
Spark plugs	3 for $2.20
Cans of motor oil	2 for $1.29
Baby moon hubcaps	2 for $3.15
Seat belts	2 for $11.95
Stereo tapes	3 for $19.50
Bumper guards	2 for $22.95
Shock absorbers	2 for $29.95
Chrome reverse wheels	2 for $34.50
Mag wheels	2 for $83.50
Fasteners for mag wheels	5 for $4.25
Steel-belted tires	2 for $115.75

Use proportions to find the cost of the items listed in each exercise. Round your answers to the nearest cent.

1. 4 floor mats

$$\frac{2}{4.69} = \frac{4}{c} \quad \begin{array}{l} \leftarrow \text{Number of items} \\ \leftarrow \text{Cost} \end{array}$$

2. 8 spark plugs

3. 7 cans of motor oil

4. 5 baby moon hubcaps

5. 6 seat belts

6. 10 stereo tapes

7. 4 bumper guards

8. 4 shock absorbers

9. 5 chrome reverse wheels

10. 5 mag wheels

11. 20 fasteners for mag wheels

12. 5 steel-belted tires

Analysts for a brokerage firm prepare research reports on the companies whose stocks are traded in the stock market. One figure that an analyst uses is the price-earnings ratio (P.E. ratio). The P.E. ratio of a certain stock is shown below.

$$\frac{\$70.75}{\$5.37}$$ ⟵ Market price per share
⟵ Earnings per share

The P.E. ratio can be written as a decimal correct to the nearest tenth.

$$5.37)\overline{70.75\,00} \quad \frac{13.17}{} \approx 13.2$$

The P.E. ratio of this stock is 13.2.

For each stock, give the P.E. ratio as a decimal correct to the nearest tenth.

	Stock	Market price (May, 1974)	Earnings per share (1973)
1.	Travelers Insurance	$25.38	$3.93
2.	Gillette	$34.25	$2.91
3.	United States Steel	$45.13	$6.01
4.	General Electric	$51.75	$3.21
5.	Aluminum Company of America	$49.38	$3.09

A. Teresa assembled a plastic model of the Grumman Gulfhawk stunt plane. The scale of this model is 1 to 32. One centimeter on the model represents 32 centimeters on the actual airplane.

The wingspan of the model is about 27 centimeters. What is the actual wingspan?

$$\frac{1}{32} = \frac{27}{n}$$ ⟵ Model airplane
⟵ Actual airplane

$$n = 864$$

The actual wingspan is about 864 centimeters, or 8.64 meters.

B. The length of the Gulfhawk model is about 22 centimeters. What is the actual length of the airplane?

$$\frac{1}{32} = \frac{22}{n}$$ ⟵ Model airplane
⟵ Actual airplane

$$n = 704$$

The actual length is about 704 centimeters, or 7.04 meters.

The wingspan and the length of model airplanes are given in the table. Use the scale to find the actual length and the actual wingspan for each airplane.

	Airplane	Scale	Wingspan (cm)	Length (cm)
1.	Corsair F 4U-1	1 to 32	39	32
2.	Phantom F-4J	1 to 32	37	55
3.	Wright Brothers Plane	1 to 39	32	17
4.	Cessna 180	1 to 41	25	19
5.	Hawk P-6E	1 to 72	13	9
6.	Boeing B-17E	1 to 72	43	30
7.	Albatross HU-16B	1 to 72	41	27
8.	SAS DC-9	1 to 96	30	38
9.	Eastern L-1011	1 to 144	33	38
10.	TWA 747	1 to 144	40	48

Similar Triangles

A. Triangle PAT is similar to triangle SUE.

We write $\triangle$ PAT ~ $\triangle$ SUE.

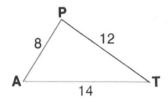

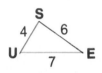

In similar triangles the corresponding angles are congruent.

$$\angle P \cong \angle S$$

$$\angle A \cong \angle U$$

$$\angle T \cong \angle E$$

In similar triangles the lengths of the corresponding sides are proportional.

$$\frac{PA}{SU} = \frac{AT}{UE} = \frac{PT}{SE}$$

$$\frac{8}{4} = \frac{14}{7} = \frac{12}{6}$$

B. These triangles are similar. Find the missing length.

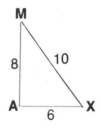

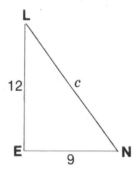

$$\frac{MA}{LE} = \frac{MX}{LN}$$

$$\frac{8}{12} = \frac{10}{c}$$

$$8 \times c = 12 \times 10$$

$$8c = 120$$

$$c = 15$$

In each exercise the two triangles are similar. Find each missing length.

1.

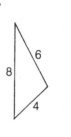
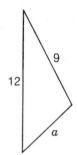

2.

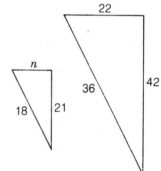

3.

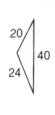
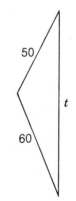

4.

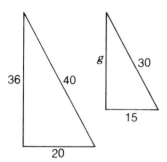

36   40

g   30

20   15

5.

16   k

26

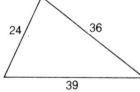

24   36

39

6.

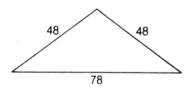

48   48

78

16   16

y

7. The triangles formed by the girl and her shadow and by the building and its shadow are similar. Find the height of the building.

h

159 cm

53 cm

212 cm

The distance from the sun to the earth, 93,000,000 miles, is called 1 astronomical unit.

In 1772, an astronomer named Johann Bode noticed a relationship concerning the distances of the planets from the sun.

To see what Bode's Law says, copy and complete this table.

	Mercury	Venus	Earth	Mars	Asteroids	Jupiter	Saturn	Uranus	Neptune	Pluto
Double each number going across the row.	0	3	6	12						
Add 4 to each number in the row above.	4	7	10							
Divide each number in the row above by 10.	.4	.7								
Average distance from the sun in astronomical units	.39	.72	1.0	1.52	2.65	5.20	9.54	19.2	30.1	39.5

Compare the results in the third row of the table with the actual distances in the fourth row.

No one has completely explained why Bode's Law works; it may be just a coincidence. The law seems inaccurate for Neptune and Pluto—perhaps because of their unusual orbits.

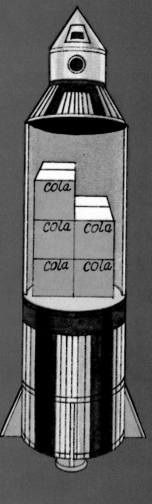

TIME OUT

If 2 space travelers drink 2 containers of Bode Cola in 2 days, how many containers of Bode Cola will 10 space travelers drink in 10 days? (The answer is not 10.)

Sides in a Right Triangle

Triangle XBT is a right triangle.

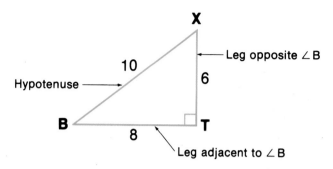

The length of the hypotenuse of △ XBT is 10.
The length of the leg opposite ∠ B is 6.
The length of the leg adjacent to ∠ B is 8.

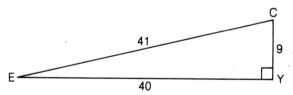

Give the length of each of these sides of △ CEY.

1. Hypotenuse

2. Leg opposite ∠ E

3. Leg adjacent to ∠ E

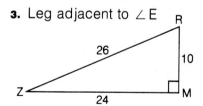

Give the length of each of these sides of △ RZM.

4. Hypotenuse

5. Leg opposite ∠ Z

6. Leg adjacent to ∠ Z

Writing Trigonometric Ratios

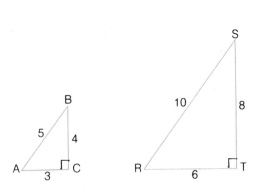 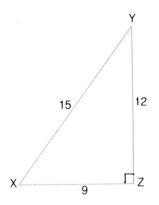

Triangles ABC, RST, and XYZ are similar right triangles. $\angle A \cong \angle R \cong \angle X$.

In any right triangle, three *trigonometric ratios* can be written for each acute angle. They are called the *tangent* (tan), the *sine* (sin), and the *cosine* (cos).

Complete this table of ratios.

Trigonometric ratios		$\angle A$	$\angle R$	$\angle X$
tan =	$\dfrac{\text{length of leg opposite angle}}{\text{length of leg adjacent to angle}}$	$\dfrac{4}{3}$	$\dfrac{8}{6}$	
sin =	$\dfrac{\text{length of leg opposite angle}}{\text{length of hypotenuse}}$	$\dfrac{4}{5}$		
cos =	$\dfrac{\text{length of leg adjacent to angle}}{\text{length of hypotenuse}}$			

The tangent, the sine, and the cosine are usually written as decimals.

$$\tan A = \frac{4}{3} \approx 1.333 \qquad \begin{array}{r} 1.3333\ldots \\ 3\overline{)4.0000} \end{array}$$

$$\tan R = \frac{8}{6} \approx 1.333 \qquad \begin{array}{r} 1.3333\ldots \\ 6\overline{)8.0000} \end{array}$$

$$\tan X = \frac{12}{9} \approx 1.333 \qquad \begin{array}{r} 1.3333\ldots \\ 9\overline{)12.0000} \end{array}$$

$\tan A = \tan R = \tan X$

Is sin A = sin R = sin X?

Is cos A = cos R = cos X?

Any angle with the same measure as $\angle A$ has the same tangent, sine, and cosine as $\angle A$.

For each exercise, give the tangent, the sine, and the cosine as ratios and also as decimals correct to the nearest thousandth.

1. a. $\tan S = \dfrac{8}{15} \approx$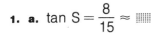

   b. $\sin S$

   c. $\cos S$

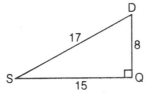

2. a. $\tan T$

   b. $\sin T$

   c. $\cos T$

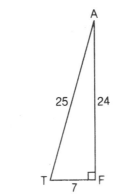

3. a. $\tan E$

   b. $\sin E$

   c. $\cos E$

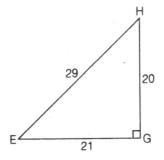

4. a. $\tan N$

   b. $\sin N$

   c. $\cos N$

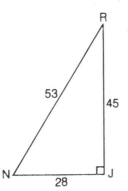

Measure the sides of these triangles to the nearest millimeter. For each exercise, give an approximation for the tangent, the sine, and the cosine. Give each answer as a ratio and as a decimal to the nearest tenth.

5. a. $\tan 50° = \dfrac{}{} \approx$

   b. $\sin 50°$

   c. $\cos 50°$

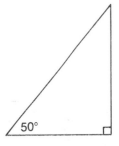

6. a. $\tan 30°$

   b. $\sin 30°$

   c. $\cos 30°$

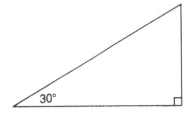

275

Reading a Table of Trigonometric Ratios

The table shows that, for a 15° angle in any right triangle, the tangent is about .268, the sine is about .259, and the cosine is about .966.

Use the table to give a decimal for each exercise.

1. sin 18°

2. cos 27°

3. tan 38°

4. tan 87°

5. sin 6°

6. cos 84°

Use the table to find the measure of ∠A.

7. cos A = .500

8. tan A = 1.881

9. sin A = .358

10. tan A = .231

11. sin A = .682

12. cos A = .682

Measure of angle	tan	sin	cos	Measure of angle	tan	sin	cos
1°	.017	.017	1.000	46°	1.036	.719	.695
2°	.035	.035	.999	47°	1.072	.731	.682
3°	.052	.052	.999	48°	1.111	.743	.669
4°	.070	.070	.998	49°	1.150	.755	.656
5°	.087	.087	.996	50°	1.192	.766	.643
6°	.105	.105	.995	51°	1.235	.777	.629
7°	.123	.122	.993	52°	1.280	.788	.616
8°	.141	.139	.990	53°	1.327	.799	.602
9°	.158	.156	.988	54°	1.376	.809	.588
10°	.176	.174	.985	55°	1.428	.819	.574
11°	.194	.191	.982	56°	1.483	.829	.559
12°	.213	.208	.978	57°	1.540	.839	.545
13°	.231	.225	.974	58°	1.600	.848	.530
14°	.249	.242	.970	59°	1.664	.857	.515
15°	.268	.259	.966	60°	1.732	.866	.500
16°	.287	.276	.961	61°	1.804	.875	.485
17°	.306	.292	.956	62°	1.881	.883	.469
18°	.325	.309	.951	63°	1.963	.891	.454
19°	.344	.326	.946	64°	2.050	.899	.438
20°	.364	.342	.940	65°	2.145	.906	.423
21°	.384	.358	.934	66°	2.246	.914	.407
22°	.404	.375	.927	67°	2.356	.921	.391
23°	.424	.391	.921	68°	2.475	.927	.375
24°	.445	.407	.914	69°	2.605	.934	.358
25°	.466	.423	.906	70°	2.748	.940	.342
26°	.488	.438	.899	71°	2.904	.946	.326
27°	.510	.454	.891	72°	3.078	.951	.309
28°	.532	.469	.883	73°	3.271	.956	.292
29°	.554	.485	.875	74°	3.487	.961	.276
30°	.577	.500	.866	75°	3.732	.966	.259
31°	.601	.515	.857	76°	4.011	.970	.242
32°	.625	.530	.848	77°	4.332	.974	.225
33°	.649	.545	.839	78°	4.705	.978	.208
34°	.675	.559	.829	79°	5.145	.982	.191
35°	.700	.574	.819	80°	5.671	.985	.174
36°	.727	.588	.809	81°	6.314	.988	.156
37°	.754	.602	.799	82°	7.115	.990	.139
38°	.781	.616	.788	83°	8.144	.993	.122
39°	.810	.629	.777	84°	9.514	.995	.105
40°	.839	.643	.766	85°	11.430	.996	.087
41°	.869	.656	.755	86°	14.301	.998	.070
42°	.900	.669	.743	87°	19.081	.999	.052
43°	.933	.682	.731	88°	28.636	.999	.035
44°	.966	.695	.719	89°	57.290	1.000	.017
45°	1.000	.707	.707				

Using the Tangent Ratio: Indirect Measurement

How far above Graytown is the
airplane? Give your answer to the
nearest kilometer.

For each exercise, use
the tangent ratios in the
table to help you find
the missing measure.
Round your answers to
the nearest whole
number.

Use the tangent ratio
to write an equation.

$$\tan 56° = \frac{s}{6}$$

Find the tangent $\tan 56° \approx 1.483$
of 56° in the table.
Write the decimal in
the equation.

$$1.483 = \frac{s}{6}$$

Find *s*.

$$8.898 = s$$

Answer the
question.

The airplane is about
9 kilometers above Graytown.

s

56°
Smithville   **6 km**   Graytown

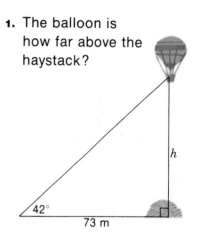

1. The balloon is
how far above the
haystack?

h

42°
73 m

2. The helicopter is
how far above the
spacecraft?

b
20°
300 m

3. How tall is the tree?

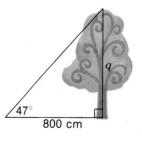

q

47°
800 cm

Using the Sine and Cosine Ratios: Indirect Measurement

A. How far above the ground is the airplane? Give your answer to the nearest meter.

$$\sin 23° = \frac{n}{900}$$

$\sin 23° \approx .391$

$$.391 = \frac{n}{900}$$

$$n = 351.900$$

The airplane is about 352 meters above the ground.

B. How far from the building is the foot of the ladder? Give your answer to the nearest centimeter.

$$\cos 75° = \frac{n}{730}$$

$\cos 75° \approx .259$

$$.259 = \frac{n}{730}$$

$$189.070 = n$$

The foot of the ladder is about 189 centimeters from the building.

For each exercise, use the sine and cosine ratios in the table on page 276 to help you find the missing measure. Round your answers to the nearest whole number.

1. How high is the kite?

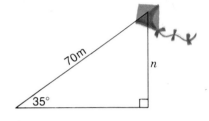

2. How far from Princeton is the boat?

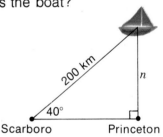

3. How wide is the television screen?

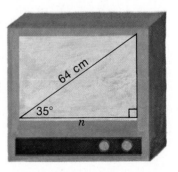

LABORATORY ACTIVITY

1. Ask your classmates
which of these
rectangles they
like best.
Tally the results.

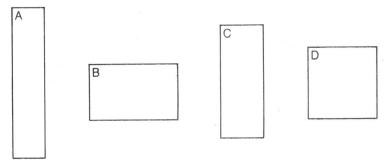

The shape of the Golden Rectangle is said to be pleasing
to the eye. A Golden Rectangle has a special ratio of its
length to its width.

2. A Golden Rectangle is outlined in the
picture. Measure the red rectangle in
millimeters and write the ratio of the
length to the width.

The Metropolitan Museum of Art. Bequest of Stephen C. Clark. 1960.

3. Give the ratio of the length
to the width in the Golden
Rectangle as a decimal
correct to the nearest
tenth.

4. Measure rectangles
A, B, C, and D. For each
rectangle, give the ratio
of the length to the width
as a decimal correct to the
nearest tenth.

5. Which of rectangles
A, B, C, or D is a Golden
Rectangle? Is it the
rectangle that your
classmates liked best?

6. Try to find an example of
a Golden Rectangle in
your classroom.

279

Chapter 13 Test
Ratio, Proportion, and Trigonometry, Pages 260-279

Writing ratios and proportions, pages 260-261

1. The Harris School Tigers won 7 games and lost 4 games. Write the ratio of games won to games lost.

Tell whether each pair of ratios would form a proportion.

2. $\dfrac{15}{20}$ $\dfrac{12}{16}$

3. $\dfrac{2.5}{10}$ $\dfrac{2.1}{8}$

Find the missing number in each proportion.

4. $\dfrac{4}{30} = \dfrac{6}{n}$

6. $\dfrac{c}{1.2} = \dfrac{9}{36}$

5. $\dfrac{35}{a} = \dfrac{15}{9}$

7. $\dfrac{8}{1.4} = \dfrac{28}{w}$

Writing trigonometric ratios, pages 273-276

Give the tangent, the sine, or the cosine as a ratio and also as a decimal correct to the nearest thousandth.

8. tan X

9. sin X

10. cos X

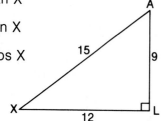

Problem solving, pages 262-266, 268-271, 277-278

11. Researchers tagged 140 fish in Silver Lake. In a later sample, they found 8 out of 400 fish were tagged. About how many fish were in Silver Lake?

12. Stereo tapes are on sale at 2 for $11.50. How much would 5 tapes cost?

13. Tosh made a model 727 that had a scale of 1 to 96. The wingspan of the model is 34 centimeters. What is the wingspan of the actual airplane?

14. These triangles are similar. Find n.

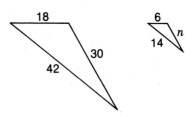

15. Find the height of the cliff. Round your answer to the nearest whole number. (tan 38° ≈ .781)

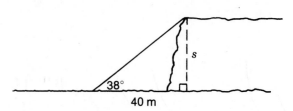

280

4 is what percent of 10?

Percent

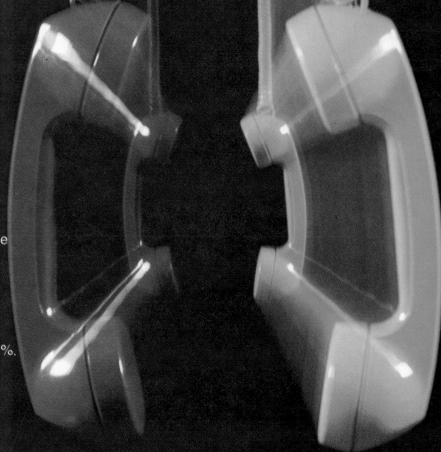

A. In 1972, about 95 out of every 100 out-of-country telephone calls made in Canada were to points in the United States.

"95 out of 100" can be written as $\frac{95}{100}$ or as 95 *percent*.

Percent means "hundredths." The symbol for percent is %.

$$\frac{95}{100} = 95\%$$

B. In 1972, about 90% of the households in New Brunswick had telephones. What fraction of the households was this?

$$90\% = \frac{90}{100} = \frac{9}{10}$$

$\frac{9}{10}$ of the households had telephones.

Write each fraction as a percent.

1. $\frac{17}{100}$

2. $\frac{35}{100}$

3. $\frac{78}{100}$

4. $\frac{41}{100}$

5. $\frac{65}{100}$

6. $\frac{9}{100}$

7. $\frac{73}{100}$

Write each percent as a fraction in lowest terms.

8. 50%

9. 20%

10. 75%

11. 30%

12. 45%

13. 60%

14. 54%

15. 24%

Percents and Fractions

A. In 1972, about $66\frac{2}{3}\%$ of the telephones in Nova Scotia had access to direct distance dialing. What fraction of the telephones was this?

$$66\frac{2}{3}\% = \frac{66\frac{2}{3}}{100} = 66\frac{2}{3} \div 100$$

$$66\frac{2}{3} \div 100$$

$$\frac{200}{3} \div \frac{100}{1} = \frac{200}{3} \times \frac{1}{100} = \frac{200}{300} = \frac{2}{3}$$

$$66\frac{2}{3}\% = \frac{2}{3}$$

$\frac{2}{3}$ of the telephones in Nova Scotia had access to direct distance dialing.

B. In 1972, about $\frac{5}{6}$ of the telephones in Ontario had access to direct distance dialing. What percent was this?

You can use cross-products to write $\frac{5}{6}$ as hundredths.

$$\frac{c}{100} = \frac{5}{6}$$

$$c \times 6 = 100 \times 5$$

$$6c = 500$$

$$c = 83\frac{1}{3}$$

$$\frac{5}{6} = \frac{83\frac{1}{3}}{100} = 83\frac{1}{3}\%$$

$83\frac{1}{3}\%$ of the telephones in Ontario had access to direct distance dialing.

Write each percent as a fraction in lowest terms.

1. $33\frac{1}{3}\%$

2. $12\frac{1}{2}\%$

3. $11\frac{1}{9}\%$

4. $8\frac{1}{3}\%$

5. $62\frac{1}{2}\%$

6. $4\frac{1}{2}\%$

7. $28\frac{4}{7}\%$

Write each fraction as a percent.

8. $\frac{2}{5}$

9. $\frac{7}{10}$

10. $\frac{1}{4}$

11. $\frac{7}{20}$

12. $\frac{3}{8}$

13. $\frac{1}{6}$

14. $\frac{7}{8}$

15. $\frac{5}{12}$

283

Percents and Decimals

A. To change a percent to a decimal, write the percent as a fraction with a denominator of 100. Then change the fraction to a decimal.

$$21\% = \frac{21}{100} = .21$$

$$6\% = \frac{6}{100} = .06$$

$$\frac{37.5}{100} = 37.5 \div 100$$

$$37.5\% = \frac{37.5}{100} = .375$$

B. To change a decimal to a percent, write the decimal as a fraction with a denominator of 100. Then change the fraction to a percent.

$$.52 = \frac{52}{100} = 52\%$$

$$.07 = \frac{7}{100} = 7\%$$

$$.3 = \frac{3}{10} = \frac{30}{100} = 30\%$$

$$\frac{n}{100} = \frac{784}{1000}$$
$$n = 78.4$$

$$.784 = \frac{784}{1000} = \frac{78.4}{100} = 78.4\%$$

Write each percent as a decimal.

1. 15%

2. 87%

3. 1%

4. 50%

5. 38%

6. 3%

7. 18.9%

8. 73.5%

9. 20.4%

10. 4.5%

11. 67.5%

12. 6.75%

13. 25%

14. 2.5%

15. .25%

● **Discuss** Do you see an easy way to change a percent to a decimal?

More practice
Set B, page 318

Write each
decimal as
a percent.

16. .34

17. .89

18. .57

19. .08

20. .05

21. .7

22. .9

23. .927

24. .681

25. .309

26. .8

27. .44

28. .02

29. .659

30. .074

31. .081

32. .002

33. .6

34. .006

● **Discuss** Do you
see an easy way to
change a decimal
to a percent?

Laboratory Activity

One week, Kurt's family kept a record
of how many minutes the members of the
family spent talking on their home telephone.

Kurt organized the information in a table.
Complete the table.

Person	Minutes spent on the telephone	Part of total time that each person spent on the telephone		
		Fraction	Percent	Decimal
Mother	75	$\frac{75}{500}$	15 %	.15
Father	84	$\frac{84}{500}$	16.8 %	.168
Judy	125			
Martin	56			
Kurt	160			
Total	500			

Collect information about some daily activity and
construct a table like Kurt's.

Finding a Percent of a Number

A. Joan bought a saxophone priced at $320. The sales tax was 5% of the price. What was the amount of sales tax?

Find 5% of 320.

$$\frac{5}{100} = \frac{n}{320}$$

$$5 \times 320 = 100 \times n$$

$$1600 = 100n$$

$$n = 16.00$$

The sales tax was $16.00.

B. Here is another way to find 5% of 320.

Write an equation. $5\% \times 320 = b$

Change the percent to a decimal. $.05 \times 320 = b$

Find b. $16.00 = b$

Answer the question.   The sales tax was $16.00.

C. Here is a third way to find 5% of 320.

Write an equation. $5\% \times 320 = c$

Change the percent to a fraction. $\frac{1}{20} \times 320 = c$

Find c. $16 = c$

Answer the question.   The sales tax was $16.

Find each missing number.

1. 10% of 70 is a.

2. 25% of 64 is n.

3. 70% of 120 is b.

4. 15% of 80 is t.

5. 20% of 65 is y.

6. 7% of 300 is g.

7. 50% of 76 is c.

8. 18% of 200 is w.

9. 82% of 150 is h.

10. 46% of 350 is k.

11. $12\frac{1}{2}$% of 800 is m.

12. 48% of 125 is c.

13. 30% of 140 is d.

14. 85% of 40 is a.

15. $66\frac{2}{3}$% of 90 is n.

16. y is 75% of 56.

17. s is 92% of 45.

18. a is 60% of 112.

19. v is $33\frac{1}{3}$% of 150.

20. u is 95% of 38.

Find the amount of sales tax on each of these items if the tax is 5%.

21. Trumpet: $165

22. Bassoon: $950

23. Cornet: $137

24. Baritone horn: $375

Find the amount of sales tax on each of these items if the tax is 6%.

25. Flute: $197

26. Trombone: $205

27. Clarinet: $155

28. Violin: $92

Find the amount of sales tax on each of these items if the tax is 4.5%.

29. Oboe: $350

30. Bass drum: $200

31. French horn: $410

32. Cello: $390

More practice
Set C, page 318

Pages 305

Using Percent: Computing Interest

A. Ms. Lopez had a $3000 bond that paid 7% interest each year. How much interest did she receive in 2 years?

To find the amount of interest, use the following formula:

interest = principal × rate × time

The principal is $3000.

The rate of interest is 7%.

The time is 2 years.

$$i = prt$$

$$i = 3000 \times 7\% \times 2$$

$$7\% = .07$$

$$i = 3000 \times .07 \times 2$$

$$i = 420.00$$

Ms. Lopez received $420.00 interest in 2 years.

B. Chuck borrowed $500 from his uncle and agreed to pay 6% interest per year. How much interest did he owe at the end of 6 months? (6 months = $\frac{1}{2}$ year)

$$i = prt$$

$$i = 500 \times 6\% \times \frac{1}{2}$$

$$6\% = .06$$
$$\frac{1}{2} = .5$$

$$i = 500 \times .06 \times .5$$

$$i = 15.00$$

Chuck owed $15.00 interest after 6 months.

For each exercise, find the amount of interest.

	Principal	Rate	Time
1.	$100	5%	1 year
2.	$275	6%	1 year
3.	$600	4%	2 years
4.	$150	7%	5 years
5.	$800	7%	10 years
6.	$2000	9%	3 years
7.	$10,000	6%	8 years
8.	$1000	5.5%	1 year
9.	$600	4.5%	2 years
10.	$8000	7.25%	4 years
11.	$700	6%	$\frac{1}{2}$ year
12.	$2000	5%	$\frac{1}{4}$ year
13.	$4000	6%	$\frac{3}{4}$ year
14.	$2500	4%	$1\frac{1}{2}$ years
15.	$6200	6%	$3\frac{1}{2}$ years
16.	$1200	4%	6 months
17.	$900	8%	3 months
18.	$6000	7%	9 months
19.	$10,000	4.5%	6 months
20.	$10,000	8.2%	6 months

TIME OUT

Use the facts below to find out whose portraits are on the $1, $5, $10, $20, $50, $100, $500, $1000, $5000, and $10,000 bills.

Hamilton's portrait is on the $10 bill.

Grant, Franklin, and Washington together make $151.

Madison, Grant, and Cleveland together make $6050.

Franklin, Jackson, and Lincoln together make $125.

McKinley and Jackson together make $520.

Chase and Madison together make $15,000.

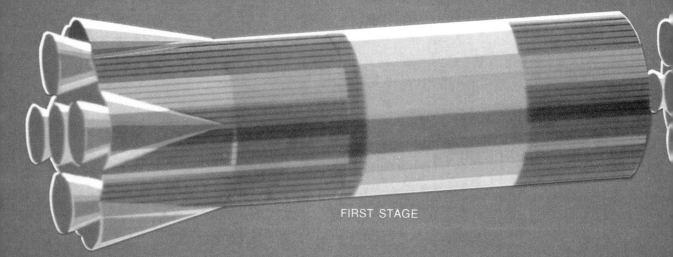

FIRST STAGE

The total length of the Saturn V launch vehicle is about 280 feet. The length of the second stage of the Saturn V is about 80 feet. The length of the second stage is what percent of the total length?

80 is what percent of 280?

$$\frac{c}{100} = \frac{80}{280}$$

$$c \times 280 = 100 \times 80$$

$$280c = 8000$$

$$c = 28\frac{4}{7}$$

The length of the second stage is $28\frac{4}{7}$% of the total length.

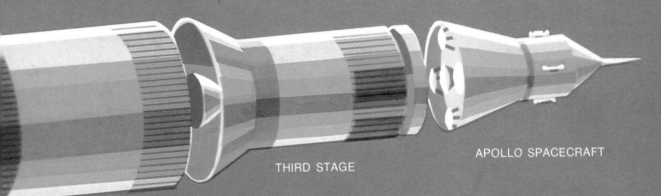

SECOND STAGE

THIRD STAGE

APOLLO SPACECRAFT

Find each percent.

1. 60 is what percent of 80?

2. 12 is what percent of 15?

3. 21 is what percent of 30?

4. 28 is what percent of 50?

5. 24 is what percent of 75?

6. 16 is what percent of 200?

7. 63 is what percent of 140?

8. 9 is what percent of 24?

9. 2.5 is what percent of 4?

10. 200 is what percent of 300?

11. What percent of 20 is 18?

12. What percent of 50 is 32?

13. What percent of 400 is 12?

14. What percent of 9 is 7?

15. What percent of 120 is 10?

16. What percent of 23 is 2.3?

Solve these problems.

17. The total length of the Saturn V is about 280 feet. The length of the first stage is about 140 feet. The length of the first stage is what percent of the total length?

18. The Apollo spacecraft weighs about 48 tons when fully fueled. Its lunar module weighs about 16 tons. What percent of the total weight of Apollo is the weight of the lunar module?

19. The Saturn V, when fully fueled, weighs about 6.4 million pounds. The first stage weighs about 5 million pounds with fuel. What percent of the total weight is the weight of the first stage?

20. The Saturn V can launch 140 tons of payload into earth orbit and send about 48 tons of that payload to the moon. The tonnage sent to the moon is what percent of the tonnage put into earth orbit?

**More practice
Set D, page 318**

Finding a Number When a Percent Is Known

The Erie High School tennis team won 80% of their matches for the season. They won 12 matches. How many matches did they play?

80% of what number is 12?

$$\frac{80}{100} = \frac{12}{v}$$

$$80 \times v = 100 \times 12$$

$$80v = 1200$$

$$v = 15$$

The team played 15 matches.

Find each missing number.

1. 30% of t is 6.
2. 90% of a is 18.
3. 50% of d is 7.
4. 10% of c is 9.
5. 15% of y is 12.
6. 40% of b is 22.
7. 25% of w is 37.
8. 65% of z is 26.
9. 20% of n is 45.
10. 4% of s is 11.

11. 70% of g is 63.
12. 35% of h is 84.
13. 58% of k is 29.
14. 48% of a is 96.
15. 80% of d is 56.
16. 27 is 9% of n.
17. 28 is 16% of b.
18. 38 is 95% of w.
19. 53 is 50% of n.
20. 33 is 60% of t.

Solve these problems.

21. At a sale, Suzanne saved 20% on the price of a tennis racket. She saved $6. What was the regular price?

22. In Frank's school, 150 of the students play tennis. This is 30% of all the students. How many students are in Frank's school?

24. The strings on Jan's tennis racket weigh .5 ounce. This is 4% of the total weight of her racket. What is the weight of her tennis racket?

23. The singles tennis court is 75% as wide as the doubles tennis court. The singles court is 27 feet wide. How wide is the doubles court?

More practice Set E, page 318

Percents Greater Than 100%

A. Write 126% as a decimal.

$$126\% = \frac{126}{100} = 1\frac{26}{100} = 1.26$$

B. Write 475% as a mixed number.

$$475\% = \frac{475}{100} = 4\frac{75}{100} = 4\frac{3}{4}$$

C. Write 7.3 as a percent.

$$7.3 = 7\frac{3}{10} = \frac{73}{10} = \frac{730}{100}$$
$$7.3 = 730\%$$

D. Write $9\frac{1}{2}$ as a percent.

$$9\frac{1}{2} = \frac{19}{2}$$
$$\frac{a}{100} = \frac{19}{2}$$
$$a = 950$$
$$9\frac{1}{2} = 950\%$$

Write each
percent as
a decimal.

1. 215%

2. 150%

3. 321%

4. 500%

5. 625%

6. 275%

7. 490%

8. 175%

Write each
percent as
a mixed number.

9. 743%

10. 819%

11. 507%

12. 225%

13. 390%

14. 460%

15. 635%

16. 998%

Write each decimal
as a percent.

17. 6.55

18. 2.39

19. 4.17

20. 1.82

21. 3.8

22. 5.6

23. 1.4

24. 3.0

Write each mixed
number as a percent.

25. $3\frac{7}{100}$

26. $2\frac{1}{2}$

27. $3\frac{1}{4}$

28. $7\frac{2}{5}$

29. $6\frac{3}{4}$

30. $4\frac{3}{5}$

31. $5\frac{7}{10}$

32. $1\frac{1}{20}$

More practice
Set F, page 319
Set G, page 319

Percent of Increase

It costs $5 to manufacture a pair of pants. At a store, the pants are sold for $12. What is the percent of increase from manufacturing cost to selling price?

Subtract the cost from the selling price.

$$\begin{array}{r} \$12 \\ -\ 5 \\ \hline \$\ 7 \end{array}$$

The amount of increase is $7.

$7 is what percent of $5?

$$\frac{k}{100} = \frac{7}{5}$$

$$k \times 5 = 100 \times 7$$

$$5k = 700$$

$$k = 140$$

The percent of increase is 140%.

Complete this table.

	Cost	Selling price	Amount of increase	Percent of increase	
1. Shirt	$4	$11	$7		$\leftarrow \dfrac{n}{100} = \dfrac{7}{4}$
2. Sweater	$12	$24	$12		
3. Belt	$3	$8			
4. Gloves	$4	$10			
5. Boots	$15	$35			
6. Swimsuit	$10	$27			
7. Dress	$25	$58			
8. Jacket	$30	$72			
9. Suit	$44	$99			
10. Coat	$60	$126			

Percents Less Than 1%

Milk is .1% iron. How many grams of iron are in 250 grams of milk?

Find .1% of 250.

First, change
.1% to a decimal.

$$.1\% = \frac{.1}{100} = .1 \div 100 = .001$$

Write an equation.

$$.1\% \times 250 = k$$

Write the percent as a decimal.

$$.001 \times 250 = k$$

Find k.

$$.25 = k$$

Answer the question.   There is 0.25 gram of iron in 250 grams of milk.

Write each percent as a decimal.

1. .3%

2. .7%

3. .21%

4. .17%

5. .04%

Find each missing number.

6. .3% of 713 is n.

7. .9% of 3200 is s.

8. .7% of 450 is y.

9. .5% of 281 is t.

10. .4% of 65 is w.

11. .25% of 80 is c.

12. .75% of 5600 is b.

13. .08% of 970 is z.

14. a is .6% of 358.

15. v is .2% of 2400.

**More practice
Set H, page 319**

CAREERS Nutritionist

Nutritionists are concerned with the amount of vitamins, minerals, and other nutrients in various foods. Nutritionists working for food processing companies determine the nutrition information that appears on the side panels of cereal boxes.

The U.S. recommended daily allowance of vitamin A is 5000 International Units (I.U.). One serving of corn flakes contains about 1250 International Units of vitamin A. What percent of the recommended daily allowance of vitamin A is contained in one serving of corn flakes?

1250 is what percent of 5000?

$$\frac{v}{100} = \frac{1250}{5000}$$

$$v \times 5000 = 100 \times 1250$$

$$5000v = 125{,}000$$

$$v = 25$$

One serving of corn flakes contains 25% of the recommended daily allowance of vitamin A.

For each nutrient, compute the percent of the recommended daily allowance that is contained in one serving of corn flakes.

	Nutrient	Recommended daily allowance	Amount in one serving of corn flakes
1.	Vitamin D	400 I.U.	40 I.U.
2.	Vitamin C	45 mg	11.25 mg
3.	Thiamine	1.3 mg	0.325 mg
4.	Riboflavin	1.6 mg	0.4 mg
5.	Niacin	16 mg	4 mg
6.	Iron	18 mg	1.8 mg
7.	Protein	50 g	1 g
8.	Phosphorus	800 mg	16 mg

Using Percent: Gravitational Force

As an object moves away from Earth, its weight is less because the force of gravity from Earth is less. When the object nears the moon or a planet, its weight changes according to the force of gravity on the moon or the planet.

The picture shows the percent of weight on Earth that an object weighs at various locations in space.

▼
64,000 miles from Earth
.4% of weight on Earth

▼ 16,000 miles from Earth
6.7% of weight on Earth

▼
8000 miles from Earth
25% of weight on Earth

Use the percents shown in the picture to complete this table. Round your answers to the nearest tenth.

	Location	Weights of Apollo 17 astronauts		
		Eugene Cernan	Harrison Schmitt	Ronald Evans
	On Earth	175 pounds	165 pounds	160 pounds
1.	8000 miles from Earth	(25% of 175)		
2.	16,000 miles from Earth			
3.	64,000 miles from Earth			
4.	210,000 miles from Earth			
5.	On the moon			

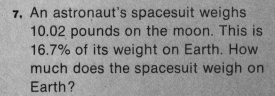

On the moon
16.7% of weight on Earth

▼
210,000 miles from Earth
0% of weight on Earth

Solve these problems.

6. A rock brought back from the moon weighs 3 pounds when it is 8000 miles from Earth. This is 25% of its weight on Earth. What would the rock weigh on Earth?

3 is 25% of what number?

7. An astronaut's spacesuit weighs 10.02 pounds on the moon. This is 16.7% of its weight on Earth. How much does the spacesuit weigh on Earth?

10.02 is 16.7% of what number?

8. An astronaut weighing 200 pounds on Earth would weigh 76 pounds on Mars. The weight on Mars is what percent of the weight on Earth?

76 is what percent of 200?

9. A spaceship weighing 50 tons on Earth would weigh 130 tons on Jupiter. The weight on Jupiter is what percent of the weight on Earth?

130 is what percent of 50?

10. A satellite weighing 30,000 pounds on Earth would weigh 30,600 pounds on Saturn. The weight on Saturn is what percent of the weight on Earth?

30,600 is what percent of 30,000?

More practice
Set I, page 319

Writing fractions, decimals, and percents, pages 282–285

Write each fraction as a percent.

1. $\frac{23}{100}$ **2.** $\frac{9}{10}$ **3.** $\frac{5}{8}$

Write each percent as a fraction in lowest terms.

4. 40%   **5.** 25%   **6.** $16\frac{2}{3}$%

Write each percent as a decimal.

7. 43%   **8.** 9%   **9.** 62.5%

Write each decimal as a percent.

10. .72   **11.** .04   **12.** .365

Using percent, pages 286–287, 290–293

Find each missing number.

13. 30% of 80 is b.

14. 75% of 64 is n.

15. 50% of c is 13.

16. 80% of y is 28.

Find each percent.

17. 4 is what percent of 16?

18. 36 is what percent of 90?

Percents greater than 100% or less than 1%, pages 294, 296

19. Write 157% as a decimal.

20. Write 425% as a mixed number.

21. Write 9.41 as a percent.

22. Write $4\frac{1}{2}$ as a percent.

23. Write .8% as a decimal.

24. .6% of 700 is what number?

Problem solving, pages 286–293, 295, 298–299

25. Ramona bought a pair of shoes priced at $30. The sales tax was 4% of the price. What was the amount of sales tax?

26. Jane has a $400 bond that pays 5% interest each year. How much interest will she receive in 3 years? ($i = prt$)

27. An astronaut weighing 200 pounds on Earth would weigh 180 pounds on Venus. The weight on Venus is what percent of the weight on Earth?

28. A basketball team won 70% of the games they played in one season. They won 14 games. How many games did they play?

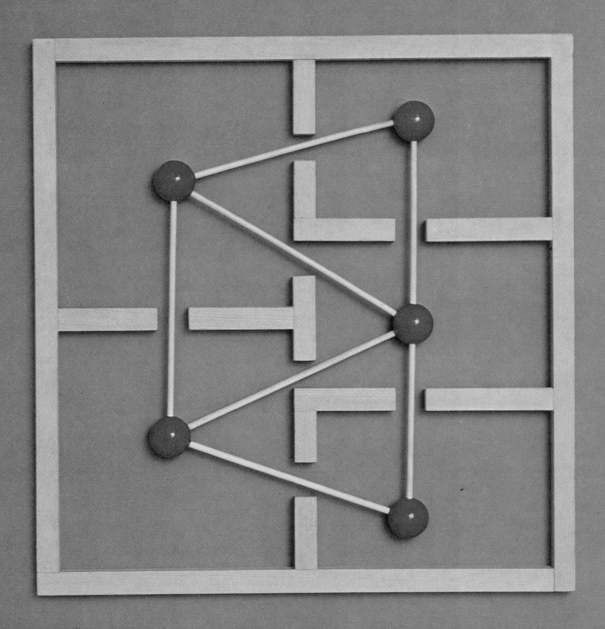

The network has 2 odd vertices.

Circle Graphs

Circle graphs are often used to picture percents.

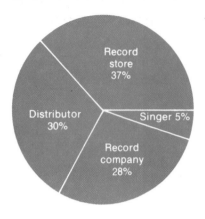

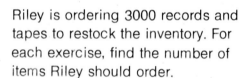

This circle graph shows how the money received from the retail sale of a certain record album is divided.

This graph shows the different types of records and tapes sold by Riley's Record Shop in one month.

If the record album sells for $5, how much money is received by

1. the distributor? (Find 30% of $5.)

2. the record store?

3. the singer?

4. the record company?

5. If $1,000,000 is received from the sale of this album, how much money will the singer receive?

Riley is ordering 3000 records and tapes to restock the inventory. For each exercise, find the number of items Riley should order.

6. LP albums (Find 35% of 3000.)

7. Reel-to-reel tapes

8. Cassette tapes

9. 8-track tapes

10. 45-rpm records

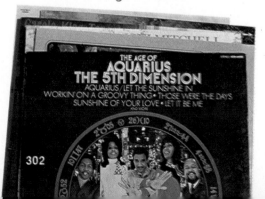

Making Circle Graphs

Grace polled 50 people on their favorite type of music. She made a table to show the results.

Complete the table.

	Type of music	Number of votes	Fraction of total votes	Percent of votes
	Rock	15	$\frac{15}{50}$	30%
1.	Classical	5	$\frac{5}{50}$	
2.	Show music	2	$\frac{2}{50}$	
3.	Country	13	$\frac{13}{50}$	
4.	Folk	12		
5.	Jazz	3		

Then Grace made a circle graph. She computed the size of each central angle on the graph. A circle has 360°.

Find the number of degrees in the angle for each type of music. Round your answers to the nearest degree.

6. Rock
(Find 30% of 360°.)

7. Classical

8. Show music

9. Country

10. Folk

11. Jazz

Grace used a protractor to draw the angle for each type of music.

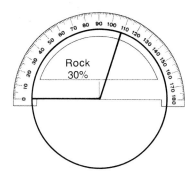

Rock
30%

12. Draw and label a circle graph to show Grace's results.

Pedro polled 100 students in his school to find which of four recording artists they preferred. Complete this table and make a circle graph to show Pedro's results.

	Recording artist	Number of votes	Fraction of total votes	Percent of votes
13.	Bob Dylan	25		
14.	Carole King	20		
15.	Diana Ross	10		
16.	Stevie Wonder	45		

Reading and Making Graphs

Many kinds of graphs are used to picture data.

This **bar graph** shows the average monthly precipitation in Des Moines, Iowa. The average amount of precipitation for January is 1.6 inches.

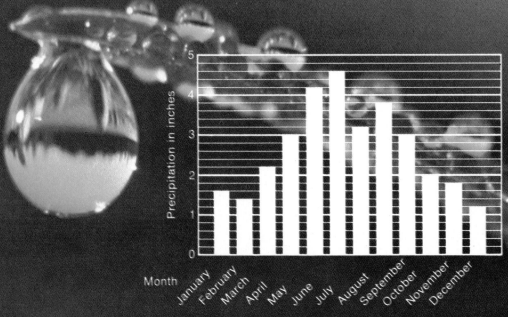

1. Give the average amount of precipitation for the other months.

2. Which month has the greatest average amount of precipitation?

3. Which month has the least average amount of precipitation?

4. Add the average monthly amounts of precipitation to find the yearly average.

5. This table lists the average monthly precipitation in Vancouver, British Columbia. Make a bar graph.

	January	February	March	April	May	June	July	August	September	October	November	December
Average precipitation (inches)	5.6	4.8	3.8	2.4	1.8	2.0	1.0	1.4	2.4	4.8	5.6	6.0

This graph shows the range in average temperatures in Perth, Australia. In January, the average high temperature is 85°F, and the average low temperature is 63°F.

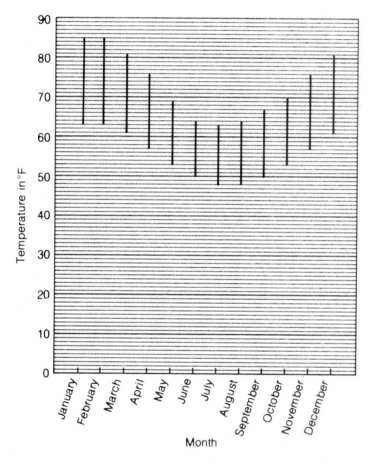

10. Use the information in the table to make a graph showing the range in average temperatures in Chicago, Illinois.

Month	Range (°F)
January	18–32
February	20–34
March	29–43
April	40–55
May	50–65
June	60–75
July	66–81
August	65–79
September	58–73
October	47–61
November	34–47
December	23–36

6. Give the average high and the average low temperatures for each of the other months.

7. Which months have the highest average high temperature?

8. Which months have the lowest average low temperature?

9. Which months have the greatest range of average temperatures?

Pages 33 7

305

Interpreting Graphs

At a sale, cola was priced at 2 cartons for $3. Sam made a graph to picture the price of the cola.

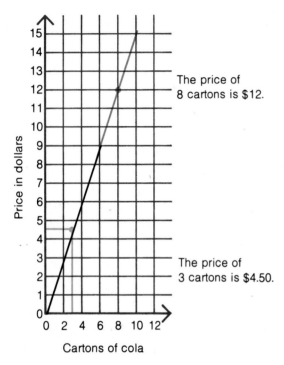

The price of 8 cartons is $12.

The price of 3 cartons is $4.50.

The blue lines show how to read between known points on the graph to find the price of 3 cartons.

The red line shows how to extend the graph to find the price of 8 cartons.

What is the price of

1. 5 cartons?

2. 7 cartons?

3. 10 cartons?

Sam recorded the number of cases of cola that his mother sold at her store in each of the first six months of the year. He marked points on a graph and connected them with line segments.

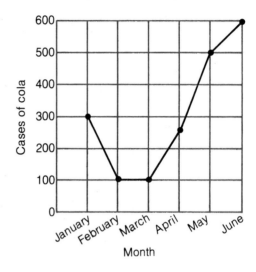

How many cases of cola were sold in

4. January?

5. March?

6. April?

7. June?

● **Discuss** Is it reasonable to read between points on this graph to find how many cases of cola were sold on January 16?

Is it reasonable to extend the graph to find how many cases of cola were sold in July?

As an experiment, Sam took a cold bottle of cola from the refrigerator and left it standing on the counter. He measured the temperature of the cola every ten minutes until it reached room temperature (22°C). This graph shows how the temperature increased during the 120 minutes (2 hours).

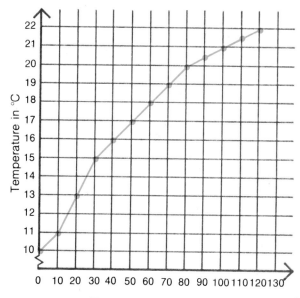

Temperature in °C

Time elapsed in minutes

What was the temperature of the cola

8. when Sam took it out of the refrigerator?

9. after 10 minutes?

10. after 20 minutes?

11. after 60 minutes?

12. after 90 minutes?

● **Discuss** Is it reasonable to read between points on this graph to estimate the temperature after 15 minutes? After 75 minutes?

Is it reasonable to extend the graph to find the temperature of the cola after $2\frac{1}{2}$ hours? 10 minutes before the experiment began?

Flow Charts

People who write computer programs sometimes make *flow charts* to outline a sequence of steps to be followed.

Here is a flow chart for deciding whether three given numbers could be the lengths of the sides of a triangle. Study the flow chart and the example next to the flow chart.

Each shape in a flow chart has a different meaning.

The circle tells you to start or stop.

The rectangle specifies an operation or an action.

The diamond contains a question to be answered *yes* or *no*.

The arrow shows the direction of flow in the flow chart.

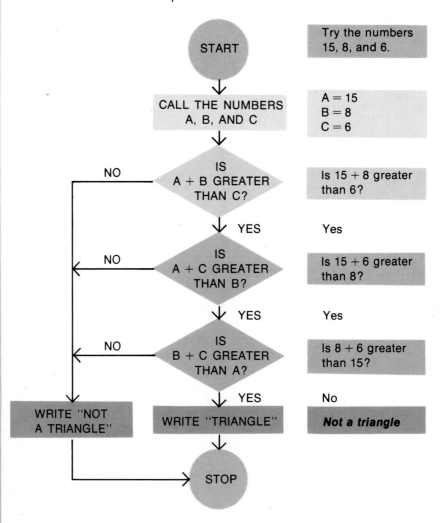

Try the numbers 15, 8, and 6.

A = 15
B = 8
C = 6

Is 15 + 8 greater than 6?

Yes

Is 15 + 6 greater than 8?

Yes

Is 8 + 6 greater than 15?

No

Not a triangle

Use the flow chart to decide whether these numbers could be the lengths of the sides of a triangle.

1. 3, 4, 5

2. 9, 10, 19

3. 17, 3, 18

4. 37, 8, 25

5. 54, 26, 32

6. 72, 41, 23

This flow chart can help you find the square root of a number to the nearest tenth.

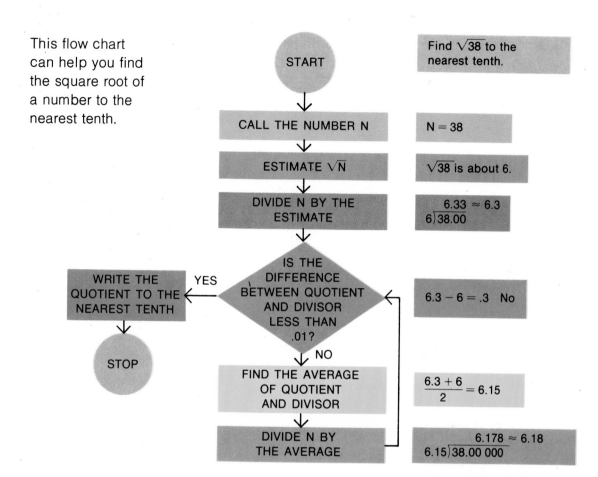

START

CALL THE NUMBER N

ESTIMATE $\sqrt{N}$

DIVIDE N BY THE ESTIMATE

IS THE DIFFERENCE BETWEEN QUOTIENT AND DIVISOR LESS THAN .01?

YES → WRITE THE QUOTIENT TO THE NEAREST TENTH → **STOP**

NO → FIND THE AVERAGE OF QUOTIENT AND DIVISOR

DIVIDE N BY THE AVERAGE

Find $\sqrt{38}$ to the nearest tenth.

$N = 38$

$\sqrt{38}$ is about 6.

$$\begin{array}{r} 6.33 \approx 6.3 \\ 6\overline{)38.00} \end{array}$$

$6.3 - 6 = .3$ No

$$\frac{6.3 + 6}{2} = 6.15$$

$$\begin{array}{r} 6.178 \approx 6.18 \\ 6.15\overline{)38.00\ 000} \end{array}$$

$6.18 - 6.15 = .03$ No

$$\frac{6.18 + 6.15}{2} = 6.165$$

$$\begin{array}{r} 6.1638 \approx 6.164 \\ 6.165\overline{)38.000\ 0000} \end{array}$$

$6.165 - 6.164 = .001$ Yes

6.2

Use the flow chart on this page to help you find the square root of each number to the nearest tenth.

7. $\sqrt{8}$

8. $\sqrt{17}$

9. $\sqrt{52}$

10. $\sqrt{95}$

THE FAMILY OF A
COMPUTER
PROGRAMMER
CONSISTS OF
EXACTLY
1 GRANDMOTHER,
1 GRANDFATHER,
2 FATHERS,
2 MOTHERS,
1 GRANDCHILD,
2 DAUGHTERS,
1 FATHER-IN-LAW,
1 MOTHER-IN-LAW,
AND 1 SON-IN-LAW.

What is the smallest
possible number of
persons in her
family?

Making Flow Charts

1. Here are the steps in a flow chart for deciding
   whether a triangle is a right triangle by using
   the lengths of the sides. Copy the flow chart and
   write in the remaining steps in the correct order.

Call the greatest
number c

Stop

Write
"right triangle"

Write "not a
right triangle"

Start

Call the other
two numbers
a and b

Is $c^2 = a^2 + b^2$?

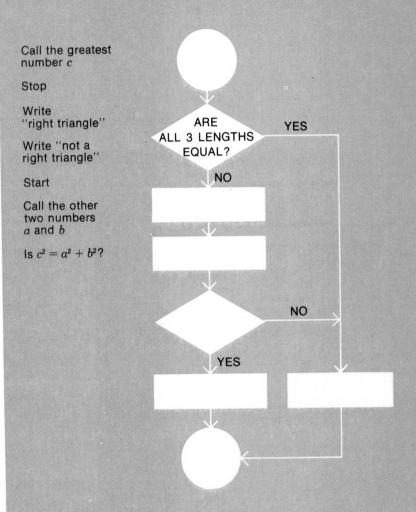

2. The lengths of the sides of triangles are given.
   Use the flow chart to decide whether these could
   be the lengths of the sides of right triangles.

   a. 9, 9, 9   b. 11, 12, 13   c. 16, 30, 34

3. Here are the steps in a flow chart for deciding whether a given number is a multiple of 6. Copy the flow chart and write in the steps in the correct order.

Write "multiple of 6"

Start

Is the last digit 0, 2, 4, 6, or 8?

Stop

Write "not a multiple of 6"

Is the sum of the digits a multiple of 3?

5. Use these steps to make a flow chart for deciding whether a number greater than 1 is prime or composite.

Are there exactly 2 different factors of a?

Stop

Write "prime"

Call the number a

Start

Write "composite"

List all the factors of a

6. Make a flow chart for deciding whether a given number is a multiple of 5.

4. Use the flow chart to decide whether these numbers are multiples of 6.

a. 438   **d.** 9156

b. 1605   **e.** 17,439

c. 3422   **f.** 8640

Networks

This diagram is called a *network*.

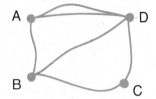

The points A, B, C, and D are *vertices*.

The vertices are connected by paths.

Trace the network without going over any path more than once and without lifting your pencil from the paper. A path may cross a path.

A network that can be traced in this way is called a *traversable network*.

Another traversable network and one way to trace it is shown below.

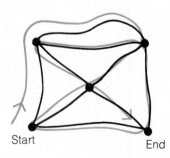

You can tell whether a network is traversable by the number of odd vertices in the network.

A vertex is odd if an odd number of paths meet at that point.

3 paths meet at vertex B.

Vertex B is odd.

A vertex is even if an even number of paths meet at that point.

2 paths meet at vertex C.

Vertex C is even.

Tell whether each vertex is even or odd.

1.

2.

3.

4.

5.

6.

7. For each exercise, find the number of odd vertices in the network and complete the table. Then show a way to trace each traversable network.

Network	Number of odd vertices	Is the network traversable?
a		yes
b		yes
c		yes
d		yes
e		yes
f		yes
g		no
h		no
i		no
j		no

a.

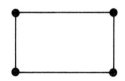

b.

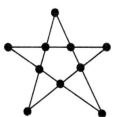

c.

d.

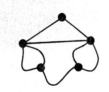

e.

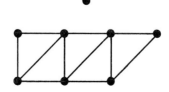

f.

g.

h.

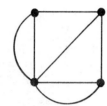

i.

j.

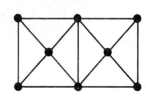

8. How many odd vertices are there in the traversable networks?

9. How can you decide whether a network is traversable or not?

Side Trip The Königsberg Bridge Problem

Königsberg was once a German city and is now Kaliningrad, U.S.S.R. It is located on the banks and on two islands of the Pregel River. The citizens of old Königsberg wondered if they could take a walk crossing each bridge exactly once.

This problem was solved by a famous mathematician, Leonhard Euler (1707–1783). He used a network to represent the map of Königsberg.

On this network, which represents the bridge problem, the regions of land are vertices. The paths connect the regions.

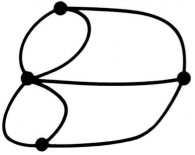

Is this a traversable network?

Could the citizens of Königsberg take a walk by crossing each bridge exactly once?

LABORATORY ACTIVITY

Regular polygons have all sides and all angles congruent. The figures on this page are regular polygons.

1. Find the measure of the angle of each polygon.

2. Make a graph to show your results. Write "Number of sides in polygon" along the horizontal axis. Use labels: 0, 1, 2, and so on, up to 24. Write "Angle of polygon" along the vertical axis. Use labels: 0°, 10°, 20°, and so on, up to 180°.

3. Plot points on the graph and connect the points with a curve.

4. Read between the points on the graph to estimate the measure of the angle of a regular polygon with 6 sides.

5. As the number of sides increases, does the measure of the angle increase or decrease?

6. Is it possible to draw a regular polygon with an angle that measures 180° or more?

7. Extend your graph and give an estimate of the measure of the angle of a 24-sided polygon.

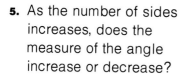
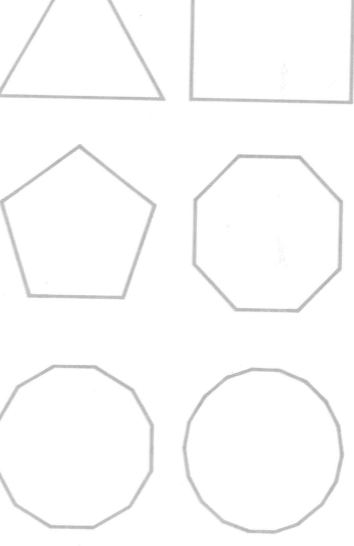

Using graphs, pages 302–307

This circle graph shows how the real estate taxes for a community are spent.

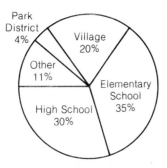

If a business pays $9000 in real estate taxes, how much is spent for

1. high school?

2. elementary school?

3. village?

4. park district?

This bar graph shows the number of birthdays of U.S. Presidents in each month.

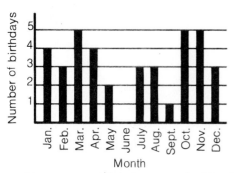

5. How many birthdays are in May?

6. Which months have the greatest number of birthdays?

7. Which month has the least number of birthdays?

Using flow charts, pages 308–311

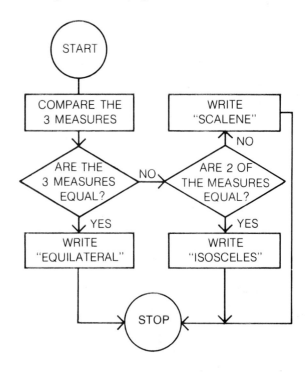

Use the flow chart to decide whether these numbers are the measures of the sides of equilateral, isosceles, or scalene triangles.

8. 15, 12, 15

9. 7, 23, 21

Networks, pages 312–313

10. Is this a traversable network?

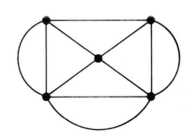

Unit 5 Test

Ratio, proportion, and trigonometry, pages 260–279

Find the missing number in each proportion.

1. $\dfrac{a}{15} = \dfrac{45}{25}$ **2.** $\dfrac{7}{28} = \dfrac{c}{.8}$

3. Jill mixed paint in a ratio of 3 parts of red for 2 parts of blue. If she used 570 milliliters of red paint, how much blue paint did she use?

4. Luis has a model railroad built in the scale of 1 to 87. The length of a model boxcar is 17 centimeters. What is the length of the actual boxcar?

5. Find the height of the girl to the nearest centimeter. (tan 25° ≈ .466)

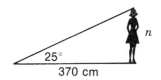

25°
370 cm
n

Percent, pages 282–299

6. Write $\frac{4}{5}$ as a percent.

7. Write 39% as a fraction.

8. Write 7% as a decimal.

9. Write .412 as a percent.

Find t.

10. 20% of 75 is t. **11.** 5% of t is 13.

12. 6 is what percent of 18?

13. Write 3.56 as a percent.

14. Write .4% as a decimal.

15. Aki bought a $28 pair of skates on sale for 10% off. How much did he save?

16. Peg earns $60 per week. She spends $9 per week on lunches. What percent of the money she earns does Peg spend on lunches?

17. In Amy's class, 8 students have brown eyes. This is 25% of all the students in the class. How many students are in Amy's class?

Graphs, flow charts, and networks, pages 302–315

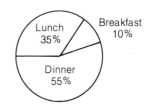

This circle graph shows the favorite daily meal of the students in Einstein School. If there are 720 students in the school, how many said that their favorite meal is

18. breakfast? **19.** dinner?

20. Is this a traversable network?

317

More Practice

Set A

Find each missing number.

1. $\dfrac{30}{12} = \dfrac{r}{14}$

2. $\dfrac{9}{x} = \dfrac{54}{12}$

3. $\dfrac{21}{3} = \dfrac{m}{7}$

4. $\dfrac{a}{21} = \dfrac{2}{3}$

5. $\dfrac{39}{65} = \dfrac{s}{20}$

6. $\dfrac{64}{92} = \dfrac{16}{c}$

7. $\dfrac{k}{78} = \dfrac{12}{13}$

8. $\dfrac{14}{y} = \dfrac{35}{25}$

9. $\dfrac{63}{n} = \dfrac{42}{48}$

10. $\dfrac{35}{g} = \dfrac{15}{21}$

11. $\dfrac{18}{33} = \dfrac{h}{77}$

12. $\dfrac{26}{38} = \dfrac{t}{5.7}$

Set B

Write each percent as a decimal.

1. 3.5% **9.** 24%

2. 4% **10.** 68.43%

3. 54.9% **11.** 7%

4. 37% **12.** 40%

5. 2% **13.** .75%

6. 89.5% **14.** 32.3%

7. 72% **15.** 91.25%

8. 11% **16.** 22.6%

Set C

Find each missing number.

1. 35% of 60 is t.

2. 80% of 120 is c.

3. $37\frac{1}{2}$% of 200 is m.

4. 40% of 240 is x.

5. 55% of 98 is d.

6. 17% of 400 is s.

7. 60% of 55 is a.

8. y is 88% of 65.

9. h is 70% of 50.

10. v is 30% of 116.

11. k is $66\frac{2}{3}$% of 81.

Set D

Find each missing number.

1. 63 is n percent of 350.

2. 18 is e percent of 75.

3. 81 is p percent of 180.

4. 49 is c percent of 70.

5. 27 is s percent of 90.

6. 63 is z percent of 75.

7. h percent of 5 is 2.7.

8. a percent of 40 is 14.

9. w percent of 60 is 57.

10. k percent of 140 is 91.

Set E

Find each missing number.

1. 28% of x is 7.

2. 55% of d is 44.

3. 84% of y is 63.

4. 12% of g is 15.

5. 75% of t is 18.

6. 24% of b is 6.

7. 138 is 92% of m.

8. 112 is 64% of r.

9. 54 is 45% of a.

10. 72 is 32% of p.

More Practice

Set F

Write each percent as a decimal.

1. 312%
2. 190%
3. 509%
4. 125%
5. 447%
6. 233%
7. 572%
8. 287%
9. 162%
10. 638%
11. 171%
12. 258%
13. 618%
14. 205%
15. 659%
16. 341%
17. 140%
18. 523%
19. 218%
20. 474%

Write each percent as a mixed number.

1. 205%
2. 880%
3. 370%
4. 115%
5. 595%
6. 756%
7. 184%
8. 616%
9. 472%
10. 332%
11. 731%
12. 420%
13. 124%
14. 625%
15. 964%
16. 216%
17. 948%
18. 150%
19. 875%
20. 508%

Set G

Write each decimal as a percent.

1. 8.6
2. 6.48
3. 2.1
4. 1.13
5. 4.77
6. 9.0
7. 3.57
8. 4.7
9. 7.66
10. 6.8
11. 4.28
12. 5.4
13. 2.9
14. 9.45
15. 7.5
16. 8.90
17. 5.39
18. 3.2

Write each mixed number as a percent.

1. $9\frac{11}{25}$
2. $3\frac{43}{100}$
3. $7\frac{1}{4}$
4. $4\frac{11}{20}$
5. $8\frac{41}{50}$
6. $1\frac{3}{10}$
7. $6\frac{3}{5}$
8. $2\frac{3}{4}$
9. $4\frac{1}{5}$
10. $7\frac{17}{20}$
11. $3\frac{9}{10}$
12. $8\frac{4}{5}$
13. $9\frac{19}{20}$
14. $2\frac{13}{100}$
15. $7\frac{1}{4}$
16. $6\frac{1}{2}$
17. $5\frac{2}{5}$
18. $3\frac{9}{20}$

Set H

Find each missing number.

1. .6% of 572 is g.
2. .75% of 70 is n.
3. .2% of 648 is a.
4. .7% of 228 is r.
5. .03% of 890 is y.
6. .8% of 436 is d.
7. .25% of 2700 is s.
8. .3% of 770 is h.
9. b is .9% of 394.
10. m is .5% of 1800.

Set I

Solve each problem.

1. 45% of 120 is m.
2. 92 is q percent of 368.
3. 32% of s is 16.
4. 16 is b percent of 80.
5. 24% of 75 is a.
6. 12% of d is 15.
7. 42 is n percent of 56.
8. 30% of p is 27.
9. 20% of 85 is s.
10. 2 is x percent of 50.

Individualized Skills Maintenance

Diagnosis	Practice

Diagnosis

A. $5\frac{1}{6} \times 1\frac{2}{3}$

$\frac{3}{4} \times 3\frac{4}{5}$

$6\frac{1}{2} \times 2\frac{7}{8}$

B. $3\frac{7}{10} \div \frac{2}{3}$

$4\frac{1}{8} \div 1\frac{1}{4}$

$3\frac{5}{6} \div 2\frac{2}{5}$

C. $2\frac{2}{3} + \frac{1}{2}$

$4\frac{11}{12} + 2\frac{5}{6}$

$1\frac{5}{8} + 2\frac{1}{3}$

D. $6\frac{1}{12} - 4\frac{2}{3}$

$4\frac{7}{8} - \frac{3}{4}$

$5\frac{2}{5} - 1\frac{1}{2}$

Practice

Set A (pp. 140–145)

1. $3\frac{1}{2} \times \frac{6}{7}$

2. $\frac{3}{4} \times \frac{5}{9}$

3. $4\frac{1}{4} \times 3\frac{3}{5}$

4. $1\frac{3}{5} \times 5\frac{3}{4}$

5. $6\frac{1}{3} \times 2\frac{4}{7}$

6. $\frac{2}{5} \times 4\frac{3}{8}$

7. $2\frac{4}{5} \times 6\frac{3}{7}$

8. $5\frac{2}{3} \times 1\frac{1}{5}$

Set B (pp. 146–148)

1. $4\frac{1}{2} \div 3\frac{3}{8}$

2. $\frac{2}{3} \div \frac{4}{9}$

3. $5\frac{3}{5} \div 4\frac{9}{10}$

4. $7\frac{1}{3} \div 1\frac{5}{6}$

5. $2\frac{1}{4} \div 2\frac{5}{8}$

6. $\frac{3}{4} \div 7\frac{1}{2}$

7. $6\frac{2}{5} \div 9\frac{1}{7}$

8. $3\frac{3}{7} \div 5\frac{1}{3}$

Set C (pp. 158–161)

1. $7\frac{1}{2} + 4\frac{5}{6}$

2. $3\frac{1}{6} + \frac{2}{3}$

3. $\frac{2}{5} + 5\frac{7}{10}$

4. $9\frac{3}{7} + 3\frac{2}{5}$

5. $4\frac{2}{3} + 1\frac{4}{9}$

6. $3\frac{1}{5} + 4\frac{5}{8}$

7. $\frac{5}{6} + \frac{3}{4}$

8. $1\frac{2}{7} + 2\frac{3}{8}$

9. $5\frac{4}{7} + \frac{4}{5}$

10. $2\frac{3}{5} + 4$

11. $6\frac{1}{3} + 1\frac{1}{6}$

12. $\frac{3}{8} + \frac{5}{9}$

13. $2\frac{1}{4} + 6\frac{1}{4}$

14. $8\frac{5}{8} + 1\frac{3}{4}$

15. $\frac{3}{4} + 3\frac{7}{8}$

16. $5\frac{4}{5} + 7\frac{1}{2}$

17. $4\frac{5}{7} + 2\frac{1}{3}$

Set D (pp. 162–163)

1. $5 - 1\frac{2}{3}$

2. $3\frac{1}{3} - 2\frac{5}{6}$

3. $8\frac{1}{6} - 6\frac{4}{5}$

4. $7\frac{3}{4} - 4\frac{1}{2}$

5. $5\frac{5}{7} - 3\frac{3}{10}$

6. $4\frac{3}{5} - 2\frac{2}{5}$

7. $5\frac{2}{3} - 2\frac{5}{9}$

8. $6\frac{4}{7} - 1\frac{5}{21}$

9. $9\frac{5}{6} - 4\frac{1}{3}$

10. $8\frac{4}{5} - 2\frac{7}{12}$

11. $6\frac{2}{7} - 3\frac{4}{9}$

12. $7\frac{1}{4} - 1\frac{3}{8}$

13. $4\frac{3}{7} - 3\frac{3}{5}$

14. $3\frac{1}{5} - 1\frac{7}{10}$

15. $8\frac{1}{2} - 3\frac{3}{4}$

16. $4\frac{1}{7} - 2\frac{3}{14}$

17. $7\frac{2}{5} - 5\frac{2}{9}$

Unit 6

Counting, Probability, and Statistics

Number of choices of lunch meat		Number of choices of cheese		Number of choices of bread		Number of choices of sandwiches
3	**×**	**2**	**×**	**3**	**=**	**18**

Counting: Guessing and Estimating

A. Cathi unloaded a crate of oranges. She counted the oranges to find exactly how many were in the crate.

B. Jorge wondered how many oranges were in 300 crates. He guessed and then checked his guess by counting the number of oranges in one crate and multiplying by 300.

C. Jennifer wondered how many oranges were on the display counter at the grocery store. She guessed. Then she checked her guess by multiplying the number of oranges in one row by the number of oranges in one column.

When the total number of items is very large, it sometimes is not practical to count. Then a person can estimate the answer as Jorge and Jennifer did.

Tell whether you would make an exact count or try to make a reasonable estimate if you want to know

1. the number of trees in a forty-acre orange grove.

2. the number of oranges in an orange grove.

3. the number of oranges in a bag at the grocery store.

4. the number of oranges in 500 bags.

5. the number of oranges it takes to make one glass of orange juice.

6. the number of oranges in a crate.

7. the number of orange crates on a fleet of trucks.

8. the number of candidates for queen of the Orange Festival.

9. the number of people in the stadium at the Orange Festival.

Find each answer.

10. Guess how many oranges are in the picture.

11. Check your guess by counting.

12. Guess how many oranges you can put across the length of your desk. Across the width.

13. About how many oranges would cover the top of your desk?

14. Guess how many words are on this page.

15. Check your guess by counting. Do not count numerals, punctuation, or the words in the cartoon.

16. Guess how many letters are on this page.

17. Check your guess by counting. Do not count numerals, punctuation, or the words in the cartoon.

Alfred is going to buy a Spider Six automobile.

The Spider Six Company offers these colors for the exterior: white, light blue, or dark red.

The same colors are offered for the interior. The interior color must be the same as or lighter than the exterior.

The company offers a rally stripe only on those cars with a dark red exterior.

A tree diagram shows how many styles are available.

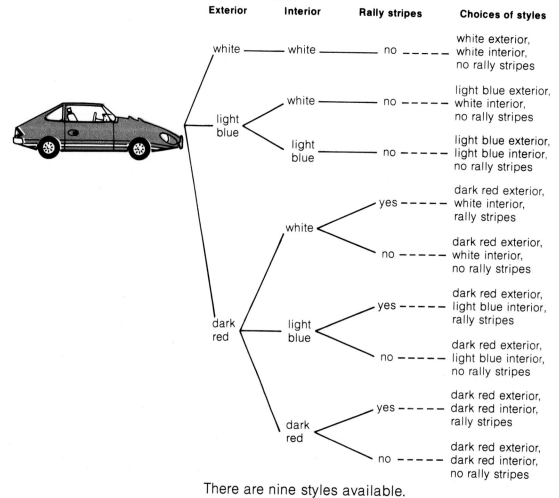

There are nine styles available.

How many available
styles have

1. rally stripes?

2. a light blue exterior?

3. a light blue interior?

4. a red or white
interior?

5. a light blue or
white interior?

6. an interior that is
a different color
from the exterior?

Solve each problem.
Use a tree diagram
to help you.

7. Suppose that the
Spider Six Company
decides to offer
rally stripes on
all cars. How many
styles will then be
available?

8. If the company then
removes its
restrictions on
choices of interior
color, how many
styles will be
available?

Here is a schedule
of next Saturday's
four basketball games.

Game	Home team	Visiting team
1	Central	Northern
2	Hannibal	Quincy
3	Mayfield	Artesia
4	Vallonia	Freetown

9. Ted wants to find
the number of ways
to guess outcomes,
or winners, of the
first three games.
Complete his tree
diagram (no ties).
Use the first letter
of each team's name.

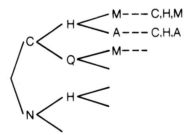

10. Make a tree diagram
to find the number
of ways Ted can
guess the outcomes
of four games.

Here is a schedule
of next Saturday's
three football games.

Game	Home team	Visiting team
1	Seymour	Albany
2	Goshen	Dunlap
3	Bedford	Mitchell

11. Ann wants to find
the number of ways
to guess outcomes
of the first two
games. Either team
may win, or they
may tie. Complete
her tree diagram.

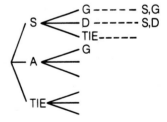

12. Make a tree diagram
to find the number
of ways Ann can
guess the outcomes
of three games.

The Counting Principle

Tina, a beginning ballerina, has two pairs of ballet slippers and three leotards. How many ballet costumes does she have?

A. Olive made a tree diagram.

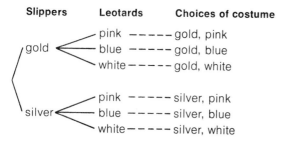

Slippers	Leotards	Choices of costume
gold	pink	gold, pink
	blue	gold, blue
	white	gold, white
silver	pink	silver, pink
	blue	silver, blue
	white	silver, white

She found that Tina has a choice of six ballet costumes.

B. Wayne multiplied.

Number of choices of slippers		Number of choices of leotards		Number of choices of costumes
2	**×**	**3**	**=**	**6**

He, too, found that Tina has a choice of six ballet costumes. Sometimes it is easier to multiply to find the total number of choices.

■ *If there is a number of successive choices to make, the total number of choices is the product of the number of choices at each stage.*

Multiply to find the answers.

1. If Tina had three pairs of ballet slippers and four leotards, how many ballet costumes would she have?

Number of choices of slippers		Number of choices of leotards		Number of choices of costumes
▦	×	▦	=	▦

2. If Tina had four pairs of ballet slippers, five leotards, and three hair ribbons, how many ballet costumes would she have?

Number of choices of slippers		Number of choices of leotards		Number of choices of ribbons		Number of choices of costumes
▦	×	▦	×	▦	=	▦

Complete the table to show how many choices of costumes each ballerina has.

	Name	Number of choices of slippers	Number of choices of leotards	Number of choices of ribbons	Number of choices of costumes
3.	Mona	3	3	3	
4.	Andrea	2	3	4	
5.	Jeanne	3	3	5	
6.	Bette	3	5	8	
7.	Nanette	4	6	10	
8.	Mia	3		5	60

Tina decided to adopt a new stage name. She listed all the names suggested by her friends.

Choices for first name — Anita
Teresa
Conchita
Bea
Cecile
Margot
Stella

Choices for second name — Maria
Rosa
Celeste
Lolita
Ramona
Bella

Choices for third name — Melina
Alexandra
Margarita
Lupe

9. How many name combinations are there if Tina chooses one first name and one second name?

10. How many name combinations are there if Tina chooses one first name, one second name, and one third name?

Using the Counting Principle

A. The Postal Service uses the counting principle
to find the number of possible Zip Codes.
Each Zip Code consists of five digits. Remember,
the digits are the numbers 0 through 9.

Number of choices for first digit		Number of choices for second digit		Number of choices for third digit		Number of choices for fourth digit		Number of choices for fifth digit		Number of choices for Zip Code numbers
10	×	**10**	×	**10**	×	**10**	×	**10**	=	**100,000**

There are 100,000 possible Zip Code numbers.

B. How many possible Zip Code numbers are there
if the first digit is a 7?

Number of choices for first digit		Number of choices for second digit		Number of choices for third digit		Number of choices for fourth digit		Number of choices for fifth digit		Number of choices for Zip Code numbers
1	×	**10**	×	**10**	×	**10**	×	**10**	=	**10,000**

There are 10,000 possible Zip Code numbers whose first digit is 7.

How many possible Zip Code numbers are there if

1. the second digit is 4?

2. the last digit is 9?

3. the first digit is 7 and the second digit is 4?

4. the second digit is 5, the fourth digit is 6, and the last digit is 1?

5. the first digit is even?

6. each of the first two digits is even?

7. each of the first three digits is even?

★8. all the digits are the same?

★9. all the digits are prime?

★10. none of the digits is prime?

The call letters of United States radio stations begin with either K or W. The radio station WGN has three call letters. How many stations could have

11. three call letters?

Number of choices for first letter	Number of choices for second letter	Number of choices for third letter	Number of choices for three call letters
2	× 26	× 26	= ▦

12. four call letters?

Time Out

4	2	5	8
9	7	1	4
3	4	0	6
5	1	7	1

All digits can be thought of as "straight" or "curvy."

Straight digits   1   4   7
Curvy digits   0   2   3   5   6   8   9

To play the game, follow these steps.

1. Put a coin or a paper clip on any curvy digit.

2. Move left or right until you reach a square with a straight digit.

3. Move up or down until you reach a square with a curvy digit.

4. Move diagonally until you reach a square with a straight digit.

5. Move down or right until you reach a square with a curvy digit.

6. Are you now at zero?

Play this game several times. Do you always end up at zero?

Independent Choices

A. Some choices are made by people. Suppose that you were to take a true-false test. Are exactly two choices possible for question 5 if questions 1 through 4 have been answered? How many choices are possible for question 5 if questions 1 and 3 have been answered? If question 1 has been answered? If question 3 has not yet been answered?

The choices of answers on a true-false test are *independent* because they have no influence on each other.

B. Some choices are made by chance. Suppose that you were to roll a pair of dice. How many outcomes are there for the second die if the first die shows one? Two? Six? Are the outcomes for rolling a pair of dice independent?

C. Independent choices often occur in repeated trials. Suppose that you were to roll a die several times. There are 6 possible outcomes on the first roll. How many outcomes are possible on the second roll? The third roll? How many outcomes are possible for two rolls?

Ways die can land on first roll	Ways die can land on second roll	Possible outcomes
6 ×	**6** =	**36**

There are 36 possible outcomes for two rolls. How many outcomes are possible for three rolls?

Suppose that you toss a coin several times.

1. How many outcomes can occur on the first toss? The second toss? The third toss?

2. How many outcomes are possible for two tosses? Three tosses?

Suppose you toss a coin eight times, and it comes up heads each time.

3. How many outcomes can occur the ninth time the coin is tossed?

4. Does the outcome of one toss affect the outcome of another toss?

● **Discuss** Suppose that a coin were tossed 50 times and showed heads each time. What do you think would happen on the 51st toss?

The manager of a shoe store uses independent choices to help him classify shoes according to style, color, size, and the name of the manufacturer.

Each classification has a code label. The store's coding system uses P, Q, R, S, or T followed by three digits.

5. How many code labels are possible?

Choices for letter	Choices for first digit	Choices for second digit	Choices for third digit	Number of code labels
5 ×	10 ×	▦ ×	▦ =	▦

6. How many possible code labels

   a. begin with Q?

   b. begin with P or Q?

   c. end with 7?

   d. end with 7 or 8?

The store manager decides to include more styles and sizes. He still wants the code to consist of one letter and three digits. How many letters will be needed to have

7. 9000 code labels?

Choices for letter	Choices for first digit	Choices for second digit	Choices for third digit	Number of code labels
▦ ×	10 ×	10 ×	10 =	9000

8. 13,000 code labels?

★9. at least 15,670 code labels?

Bob and Linda are playing a game. Each has written the letters *O N E* on three cards like these.

O   N   E

Each player has shuffled the three cards and put them face down on the floor.

Bob and Linda each have picked a card and turned it face up. How many choices of cards did each of them have for the first letter?

Next, Bob and Linda each will pick a second card and put it beside the first card. How many choices of cards will each of them have for the second letter?

Finally, Bob and Linda each will turn the last card face up and put it beside the second card. How many choices will each of them have for the third letter?

If Bob's or Linda's cards show the word *ONE*, he or she gets one point. The first player to get three points wins the game.

A. Sometimes choices are made that are affected by previous choices. Bob used the counting principle to find the number of ways he could arrange the letters in ONE.

Number of choices for first letter	Number of choices for second letter	Number of choices for third letter	Number of possible arrangements
3 ×	2 ×	1 =	6

The choices are *dependent* because they have some influence on each other.

B. Sometimes choices are made that will affect future choices. The director of Super Spy, Inc., wanted to issue a reverse code number, such as 060, to each secret agent. (A reverse number does not change when the digits are reversed.) He used the counting principle to find how many three-digit reverse code numbers are possible.

Number of choices for first digit	Number of choices for second digit	Number of choices for third digit	Number of possible three-digit reverse numbers
10 ×	10 ×	1 =	100

Notice that there is only one choice for the third digit because it must be the same as the first digit. Do you think the choices are dependent?

How many ways can you arrange the letters in each exercise?

1. A R M

2. N O S E

3. M O U T H

4. F I N G E R

How many reverse code numbers are possible that have

5. four digits?

6. five digits?

7. six digits?

8. seven digits?

At Valley School, all room numbers have three digits. All room numbers on the first floor have 1 as the first digit. All room numbers on the second floor have 2 as the first digit.

9. How many room numbers are possible?

10. How many reverse room numbers are possible?

A. Joan, Andy, and Maria are officers of the Photography Club. At the first meeting, they were seated in a row. Arrangements of people or objects in order are called *permutations*. If, at every meeting, the seating order is different, how many meetings can they attend without duplicating any seating arrangement?

Joan used the counting principle to find the number of permutations, or seating arrangements.

Number of choices for first seat	Number of choices for second seat	Number of choices for third seat	Number of seating arrangements
3	× 2	× 1	= 6

There are six seating arrangements. The officers can attend six meetings without duplicating any arrangement.

B. The product $3 \times 2 \times 1$ can be written 3! and is read "three factorial." $3! = 3 \times 2 \times 1$

C. Here is a list of some other *factorials*.

$4! = 4 \times 3 \times 2 \times 1$
$5! = 5 \times 4 \times 3 \times 2 \times 1$
$6! = 6 \times 5 \times 4 \times 3 \times 2 \times 1$
$7! = 7 \times 6 \times 5 \times 4 \times 3 \times 2 \times 1$

The members of the Photography Club decided they needed more officers. How many different seating arrangements are there if the members decide to elect

1. four officers?

2. five officers?

3. six officers?

4. seven officers?

● **Discuss** Can you write the answers to the above exercises by using the factorial symbol?

If the Photography Club meets once a month, how many years could pass without repeating a seating arrangement if there are

5. four officers?

6. five officers?

7. six officers?

8. seven officers?

Write each factorial as a product.

Here's how

3!   **3 × 2 × 1**

9. 2!

10. 8!

11. 9!

12. 10!

Compute the value of each factorial.

Here's how

3!   **3 × 2 × 1 = 6**

13. 2!

14. 4!

15. 5!

16. 6!

17. 7!

18. 8!

19. 9!

20. 10!

Find the value of each expression.

21. 3! + 2!

22. 3! × 2!

23. 6! − 3!

24. 6! ÷ 2!

25. 6! ÷ 3!

Tell whether each sentence is true or false.

26. 3! + 2! = 5!

27. 3! × 2! = 6!

28. 6! − 3! = 3!

29. 6! ÷ 2! = 3!

30. 6! ÷ 3! = 2!

Using Diagrams

Mr. Char collected these data.

There are 32 students in his class.
14 are in the Letter Club.
16 are in the Music Club.
12 are *not* in either club.

He asked Barbara and Lillian to find how many
students are in both the Letter Club and the Music Club.

A. Barbara used dots
to find the answer.
She marked 32 dots
to represent
32 students.

First, she circled
12 dots to
represent those
students who are
not in either club.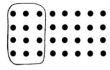

Then she shaded
14 of the remaining
dots gray to
represent the
members of the
Letter Club.

She then shaded
16 dots red to
represent the
members of the
Music Club.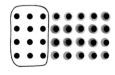

The 10 dots that Barbara shaded both
gray and red represent the
students who are in both clubs.

B. Lillian computed her answer.
She subtracted to find the number
of students in one or both clubs.

Students in class	Students who are not in either club	Students who are in one or both clubs
32	− 12	= 20

She then added to find the number
of club memberships among these
20 students.

Students in Letter Club	Students in Music Club	Club memberships
14	+ 16	= 30

Next, she subtracted to find the
number of students who must be
in both clubs.

Club memberships	Students who are in one or both clubs	Students who are in both clubs
30	− 20	= 10

There are 10 students who are
in both the Letter Club and the
Music Club.

c. Mr. Char made a *Venn diagram* to show the data.

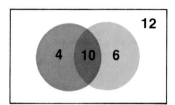

12

4 10 6

The gray circle shows how many students are in the Letter Club.

$10 + 4 = 14$

The red circle shows how many students are in the Music Club.

$10 + 6 = 16$

The *intersection* of the two circles (where they overlap) shows how many students are in both clubs. There are 10.

The number 12 outside the circles shows how many students are not in either club.

1. Bob collected these data.

There are 30 students in his class.
8 are in Spanish Club.
10 are in Debate Club.
15 are *not* in either club.

a. How many students are in both clubs?

b. How many students are not in both clubs?

2. Sue collected these data.

There are 48 students in her class.
24 have blonde hair.
18 have blue eyes.
16 do *not* have blonde hair or blue eyes.

a. How many students have both blonde hair and blue eyes?

b. How many students do *not* have blonde hair?

c. How many students do *not* have blue eyes?

LABORATORY ACTIVITY

Take a poll of your class. Make a Venn diagram for each set of data.

1. Find the number of students who

a. watch a medical show regularly on television.

b. watch a detective show regularly on television.

c. do *not* watch either a medical or detective show regularly on television.

2. Find the number of students who

a. like to read mysteries.

b. like to read biographies.

c. do *not* like to read either mysteries or biographies.

Guessing and estimating, pages 324–325

Tell whether you would make an exact count or try to make a reasonable estimate if you want to know

1. the number of people at a concert.

2. the number of coins in your pocket.

Finding possible outcomes by using tree diagrams, pages 326–327

3. Sandy has two sweaters and three skirts.

Sweater	Skirt
yellow	gray
orange	brown
	green

Complete the tree diagram. Sandy has how many choices of costume?

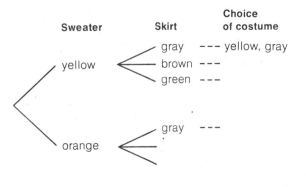

Sweater	Skirt	Choice of costume
yellow	gray	--- yellow, gray
	brown	---
	green	---
orange	gray	---

Finding possible outcomes by multiplying, pages 328–337

4. How many different ways can you choose a four-digit code number?

5. How many different ways can you choose a four-digit code number if the first digit is 0?

6. A coding system uses G and B followed by two digits. How many codes are possible?

How many different ways can you arrange the letters in each exercise?

7. B O Y

8. G I R L

9. Suppose that five objects were arranged in a row. How many different arrangements of the five objects are possible?

Venn diagrams, pages 338–339

10. Carmen collected these data.

There are 30 students in her class.
15 like to play basketball.
15 like to play baseball.
10 do *not* like to play either basketball or baseball.

How many students like to play both basketball and baseball?

The probability of getting a 6 is $\frac{1}{6}$.

Measuring Chances

PROBABLITIES

Laura has made cards like these.
She has placed them in a bag and shaken the bag.
She is going to draw a card at random.

A. What are the chances that Laura
will draw a card showing *B*?

She can pick any of 13 cards.
There are 13 possible outcomes.
All are equally likely to occur.
There are 2 cards showing *B*.
So there are 2 chances out of 13
to draw a card showing *B*.
The *probability* that Laura will
draw a card showing *B* is $\frac{2}{13}$.

$\underline{2}$ ← Number of favorable outcomes
13 ← Number of possible outcomes

B. What is the probability that Laura
will draw a card showing *B* or *E*?

There are 13 possible outcomes.
All are equally likely to occur.
Two cards show *B*, and one card
shows *E*. Therefore, there
are 3 favorable outcomes.
The probability that Laura will
draw a card showing *B* or *E* is $\frac{3}{13}$.

$\underline{3}$ ← Number of favorable outcomes
13 ← Number of possible outcomes

You can use this formula to find the
probability of a given outcome when
all outcomes are equally likely.

$$\text{probability} = \frac{\textbf{number of favorable outcomes}}{\textbf{number of possible outcomes}}$$

May						
				1	2	3
4	5	6	7	8	9	10
11	12	13	14	15	16	17
18	19	20	21	22	23	24
25	26	27	28	29	30	31

Each time Laura draws a card, she replaces it before she draws another. Give the probability that she will draw a card showing

1. *A.*

2. *E.*

3. *I.*

4. *A* or *E.*

5. *A*, *E*, or *I.*

6. a letter that occurs in the word "able."

7. a letter that occurs in the word "bite."

8. a letter that occurs in your last name.

9. a letter that occurs in your first name.

10. a letter that occurs in your first name or your last name.

Kikuye is going to roll a die. What is the probability that the roll will result in

11. one?

$$\frac{\text{▦}}{6} \begin{array}{l} \longleftarrow \text{Favorable outcomes} \\ \longleftarrow \text{Possible outcomes} \end{array}$$

12. three?

13. six?

14. two or four?

15. two, four, or five?

16. an even number?

17. an odd number?

18. a number greater than one?

19. a number less than one?

20. a number less than seven?

Monte is going to choose a date from the month of May at random. Give the probability that he will choose

21. May 15.

$$\frac{\text{▦}}{31} \begin{array}{l} \longleftarrow \text{Favorable outcomes} \\ \longleftarrow \text{Possible outcomes} \end{array}$$

22. May 28.

23. May 9 or May 16.

24. May 2, May 4, or May 30.

25. a date consisting of two digits.

26. a date that has one in it.

27. a date that has three in it.

28. a date that has one or three in it.

29. a date that is an even number.

Computing Probabilities

Mrs. Anaya's class is going to select a class representative and an alternate. Mrs. Anaya has written each student's name on a slip of paper and placed the slips in a jar. She is going to draw two slips at random. She will not replace the first slip before she draws the second slip.

Of the 34 students in the class, 18 are girls. What is the probability that both the representative and the alternate will be girls?

Mrs. Anaya computes the number of ways to choose both the representative and the alternate.

Number of choices for the representative	Number of choices left for the alternate	Number of possible outcomes
34 ×	**33** =	**1122**

There are 1122 possible outcomes.

Then she computes the number of ways to choose a girl for both the representative and the alternate.

Number of choices of girls for the representative	Number of choices of girls left for the alternate	Number of favorable outcomes
18 ×	**17** =	**306**

There are 306 favorable outcomes.

Remember, if all outcomes are equally likely:

$$\text{probability} = \frac{\text{number of favorable outcomes}}{\text{number of possible outcomes}}$$

Therefore, the probability that both the representative and the alternate will be girls is $\frac{306}{1122}$, or $\frac{3}{11}$.

Use these data about Mrs. Anaya's class to help you solve each problem.

Number of students in class		
	Age in years	
	Under 14	14 or over
Boys	2	14
Girls	5	13

Find the answers to each exercise to help you find the probability that both the representative and the alternate will be under 14 years of age.

1. How many students are in the class?

2. Multiply to find the possible outcomes.

Choices for the representative	Choices left for the alternate	Possible outcomes
34	× 33	= ▦

3. How many students are under 14 years of age?

4. Multiply to find the favorable outcomes.

Choices of students under 14 for the representative	Choices of students under 14 left for the alternate	Favorable outcomes
7	× 6	= ▦

5. What is the probability that both the representative and the alternate will be under 14 years of age?

In the class drawing, what is the probability that both the representative and the alternate will be

6. boys?

7. 14 years of age or older?

8. girls under 14 years of age?

9. boys under 14 years of age?

10. girls 14 years of age or over?

11. boys 14 years of age or over?

12. Give the probability that the representative will be a girl and the alternate will be a boy.

13. Give the probability that the representative is under 14 years of age and the alternate is 14 years of age or over.

★ 14. Make a table for your class that shows the number of boys and girls under 14 years of age and 14 years of age or over.

★ 15. Use the data in your table to compute the probabilities for exercises 1 to 13.

Using Probabilities to Make Predictions

You can use probabilities to help you make predictions.

Alan is going to roll a die 50 times. He wants to estimate the number of rolls that will result in two.

First he finds the probability.

$\frac{1}{6}$ ⟵ Number of favorable outcomes
⟵ Number of possible outcomes

Then he multiplies to find the *expected* number of favorable outcomes.

Probability of rolling a two	Number of rolls	Expected number of favorable outcomes
$\frac{1}{6}$	× 50	= $8\frac{1}{3}$

Alan estimates that a two will occur on about 8 of the 50 rolls.

Suppose that you roll a die 50 times.

1. Give the probability of getting

    a. five.

    b. a number less than five.

    c. an even number.

2. Give the expected number of rolls that will result in

    a. five.

    b. a number less than five.

    c. an even number.

A manufacturer of television sets tests each set when it is completed. The company records show that there is a probability of $\frac{16}{1000}$, or .016, that a set will need to be scrapped.

3. If 750 sets are made per day, about how many will be scrapped?

Probability that a set will be scrapped	Number of sets	Expected number of sets to be scrapped
.016	× 750	= ▦

4. About how many sets will be scrapped in a 5-day work week?

5. About how many sets will be scrapped in a 22-day work month?

If you were to guess the answer to a question on a multiple-choice test, what is the probability that you would get a correct answer if there were

6. six choices?

7. five choices?

8. four choices?

9. three choices?

10. two choices?

If there were 25 questions on a multiple-choice test, what is the expected number of correct answers if each question had

11. six choices?

12. five choices?

13. four choices?

14. three choices?

15. two choices?

Laboratory Activity

Take this multiple-choice test just for fun. Guess each answer.

1. The Rodeo Cowboy Champion in 1959 was
   (a) Jim Shoulders   (b) Dean Oliver   (c) Phil Lyne

2. The largest industry in the Republic of Botswana is
   (a) diamond mining   (b) tourism   (c) cattle

3. The unit of money in the Republic of Lesotho is the
   (a) dirhan   (b) baht   (c) rand

4. The eighth highest volcano in Russia is
   (a) Tolbachik   (b) Avachinskaya   (c) Shiveluch

5. The 88th word in Lincoln's Gettysburg Address is
   (a) that   (b) lives   (c) their

6. The number of tornadoes in the U.S. in 1923 was
   (a) 108   (b) 102   (c) 130

7. The Women's Duckpin Bowling Champion in 1973 was
   (a) Nancy Brindle   (b) Miki Irish   (c) Agnes Claughsey

8. The number of miles of gravel road in Saskatchewan in 1972 was
   (a) 60,868   (b) 67,528   (c) 59,482

9. The Zip Code for Culebra, Puerto Rico, is
   (a) 00632   (b) 00645   (c) 00670

1. Give the probability of guessing the correct answer for one exercise.

2. What is the expected number of correct answers for the test?

3. Compare your answers with the correct answers on page 353. Is the expected number of correct answers the same as your actual number of correct answers?

4. What is the expected number of correct answers for the entire class? The actual number of correct answers?

CAREERS Medical Researcher

Nai-Ying Lim works in the research department of a medical laboratory. She tests new medicines and often cares for those patients suffering from side effects of the new medications.

Nai-Ying recently tested a new drug for arthritis on 672 volunteer patients. She made a table to show the number of patients suffering from certain side effects.

Side effects	Nausea	Dizziness	Weight loss	Nervous tension	Muscular pain
Number of patients	42	96	28	11	7

Use her table to give the probability that a patient taking the drug will suffer from

1. nausea.

2. dizziness.

3. weight loss.

4. nervous tension.

5. muscular pain.

In the United States, about 7,000,000 people have arthritis. If they all used the new drug, give the expected number of people who would experience

6. nausea.

7. dizziness.

8. weight loss.

9. nervous tension.

10. muscular pain.

She later tested a more advanced form of the same drug on 882 different volunteer patients. She again made a table to show the number of patients suffering from certain side effects.

Side effects	Nausea	Dizziness	Weight loss	Nervous tension	Muscular pain
Number of patients	14	9	49	3	0

Use her new table to give the probability that a new patient taking the improved drug will suffer from

11. nausea.

12. dizziness.

13. weight loss.

14. nervous tension.

If about 7,000,000 victims of arthritis in the United States take the improved drug, what is the expected number of people who would experience

15. nausea?

16. dizziness?

17. weight loss?

18. nervous tension?

Page 364

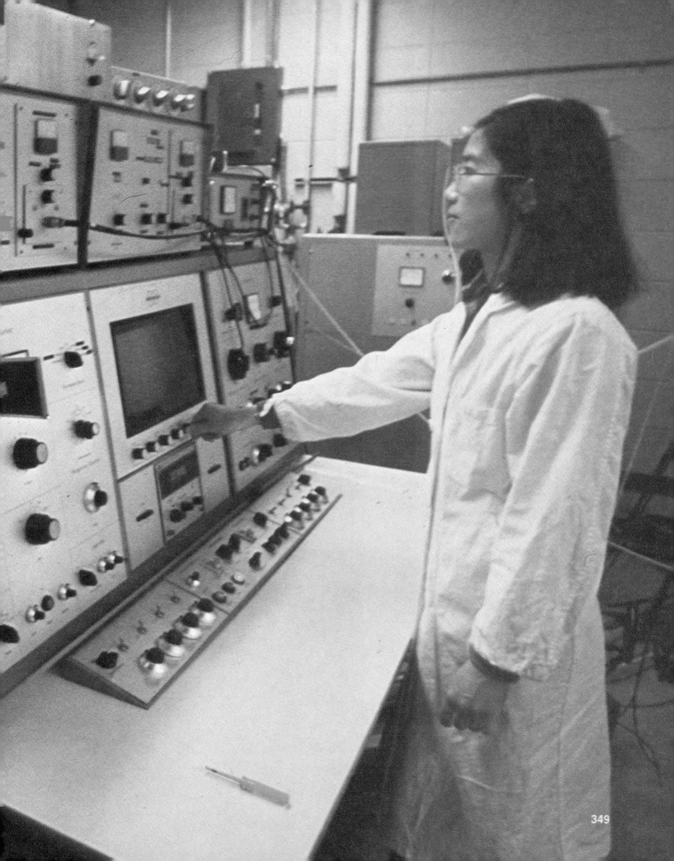

Multiplying Probabilities: Independent Events

EXPERIMENT

Put six cards like these in a bag.

B	A	N	A	N	A

Draw a card at random and *replace* it.
Draw another card.

The outcomes of the two draws are *independent* of each other
because they have no influence on each other.

Amy and Gayle use different methods to find
the probability of making two draws that show *N*.

A. Amy multiplies to find the
number of possible outcomes.

Ways to choose first card	Ways to choose second card	Possible outcomes
6 ×	**6**	**= 36**

She multiplies again to find
the number of favorable outcomes.

Ways to choose *N* for the first card	Ways to choose *N* for the second card	Favorable outcomes
2 ×	**2**	**= 4**

She then finds the probability
of making two draws that show *N*.

$\dfrac{4}{36}$ ⟵ Number of favorable outcomes
⟵ Number of possible outcomes

The probability is $\frac{4}{36}$, or $\frac{1}{9}$.

B. Gayle first finds the probability
of making one draw that shows *N*.

$\dfrac{2}{6}$ ⟵ Number of favorable outcomes
⟵ Number of possible outcomes

The probability is $\frac{2}{6}$, or $\frac{1}{3}$.

Then she multiplies to find the
probability of making two draws
that show *N*.

Probability of drawing *N* on first card	Probability of drawing *N* on second card	Probability of drawing *N* on both cards
$\frac{1}{3}$ ×	$\frac{1}{3}$ =	$\frac{1}{9}$

The probability of making two draws
that show *N* is $\frac{1}{9}$.

Suppose that you try the experiment. Each time you draw a card, you must replace it before you make another draw.

1. If you make two draws, what is the probability that both draws show

   a. *A*?

   b. *B*?

2. If you make three draws, what is the probability that the three draws show

   a. *N*?

   b. *A*?

   c. *B*?

   d. *B*, *A*, and *N* in that order?

Suppose that you roll a red die and a green die. Give the probability that the red die will show a five if the green die shows a

3. three.

4. six.

5. five.

6. When two dice are rolled, is the outcome of one die independent of the outcome of the other?

Give the probability of getting these outcomes.

7. The green die shows a three and the red die shows a five.

8. The green die shows a six and the red die shows a five.

9. Both the green die and the red die show five.

Suppose that you toss a coin and roll a die. Give the probability of getting these outcomes.

10. The coin shows heads and the die shows six.

11. The coin shows tails and the die shows six.

Suppose that you toss a coin several times. What is the probability that the coin will show heads on the

12. first toss?

13. second toss?

14. first two tosses?

15. first three tosses?

● **Discuss** If a coin is tossed 50 times, what is the probability that it will show heads on the 51st toss?

Multiplying Probabilities: Dependent Events

EXPERIMENT

Put six cards like these in a bag.

B A N A N A

Draw a card at random.
Do *not* replace it.
Draw another card.

The outcomes of the two draws are *dependent* because the outcome of the first draw influences the outcome of the second draw.

Ron and Norm use different methods to find the probability of making two draws that show *N*.

A. Ron multiplies to find the number of possible outcomes.

Ways to choose first card	Ways to choose second card	Possible outcomes
6	× **5**	= **30**

He multiplies again to find the the number of favorable outcomes.

Ways to choose *N* for the first card	Ways to choose *N* for the second card	Favorable outcomes
2	× **1**	= **2**

He then finds the probability of making two draws that show *N*.

$\dfrac{2}{30}$ ⟵ Number of favorable outcomes
⟵ Number of possible outcomes

The probability is $\frac{2}{30}$, or $\frac{1}{15}$.

B. Norm first finds the probability of making a draw that shows *N*.

$\dfrac{2}{6}$ ⟵ Number of favorable outcomes
⟵ Number of possible outcomes

The probability is $\frac{2}{6}$, or $\frac{1}{3}$.

Then he finds the probability of making a second draw that shows *N*.

$\dfrac{1}{5}$ ⟵ Number of favorable outcomes
⟵ Number of possible outcomes

The probability is $\frac{1}{5}$.

He multiplies to find the probability of making two draws that show *N*.

Probability of drawing *N* on the first draw	Probability of drawing *N* on the second draw	Probability of drawing *N* on both draws
$\dfrac{2}{6}$	× $\dfrac{1}{5}$	= $\dfrac{2}{30}$

The probability is $\frac{2}{30}$, or $\frac{1}{15}$.

For each exercise, use the cards in the experiment. Do not replace a card once it has been drawn.

1. If you were to make two draws, what is the probability of making two draws that show *A*?

2. If you were to make three draws, what is the probability of making three draws that show *A*?

Multiply to find the probability of making two draws in order that show

3. *B* and *A*.

4. *N* and *A*.

5. *B* and *N*.

Multiply to find the probability of making three draws in order that show

6. *B*, *A*, and *N*.

Probability of drawing *B* on the first draw		Probability of drawing *A* on the second draw		Probability of drawing *N* on the third draw
$\frac{1}{6}$	×	$\frac{3}{5}$	×	$\frac{2}{4}$

7. *N*, *A*, and *B*.

8. *B*, *A*, and *A*.

9. *A*, *N*, and *N*.

10. *N*, *A*, and *N*.

Sam Smart did the following computation.

There are 365 days in a year.	365
I sleep about 8 hours per day, or about $\frac{1}{3}$ of the year.	− 122
This leaves 243 days.	243
I have 52 Saturdays and 52 Sundays off from school.	− 104
This leaves 139 days.	139
I have 3 months off for summer vacation.	− 90
This leaves 49 days.	49
I have winter and spring vacations.	− 19
This leaves 30 days.	30
Each day I spend about 2 hours eating, or $\frac{1}{12}$ of the year.	− 30
I have NO TIME left for school.	0

Explain why Sam is not so smart!

Adding Probabilities

Faye is going to roll a die.
She asks Susan and Jack to find the
probability of getting a three *or* a five.

A. Susan first finds the number of
possible outcomes. There are six.
Then she counts the number of favorable outcomes.
Three is one favorable outcome. Five is another.
Therefore, there are two favorable outcomes.
The probability that the die will show
a three or a five is $\frac{2}{6}$, or $\frac{1}{3}$.

$\dfrac{2}{6}$ ⟵ Number of favorable outcomes
⟵ Number of possible outcomes

B. Jack knows that probabilities can usually
be added when the word *or* is used.
So he adds the probability of getting a three
and the probability of getting a five.

Probability of getting a three	Probability of getting a five	Probability of getting a three or a five
$\dfrac{1}{6}$ +	$\dfrac{1}{6}$ =	$\dfrac{2}{6}$

The probability that the die will show
a three or a five is $\frac{2}{6}$, or $\frac{1}{3}$.

Sarah is going to roll a
die. Add to find the
probability that the die
shows a

1. one or six.

2. two or four.

3. two or four or six.

4. two or an odd number.

5. one or an even
   number.

Warren is going to twirl
the spinner. What is the
probability that the
spinner will stop on

6. blue or green?

7. green or yellow?

8. orange or red?

9. blue or orange?

10. red or yellow?

11. green or blue or
    orange?

12. red or orange or
    yellow?

Using Probabilities

Craig is going to pick a card at random. What is the probability that he will pick a multiple of 2 or 3?

There are 10 possible outcomes. Craig lists the multiples of 2 and the multiples of 3 to help him find the number of favorable outcomes.

Multiples of 2:   2   4   ⑥   8   10

Multiples of 3:   3   ⑥   9

Craig has listed the number six twice. However, he can count it only once as a favorable outcome because there is only one card that shows six. Craig counts 7 favorable outcomes.

$\frac{7}{10}$ ←— Number of favorable outcomes
       ←— Number of possible outcomes

The probability that Craig will pick a multiple of 2 or a multiple of 3 is $\frac{7}{10}$.

Notice that Craig cannot find the correct answer by adding the probability of picking a multiple of 2 and the probability of picking a multiple of 3.

1	2	3	4	5	6	7
8	9	10	11	12	13	14

Suppose that you pick one of these cards at random. What is the probability that you will pick

1. a multiple of 2?

2. a multiple of 3?

3. a multiple of 5?

4. a multiple of 2 or 3?

5. a multiple of 2 or 5?

6. a multiple of 3 or 5?

1	2	3	4	5	6	7
8	9	10	11	12	13	14
15	16	17	18	19	20	

Suppose that you pick one of these cards at random. What is the probability that you will pick

7. a multiple of 2 or 3?

8. a multiple of 2 or 5?

9. a multiple of 3 or 5?

★ 10. a multiple of 2 or 3 or 5?

Jerry twirled the spinner. The probability that the spinner stops on five is $\frac{1}{6}$.

After the twirl, he told Beth that the spinner had stopped on an odd number. Beth knows that now there are 3 possible outcomes but still only 1 favorable outcome. Given the additional information, Beth can say that the probability that the spinner stopped on five is $\frac{1}{3}$.

As you can see, probabilities can change if additional information is given. When Beth used the new information, she computed a *conditional probability*.

Suppose that a die is rolled. What is the probability that the die shows three if you know that the die

1. shows an odd number?

2. shows one or three?

3. shows three or six?

4. shows three, five, or six?

5. does not show two?

6. shows a number greater than one?

7. shows a number greater than two?

8. shows a number less than six?

9. shows a number less than five?

10. shows a number less than four?

Suppose that a card is picked at random. What is the probability that the card shows *M* if you know that the card

11. does not show *D*?

12. does not show *R*, *N*, or *D*?

13. shows *A* or *M*?

14. shows *R*, *N*, *D*, or *M*?

15. shows a consonant?

What is the probability that the card shows *A* if you know that the card

16. does not show *N*?

17. does not show *R*, *D*, or *M*?

18. shows *R*, *A*, or *N*?

19. shows *A* or *O*?

20. shows a vowel?

Suppose that a spinner is twirled. What is the probability that the spinner stops on six if you know that the spinner

21. does not stop on three?

22. does not stop on nine or ten?

23. stops on a number greater than three?

24. stops on a number greater than four?

25. stops on a number greater than five?

26. stops on a number less than nine?

27. stops on a number less than eight?

28. stops on an even number?

Finding probabilities, pages 342–345

Louie is going to roll a die. What is the probability that the roll will result in

1. three?

2. three or five?

3. three, five, or six?

Members of the Glee Club are going to select at random a chairman and an assistant to plan a class party.

4. Of the 34 students, 16 are boys. What is the probability that both the chairman and the assistant will be boys?

Using probabilities to make predictions, pages 346–347

5. If you were to roll a die, what is the probability of getting a two?

6. Suppose you were to roll a die 40 times. Give the expected number of rolls that will result in a two.

7. The probability that Jim will get a hit when he comes to bat is .251. Give the expected number of hits in 100 times at bat.

Multiplying probabilities, pages 350–353

Use these cards for exercises 8 to 11.

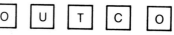

Suppose that you draw a card at random, replace it, and then draw another card. What is the probability of making two draws that show

8. O?

9. T and O?

Suppose that you draw two cards at random. Do not replace a card once it has been drawn. What is the probability of making two draws that show

10. O?

11. T and O?

Adding probabilities, pages 354–355

12. If you roll a die, what is the probability that it would show a three or a four?

Finding conditional probabilities, pages 356–357

13. Suppose that you roll a die. What is the probability that the die shows a two if you know that the die shows an even number?

Chapter 18 Statistics

Picturing Statistical Data

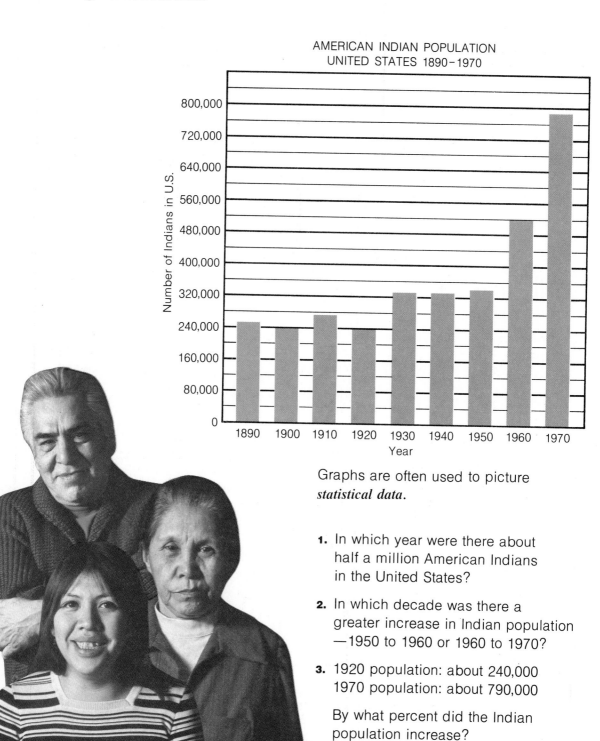

AMERICAN INDIAN POPULATION
UNITED STATES 1890–1970

Number of Indians in U.S.

800,000
720,000
640,000
560,000
480,000
400,000
320,000
240,000
160,000
80,000
0

1890 1900 1910 1920 1930 1940 1950 1960 1970
Year

Graphs are often used to picture *statistical data*.

1. In which year were there about half a million American Indians in the United States?

2. In which decade was there a greater increase in Indian population —1950 to 1960 or 1960 to 1970?

3. 1920 population: about 240,000
   1970 population: about 790,000

   By what percent did the Indian population increase?

360

DISTRIBUTION OF AMERICAN INDIAN
POPULATION IN U.S. IN 1970

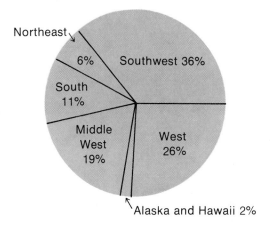

Northeast

6%   Southwest 36%

South
11%

Middle
West
19%   West
            26%

Alaska and Hawaii 2%

PERCENT OF U.S. POPULATION
5 TO 17 YEARS OF AGE

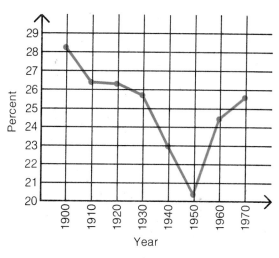

4. In 1970, which part of the United States had the largest Indian population?

5. In which part of the United States did about one-fourth of the Indians live?

6. In which part did about one-fifth of the Indians live?

7. Where did the fewest Indians live?

8. In which year did people of ages 5 to 17 make up about 20% of the total population of the United States?

9. From the graph, can you tell the number of people in 1970 who were between the ages of 5 and 17?

10. The percents for 1930 and 1970 are about the same. The total population in 1930 was about 121,770,000. The total population in 1970 was about 203,212,000. In which year were there more people between 5 and 17?

● **Discuss**   Are graphs a good source of exact information?

Collecting and Organizing Data

Statistical data are collected from a census or a sample.

A. A *census* is an examination or a count of everything that is to be studied. If, for instance, you wanted to know what hobbies the students in your mathematics class have, you would ask each student.

A *sample* is an examination or a count of only a portion of the object or objects to be studied. To find out the hobbies of teen-agers in your community, you would probably have to select a sample of people to ask.

B. In making counts, either for a census or for a sample, you often use a *frequency table*.

Gloria asked all the students in her English class what month they were born in. Then she made a frequency table of her findings.

Number of Birthdays

January	2	July	2
February	3	August	4
March	3	September	8
April	3	October	2
May	4	November	2
June	2	December	1

In which month were there the most birthdays? The fewest birthdays?

In each case, tell which you would use, a census or a sample. You wish to find—

1. the percent of students in your class whose last names begin with S or T.

2. the percent of people in Oregon whose last names begin with S or T.

3. the number of white blood cells in your body.

4. the number of students in your class who were born in January.

5. the average height of the boys in your class.

6. which of two radio programs is more popular in your community.

7. the average weekly cost of food for a family of four in your community.

8. Complete this frequency table for your class.

Initial of Last Name	
A or B	O or P
C or D	Q or R
E or F	S or T
G or H	U or V
I or J	W or X
K or L	Y or Z
M or N	

9. Which pair of letters occurs most often? Least often?

10. Make a frequency table of these test grades.

A C B C C C A A D
C A D C C F C C C
C B A

11. Make a frequency table of the occurrence of the letters in this limerick.

There was a young lady of Niger
Who smiled as she rode on a tiger;
   They returned from the ride
   With the lady inside,
And the smile on the face of the tiger.

12. Which letter occurs most often?

13. Which letters aren't used at all?

Many census statistics are so huge or change so fast that rounding the numbers is necessary. Tell which numbers you think are exact and which are rounded.

14. Willie McCovey hit 45 home runs in 1969.

15. John Tyler, the tenth President of the United States, had fourteen children.

16. There are 917,000 volumes in the Public Library in Louisville, Kentucky.

17. In 1970 the population of the United States was 203,212,000.

Sample Statistics

Here are four reasons why a sample would be better to use than a census.

A census would be:

a. impossible.

b. possible, but too expensive.

c. destructive of what is being tested.

d. foolish, because a sample gives all the needed information.

Use one or more of the above reasons to tell why a sample would be preferable to a census.

1. Measuring the public's opinion of last night's TV special

2. Testing a patient's blood

3. Testing well water for safe drinking

4. Testing soil in a garden for acid content

5. Measuring customers' opinion of a large department store

6. Checking for harmful bacteria in the water in a swimming pool

7. Seeing if the Thanksgiving turkey is done

8. Testing the bumper system on a new car model

9. Measuring the public's opinion of a person holding public office

In Lakeville, a city of 75,000, a research team interviewed 500 people to find out what languages they could speak. This is one of the tables that appeared in the report.

LANGUAGES SPOKEN IN LAKEVILLE

Language	Percent of sample
English only	58
German	9
Greek	6
Italian	15
Scandinavian languages	6
Slavic languages	7
Spanish	14
Other (includes American Indian languages, Arabic, Oriental languages)	11

10. Add the percents. Is the sum greater than 100%? What reasons might there be for this?

11. Estimate how many people in Lakeville spoke only English.

    (Find 58% of 75,000.)

Estimate how many people in Lakeville could speak

12. Greek.

13. Spanish.

14. the languages included under "Other."

15. Of the 500 people interviewed, 11 could speak Japanese. What percent was this?

16. Estimate how many people in Lakeville could speak Japanese.

The Mean

Mean is another name for "average."

To compute the mean, or average, age of the Presidents listed in the table—

a. First find the sum of the ages.

b. Then divide the sum by 16, the number of Presidents listed.

SIXTEEN YOUNGEST U.S. PRESIDENTS

President	Age when inaugurated
Martin Van Buren	54
John Tyler	51
James K. Polk	49
Millard Fillmore	50
Franklin Pierce	48
Abraham Lincoln	52
Ulysses S. Grant	46
James A. Garfield	49
Chester A. Arthur	50
Grover Cleveland	47
William McKinley	54
Theodore Roosevelt	42
William Howard Taft	51
Calvin Coolidge	51
Franklin D. Roosevelt	51
John F. Kennedy	43

The sum of the Presidents' ages is 788 years. Divide 788 by 16. The mean age is a little over 49 years.

$$16\overline{)788} \quad 49\tfrac{1}{4}$$

In exercises 1–3, compute the mean weight.

1. 40 kg   60 kg   52 kg
   48 kg

2. 20 g   18 g   21 g
   24 g   29 g   22 g
   15 g   20 g   26 g
   21 g

3. 8.2 lb.   9.6 lb.
   11.3 lb.   16.1 lb.

4. The mean cost of three dinners was $6.30. Compute the total cost.

★ 5. The mean amount of $8.11, $1.73, $2.51, and $▒▒▒ is $4.62.

   a. Compute the total amount.

   b. Fill in the missing amount.

Pages 368

The Median and the Mode

Here the Presidents mentioned on page 366 are listed in order of age, from youngest to oldest. A list like this can be used to find two other statistical measures, the median and the mode.

T. Roosevelt	42 yr.
Kennedy	43 yr.
Grant	46 yr.
Cleveland	47 yr.
Pierce	48 yr.
Polk	49 yr.
Garfield	49 yr.
Fillmore	50 yr. ⎫
Arthur	50 yr. ⎬ Median
Tyler	51 yr. ⎫
Taft	51 yr. ⎪
Coolidge	51 yr. ⎬ Mode
F. D. Roosevelt	51 yr. ⎭
Lincoln	52 yr.
Van Buren	54 yr.
McKinley	54 yr.

A. The *median* is the middle value. It separates a list of numbers so that there are as many smaller numbers before the median as larger numbers after it.

In this list the median is 50, with seven numbers before it and seven numbers after it.

B. The *mode* is the number that occurs most often. In this list the mode is 51, the most frequent number.

1. Find the median age (years).

16 10 13 11 15 14 8
11 10 12 16

2. Find the median height (centimeters).

161 160 172 147 162 166
154 181 144 158 140 181
164 166 148 180 167 160 159

3. In some cases, the median is halfway between the middle numbers. For example, the median of
1, 8, 10, 11, 18, and 20
is halfway between 10 and 11, or $10\frac{1}{2}$.

Compute the median:

20 18 15 19 24 22 21 25
27 29

4. Find the mode of these prices.

$1.07 $.99 $1.11 $1.15 $1.07
$.89 $1.07 $1.13 $1.03 $.98

5. Find the mode of these weights (kilograms).

3.5 7.2 6.0 5.1 7.3 5.1
2.4 5.1 6.2 8.9 5.1 6.3

6. Sometimes, there is no mode. At times, there are two or more modes. What are the modes?

20 18 21 24 29 22 15 24
26 21

More practice
Set A, page 382

Range and Mean Variation

WEIGHTS OF FIGHTERS IN RECENT PROFESSIONAL BOXING MATCHES

Column 1			Column 2	
Joe Roman	197 lb.	Mean weight:	Bob Foster	180 lb.
Leroy Caldwell	198 lb.	204 lb.	John Conteh	182 lb.
Earnie Shavers	206 lb.		Oscar Bonavena	211 lb.
Duane Bobick	209 lb.		George Foreman	219 lb.
Ken Norton	210 lb.		George Chuvalo	228 lb.
These weights are close to the mean.			These weights spread farther from the mean.	

A. The weights in column 2 are said to have greater *dispersion* than the weights in column 1.
First, the weights in column 2 have a greater *range*. The range is the difference between the largest and smallest numbers in the data.

In column 2, $228 - 180 = 48$.
The range is 48 lb.
In column 1, $210 - 197 = 13$.
The range is 13 lb.
The range for all ten weights is $228 - \text{▦} = \text{▦}$.

B. A second measure of dispersion is the *mean variation*—the average amount by which the data differ from the mean.

a. First compute the difference between the mean and each item of data.

Column 1		
Data	Mean	Difference
197	204	$204 - 197 = 7$
198	204	$204 - 198 = 6$
206	204	$206 - 204 = 2$
209	204	$209 - 204 = 5$
210	204	$210 - 204 = 6$

b. Then compute the mean of these differences.

$$\frac{7 + 6 + 2 + 5 + 6}{5} = \frac{26}{5} = 5.2$$

The mean variation for column 1 is 5.2 lb.

Compute the mean variation for

1. the data in column 2 on page 368.

2. the weights of all ten fighters.

For each exercise, compute the range, the mean, and the mean variation.

HOME RUN LEADERS 1969-1973

3.

American League	
Batter	Home runs
Killebrew	49
Howard	44
Melton	33
Allen	37
Jackson	32

4.

National League	
Batter	Home runs
McCovey	45
Bench	45
Stargell	48
Bench	40
Stargell	44

The tables list data for twenty professional golf tournaments in 1973. Compute the range, the mean, and the mean variation for each exercise.

5.

Winner	Prize
Rod Funseth	$27,000
Bruce Crampton	30,000
John Schlee	40,000
Bob Dickson	34,000
Lee Trevino	52,000
Brian Allin	30,000
Chi Chi Rodriguez	42,000
Homero Blancas	30,000
Jack Nicklaus	40,000
Hubert Green	20,000

6.

Winner	Prize
JoAnn Prentice	$ 4,500
Kathy Whitworth	3,750
Gloria Ehret	4,950
Betsy Cullen	4,500
Kathy Whitworth	20,000
Judy Rankin	4,500
Kathy Cornelius	25,000
Jocelyne Bourassa	10,000
Mary Mills	4,500
Mary Lou Crocker	5,250

More practice
Set B, page 382

Predictions

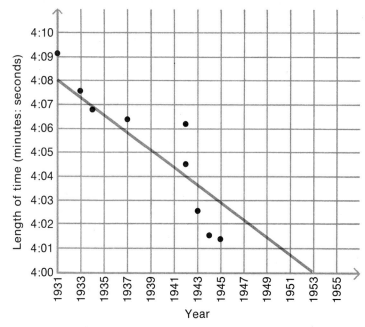

WORLD RECORDS FOR THE ONE-MILE RUN

Year	Time
1931	4 min. 9.2 sec.
1933	4 min. 7.6 sec.
1934	4 min. 6.8 sec.
1937	4 min. 6.4 sec.
1942	4 min. 6.2 sec.
1942	4 min. 4.6 sec.
1943	4 min. 2.6 sec.
1944	4 min. 1.6 sec.
1945	4 min. 1.4 sec.

A. In making predictions, statisticians sometimes make a graph of the type shown above. Points are plotted for the items of data. Then an attempt is made to draw a straight line "between" the points.

Some years ago, a line drawn "between" points for world records led people to predict that, in 1953, someone would run the mile in 4 minutes. Actually, the 4-minute barrier was broken in 1954 by Roger Bannister. His time was 3 minutes 59.4 seconds.

1. On grid paper, plot the points for the data in the following table. Label the vertical axis with the numerals 45, 46, 47, . . ., 60, to represent seconds over 3 minutes.

Record One-Mile Runs	
Year	Time
1954	3 min. 59.4 sec.
1954	3 min. 58.0 sec.
1957	3 min. 57.2 sec.
1958	3 min. 54.5 sec.
1962	3 min. 54.4 sec.
1964	3 min. 54.1 sec.
1965	3 min. 53.6 sec.
1966	3 min. 51.3 sec.
1967	3 min. 51.1 sec.

2. Draw a line "between" the points on your graph and predict the year in which a mile will be run in 3 minutes 45 seconds or less.

B. Predictions are often based on samples.

In a school of 1322 students, the names of 40 students were drawn from a hat. They were asked to name their favorite sport in the Winter Olympics. Nine students voted for bobsledding.

Predict how many students in the whole school would vote for bobsledding.

9 is $\frac{9}{40}$, or 22.5%, of 40.

Find 22.5% of 1322.

$.225 \times 1322 = 297.45$

About 297 students would vote for bobsledding.

The table shows how the sample of 40 students voted. Complete the table. Give percents to the nearest tenth.

	Sport	Number of votes	Percent of sample
	Bobsledding	9	22.5
3.	Figure skating	13	
4.	Speed skating	5	
5.	Alpine skiing	8	
6.	Nordic skiing	2	
7.	Ice hockey	3	

About how many students in the whole school would vote for

8. figure skating?

9. speed skating?

10. ice hockey?

★ 11. Alpine skiing and Nordic skiing combined?

Scattergrams and Correlation

Twenty-two students tried out for basketball.
Coach Merrill listed their heights and weights.
Then he plotted the ordered pairs (height, weight) on
a graph. For example, dot A gives the location
of (146, 34).

Height (cm)	Weight (kg)	Height (cm)	Weight (kg)
146	34	173	65
150	36	175	67
156	48	175	69
159	49	176	65
160	46	177	65
161	52	178	68
162	51	180	67
167	56	180	74
168	55	185	72
171	62	185	75
172	65	186	74

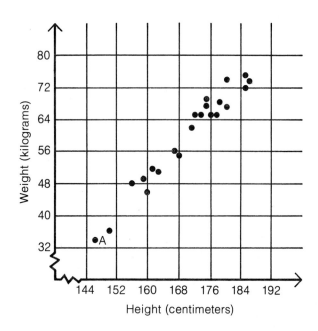

Such a graph is called a *scattergram*. The position
of the points indicates how height and weight
are related.

1. Could a line be drawn on the
   scattergram in such a way that the
   points would cluster close to the line?

2. Would you expect that, in almost
   any group of students, greater height
   would usually mean greater weight?

This scattergram shows a *positive
correlation* between height and weight.
If a line were drawn "between" the points,
it would slant upward. Most of the
points would be close to the line.

There are three kinds of correlation. These scattergrams show typical cases.

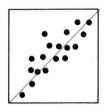

Positive Correlation
Line slants upward.

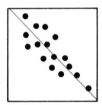

Negative Correlation
Line slants downward.

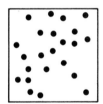

No Correlation
No definite pattern.

Which kind of correlation would you expect in scattergrams showing points for these ordered pairs?

3. (height, arm span)

4. (weight, calorie intake)

5. (score on English test, height)

6. (outside temperature, cost of heating a home)

7. (altitude, atmospheric pressure)

8. (auto speed, miles per gallon)

For each exercise, plot a scattergram for the data. Then decide what kind of correlation your graph suggests.

9.

Student	Weight (kg)	Math test score
A	50	70
B	41	85
C	52	95
D	39	80
E	36	85
F	45	60
G	48	45
H	42	75
I	40	100
J	41	55

10.

Car	Fuel-tank capacity (gallons)	Gas mileage (country driving)
A	11.6	34
B	21	23
C	11	28
D	21	19
E	16	24
F	15.8	23
G	26	16
H	24.5	17
I	25	17
J	26.5	16
K	17	22
L	22	16

Using Scattergrams

Car	Overall length (inches)	Wheelbase (inches)	Curb weight (pounds)	Turning circle (feet)	Fuel-tank capacity (gallons)
Gremlin	171	96	2775	35	21
Datsun B210	161	93	1950	33	11.6
VW Super Beetle	165	95	2025	35	11
Nova 6	197	111	3345	44	21
Valiant 6	198	111	3100	41	16
Volvo 144	188	103	2860	32	15.8
Cutlass	215	116	4020	46	22
Electra	232	127	4840	47	26
Delta 88	227	124	4655	45	26
Cadillac	231	130	5295	49	27
Challenger	199	110	3490	43	18
Mustang II	175	97	2810	38	13

The data in the table concern twelve models
of 1974 automobiles.

Use the data in the table. Make a scattergram to show
the relation of

1. overall length to wheelbase.

2. curb weight to fuel-tank capacity.

3. overall length to turning circle.

4. Which of your scattergrams seem to indicate

  a. positive correlation?

  b. negative correlation?

  c. no correlation?

Laboratory Activity

1. **a.** Each student in the class writes his or her full name. Each student reports the number of letters and the number of vowels in the name (count only a, e, i, o, and u as vowels).

   b. Using the ordered pairs (number of letters, number of vowels) for the whole class, make a scattergram.

   c. What kind of correlation is suggested?

2. **a.** Each student records his or her own height and arm span. The ordered pairs (height, arm span) are collected.

   b. Make a scattergram of the data.

   c. What kind of correlation is suggested?

3. **a.** Each student guesses the width of the chalkboard or other object of similar size. The guesses are collected.

   b. Compute the mean of the guesses.

   c. Measure the width of the chalkboard. How does the actual width compare with the mean of the guesses?

TIME OUT

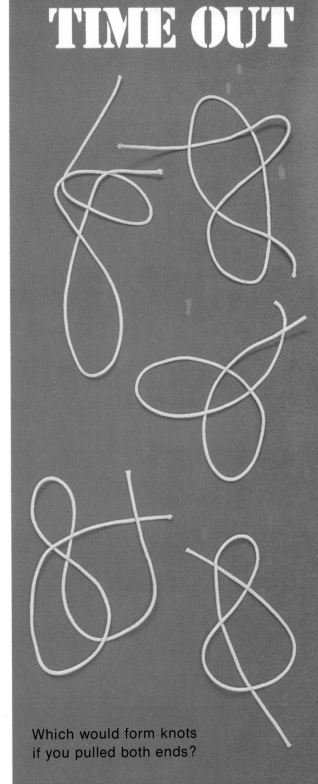

Which would form knots if you pulled both ends?

This advertisement is misleading because certain data are missing. What do you think "15% less" means?

In each exercise, tell whether the statement *might* supply missing data.

1. 15% less than $100

2. 15% less than any other automobile insurance

3. 15% less than the cost of hospitalization insurance

4. 15% less than the maximum amount allowed by the state regulations

5. 15% less than the cost of two automobile insurance policies

6. 15% less than the cost of life insurance

7. 15% less than you now pay for your automobile insurance

In each exercise, tell whether the statement *might* supply missing data in the above advertisement.

8. Minimum number of passengers required

9. Minimum number of miles required

10. Telephone number to call

11. Minimum charge for chartering a Zoomjet

Tell what is missing in each of these advertising claims.

12. Clearance—30% off

13. Guaranteed for life

14. Guaranteed against defects

15. 50% more cleansing power

16. $99\frac{44}{100}$% pure

FOOD COSTS INCREASE SLIGHTLY

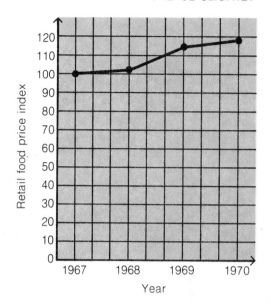

FOOD COSTS SKYROCKET

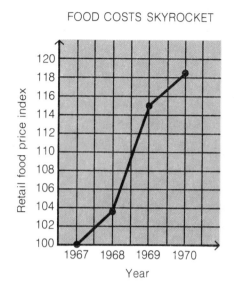

Each graph shows the increase in the cost of food from 1967 to 1970.

17. How are the horizontal scales for each graph different? How are the vertical scales different?

18. Which graph do you think was prepared by a sales executive of a major supermarket chain?

19. Which graph do you think was prepared by a director of a consumers' organization?

20. Does either graph display the data incorrectly?

CAREERS Quality-Control Engineer

In seeing that products meet certain standards, quality-control engineers use various statistical measurements.

Quality-control engineers often study samples of products. For instance, if you were a quality-control engineer at Barker Pet Foods, Inc., how would you sample the dog food to find out whether it contains the advertised ingredients? Answer *yes* or *no*.

1. Analyze the contents of every 25th can.

2. Feed every 100th can to a healthy dog; then give the dog a physical examination.

3. Take a 500-gram sample from each 1000-kilogram batch of dog food and make a chemical analysis of the sample.

4. Feed every 10th can to a group of laboratory dogs.

5. Analyze the contents of every 1000th can.

A quality-control engineer at Bright Glow Electric collected the following data on the life of the light bulbs they manufacture.

Mean life	1000 hours
Expected life	960–1040 hours
Guaranteed minimum life	950 hours

6. Could you expect every Bright Glow light bulb to burn for 1000 hours?

A sample of fifteen bulbs had these lifetimes in hours:

859	957	981	967	992
1041	1052	1002	1019	1011
1009	1020	1110	1045	1100

For this sample, compute

7. the mean lifetime.

8. the percent of bulbs that tested below the guaranteed minimum life.

9. the percent of bulbs that tested below the expected life.

10. the percent that fell within the 960–1040 range.

11. the percent that exceeded 1040 hours.

SIDE TRIP Fibonacci Numbers

1. Use the diagram of the tree to help you complete the table.

Year	Number of branches
First	1
Second	1
Third	2
Fourth	3
Fifth	5
Sixth	▦
Seventh	▦

2. If you add the number of branches for any two consecutive years, do you get the number of branches for the next year?

3. If the tree shown in the diagram continued this pattern of growth, what would be the number of branches for the eighth year? The ninth year? The tenth year?

4. Find the missing numbers for this number pattern.

   1, 1, 2, 3, 5, 8, 13, ▦, 34, ▦, ▦, ▦, 233, . . .

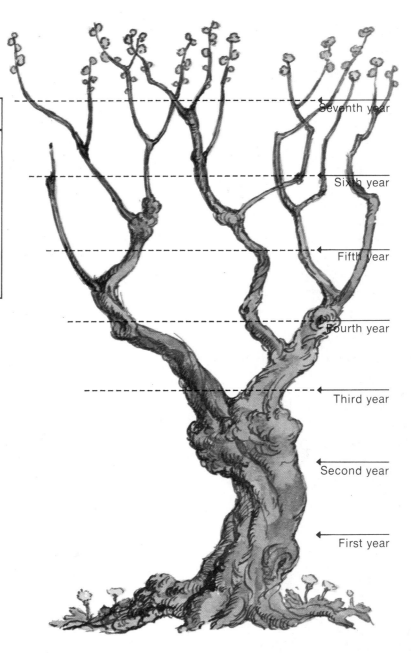

Seventh year

Sixth year

Fifth year

Fourth year

Third year

Second year

First year

An Italian mathematician known as Fibonacci recorded this interesting number pattern around 1200 A.D. The numbers in the pattern are called Fibonacci numbers.

Pictured data, pages 360–361, 376–377

This graph shows the percent of students at Glenbriar Junior High who bought their lunch at school in 1955, 1965, and 1975.

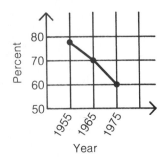

1. In which year did the students who bought their lunch make up about 60% of the student body?

2. The total number of students attending Glenbriar Junior High was 1000 in 1965 and 1500 in 1975. In which year did more students buy their lunch?

Census, sample, and frequency table, pages 362–365

In each case, tell which you would use—a census or a sample. You wish to find

3. the percent of students in your class who read a daily newspaper.

4. the percent of people in the U.S. who read a daily newspaper.

5. Make a frequency table of these test grades.

A C C B C C D C B C B
C C D C C A C F C C

6. What grade was received by the most students?

Mean, median, mode, range, and mean variation, pages 366–369

The students in Ms. Romero's class made these scores on a test.

90 87 87 86 84 81 73

7. Compute the mean.

8. Find the median.

9. Find the mode.

10. Compute the range.

11. Compute the mean variation.

Scattergrams and correlation, pages 370–374

For each exercise, tell whether the scattergram indicates positive correlation, negative correlation, or no correlation.

12.
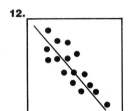

13.
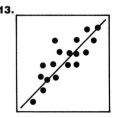

Unit 6 Test

Counting, pages 324–339

1. Hamburger Haven offers the following selections on its menu.

Sandwich	Beverage
hamburger	root beer
hot dog	lemonade
barbecue	

Complete the tree diagram. A customer would have how many choices of a sandwich and a beverage?

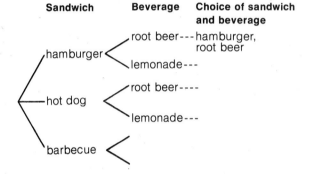

2. How many different ways can you choose a three-digit code number?

3. How many different ways can you arrange the letters in T E A M?

Probability, pages 342–357

4. If you were to roll a die, what is the probability of getting a two or a four?

5. Suppose you were to roll a die 20 times. Give the expected number of rolls that will result in a two or a four.

Use these cards for exercises 6 to 9.

Suppose that you draw a card at random, replace it, and then draw another card. What is the probability of making two draws that show

6. *P*?

7. *P* and *A*?

Suppose that you draw two cards at random. Do not replace a card once it has been drawn. What is the probability of making two draws that show

8. *P*?

9. *P* and *A*?

Statistics, pages 360–379

The students in Ms. Woo's class made these scores on a test.

84 78 95 72 78 89 85

10. Compute the mean.

11. Find the median.

12. Find the mode.

13. Compute the range.

14. Compute the mean variation.

More Practice

Set A

Find the mean, the median, and the mode for each set of data.

1. 36   42   30   40   42

2. 72   66   63   79   83   63

3. 79   81   88   75   81   82

4. 44   47   39   46   43   47   49

5. 5.5   6.7   6.9   5.5   5.1   6.8   6.1   7.0

6. 235   242   234   237   242

7. 55.9   57.6   55.2   56.7   55.2   56.3

8. 3.53   3.75   3.83   3.77   3.41   3.83   3.57

9. 616   630   627   630   617   642   620   609   630   629

10. 7425   7455   7435   7425   7445   7440   7425   7465   7475   7430

11. 149   213   278   180   164   180   152

Set B

Compute the range, the mean, and the mean variation for each set of data.

1. 25   39   21   43   37

2. 55   61   53   60   46

3. 245   211   283   194   315   230   258

4. 74   65   82   71   91   63   80   74

5. 439   376   474   414   350   426   399   466

6. 50   40   67   34   49   32   29   61   48   50

7. 880   920   800   780   830   820   850   790   890

8. 45   70   96   38   64   31   76   52

9. 48   56   42   57   53

10. 91   80   84   72   77   96   81   88   92   75

11. 464   475   456   448   469   427   451   472   433   460

Individualized Skills Maintenance

Diagnosis

A. $^+8 + {}^-3$

$^-9 + {}^-8$

$^+7 + {}^+2$

B. $^+5 - {}^-7$

$^-10 - {}^-6$

$^+3 - {}^+5$

C. $^-7 \times {}^-8$

$^-6 \times {}^+9$

$^+7 \times {}^+7$

D. $^+63 \div {}^+7$

$^-48 \div {}^-8$

$^+72 \div {}^-9$

E. 20% of 50 is a.

80% of 20 is m.

F. 36 is ▧% of 45.

25 is ▧% of 125.

G. 20% of s is 5.

60% of x is 36.

Practice

Set A (pp. 50–51)

1. $^+4 + {}^+1$
2. $^-9 + {}^+6$
3. $^-11 + {}^+5$
4. $^+2 + {}^+2$
5. $^+7 + {}^-9$
6. $^+5 + {}^+7$
7. $^-8 + {}^+11$
8. $^+10 + {}^-10$
9. $^-3 + {}^+3$
10. $^+6 + {}^-4$

Set B (pp. 52–53)

1. $^-6 - {}^-3$
2. $^-4 - {}^-4$
3. $^+8 - {}^+5$
4. $^+3 - {}^-1$
5. $^+10 - {}^+12$
6. $^-1 - {}^-7$
7. $^-7 - {}^+2$
8. $^+5 - {}^-8$
9. $^+9 - {}^+9$
10. $^+2 - {}^-2$

Set C (pp. 56–57)

1. $^-6 \times {}^+3$
2. $^-3 \times {}^-8$
3. $^+4 \times {}^+2$
4. $^-9 \times {}^-5$
5. $^+7 \times {}^-4$
6. $^+1 \times {}^-1$
7. $^+3 \times {}^+3$
8. $^-2 \times {}^+7$
9. $^+5 \times {}^-9$
10. $^+8 \times {}^+10$

Set D (p. 58)

1. $^+27 \div {}^+27$
2. $^-35 \div {}^-7$
3. $^-56 \div {}^+8$
4. $^+21 \div {}^+3$
5. $^-45 \div {}^-45$
6. $^+64 \div {}^-4$
7. $^+40 \div {}^+8$
8. $^-25 \div {}^+25$
9. $^+54 \div {}^-54$
10. $^-30 \div {}^+5$

Individualized Skills Maintenance

Practice *(continued)*

Set E (pp. 286–287)

Find each missing number.

1. 12% of 75 is x.
2. 40% of 30 is m.
3. 60% of 60 is c.
4. 64% of 75 is b.
5. 75% of 32 is s.
6. 5% of 120 is z.
7. 24% of 175 is h.
8. 90% of 140 is v.
9. 50% of 218 is a.
10. 15% of 160 is t.
11. 85% of 20 is y.
12. 32% of 50 is k.
13. 80% of 70 is p.
14. 96% of 75 is d.
15. 20% of 15 is r.
16. 45% of 60 is n.
17. 55% of 80 is b.
18. 92% of 225 is w.
19. 76% of 250 is g.
20. 8% of 25 is q.
21. 70% of 130 is e.

Set F (pp. 290–291)

Find each percent.

1. 9 is ▦% of 60.
2. 4 is ▦% of 8.
3. 63 is ▦% of 70.
4. 24 is ▦% of 30.
5. 24 is ▦% of 60.
6. 14 is ▦% of 20.
7. 81 is ▦% of 180.
8. 160 is ▦% of 500.
9. 78 is ▦% of 120.
10. 168 is ▦% of 175.
11. 3 is ▦% of 60.
12. 18 is ▦% of 24.
13. 63 is ▦% of 225.
14. 51 is ▦% of 60.
15. 42 is ▦% of 75.
16. 12 is ▦% of 30.
17. 2 is ▦% of 20.
18. 39 is ▦% of 75.
19. 9 is ▦% of 50.
20. 66 is ▦% of 150.
21. 13 is ▦% of 52.
22. 54 is ▦% of 75.

Set G (pp. 292–293)

Find each missing number.

1. 42% of s is 21.
2. 60% of c is 9.
3. 95% of n is 57.
4. 35% of x is 42.
5. 86% of e is 129.
6. 14% of v is 49.
7. 48% of a is 84.
8. 65% of z is 91.
9. 4% of k is 3.
10. 80% of g is 32.
11. 8% of u is 24.
12. 44% of d is 220.
13. 92% of q is 690.
14. 40% of w is 24.
15. 30% of x is 21.
16. 75% of r is 39.
17. 90% of h is 72.
18. 12% of t is 27.
19. 52% of m is 65.
20. 76% of b is 57.
21. 16% of p is 4.

Measures and Formulas

Metric System

Length
10 millimeters (mm) = 1 centimeter (cm)
$\left.\begin{array}{l}\text{10 centimeters}\\\text{100 millimeters}\end{array}\right\}$ = 1 decimeter (dm)
$\left.\begin{array}{l}\text{10 decimeters}\\\text{100 centimeters}\end{array}\right\}$ = 1 meter (m)
1000 meters = 1 kilometer (km)

Area
100 square millimeters (mm²) = 1 square centimeter (cm²)
10,000 square centimeters = 1 square meter (m²)
100 square meters = 1 are (a)
10,000 square meters = 1 hectare (ha)

Volume
1000 cubic millimeters (mm³) = 1 cubic centimeter (cm³)
1000 cubic centimeters = 1 cubic decimeter (dm³)
1,000,000 cubic centimeters = 1 cubic meter (m³)

1000 milliliters (ml) = 1 liter (ℓ)
1000 liters = 1 kiloliter (kl)

Mass
1000 milligrams (mg) = 1 gram (g)
1000 grams = 1 kilogram (kg)
1000 kilograms = 1 metric ton (t)

Customary System

Length
12 inches (in.) = 1 foot (ft.)
$\left.\begin{array}{l}\text{3 feet}\\\text{36 inches}\end{array}\right\}$ = 1 yard (yd.)
$\left.\begin{array}{l}\text{1760 yards}\\\text{5280 feet}\end{array}\right\}$ = 1 mile (mi.)
6076 feet = 1 nautical mile

Area
144 square inches (sq. in.) = 1 square foot (sq. ft.)
9 square feet = 1 square yard (sq. yd.)
4840 square yards = 1 acre (A.)

Volume
1728 cubic inches (cu. in.) = 1 cubic foot (cu. ft.)
27 cubic feet = 1 cubic yard (cu. yd.)

Weight
16 ounces (oz.) = 1 pound (lb.)
2000 pounds = 1 ton (T.)

Capacity
8 fluid ounces (fl. oz.) = 1 cup (c.)
2 cups = 1 pint (pt.)
2 pints = 1 quart (qt.)
4 quarts = 1 gallon (gal.)

Trigonometric Ratios

Tangent of an angle, p. 274

$$\frac{\text{length of leg opposite angle}}{\text{length of leg adjacent to angle}}$$

Sine of an angle, p. 274

$$\frac{\text{length of leg opposite angle}}{\text{length of hypotenuse}}$$

Cosine of an angle, p. 274

$$\frac{\text{length of leg adjacent to angle}}{\text{length of hypotenuse}}$$

Geometric Formulas

Area
of a circle, p. 228 $A = \pi r^2$
of a parallelogram, p. 218 $A = bh$
of a square, p. 238 $A = s^2$
of a trapezoid, p. 220 $A = h\left(\dfrac{a+b}{2}\right)$
of a triangle, p. 220 $A = \frac{1}{2}bh$

Surface Area
of a cone, p. 232 $A = \pi r^2 + \pi rs$
of a cylinder, p. 232 $A = 2\pi rh + 2\pi r^2$

Circumference
of a circle, p. 227 $C \doteq \pi d$ or $C = 2\pi r$

Perimeter
of a square, p. 238 $A = 4s$

Volume
of a cone, p. 231 $V = \frac{1}{3}\pi r^2 h$
of a cylinder, p. 230 $V = \pi r^2 h$
of a prism, p. 224 $V = Bh$
of a pyramid, p. 225 $V = \frac{1}{3}Bh$

Right-triangle relation, p. 246 $a^2 + b^2 = c^2$

Glossary

Acute angle   An angle whose measure is less than 90°.

Adjacent angles   Angles ABC and CBD are adjacent.

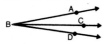

Alternate interior angles   Angles 3 and 5 are alternate interior angles.

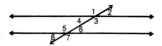

Altitude of a triangle   A segment that extends from one vertex of the triangle to the opposite side and is perpendicular to that side.

Angle   Two rays with the same endpoint.

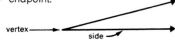

Arc   Part of a circle.

Area   A number indicating the region inside a plane figure.

Associative property of addition   The way in which numbers are grouped does not change the sum.
$$(7 + 2) + 4 = 7 + (2 + 4)$$

Associative property of multiplication   The way in which numbers are grouped does not change the product.
$$(7 \times 2) \times 4 = 7 \times (2 \times 4)$$

Average   The quotient obtained by dividing the sum of a set of numbers by the number of addends.

Central angle   An angle whose vertex is the center of a circle.

Chord   A segment whose endpoints are on a circle. A diameter is a special chord.

Circle   A closed curve in a plane, all of whose points are the same distance from a given point called the center.

Circumference   The distance around a circle.

Common denominator   A common multiple of two or more denominators. 12 is a common denominator for $\frac{2}{3}$ and $\frac{1}{4}$.

Commutative property of addition   The order in which numbers are added does not change the sum.
$$4 + 6 = 6 + 4$$

Commutative property of multiplication   The order in which numbers are multiplied does not change the product.
$$4 \times 6 = 6 \times 4$$

Composite number   A whole number greater than zero that has more than two factors.

Concentric circles   Circles in the same plane that have the same center but different radii.

Cone   A space figure shaped like this.

Congruent   Having the same size and shape.

Consecutive angles   In this quadrilateral, angles J and K are consecutive.

Cosine   For a given acute angle in a right triangle, the ratio:
$$\frac{\text{length of adjacent side}}{\text{length of hypotenuse}}$$

Counting principle   If there is a number of successive choices to make, the total number of choices is the product of the number of choices at each stage.

Cross-products   In two fractions or ratios, the products of the first number of one and the second number of the other. For $\frac{3}{4}$ and $\frac{9}{12}$, the cross-products are 3×12 and 4×9.

Cube   A rectangular prism with all square faces.

Cylinder   A space figure shaped like this.

Degree   A unit for measuring angles and arcs.

Diagonal   In a polygon, a segment that connects one vertex to another and that is not a side of the polygon.

Diameter   A segment having its endpoints on a circle and passing through the center.

Distributive property of multiplication over addition   A property that relates addition and multiplication as follows:
$$4(7 + 3) = 4(7) + 4(3)$$

Dividend   In $45 \div 6$, 45 is the dividend.

Divisor   In $45 \div 6$, 6 is the divisor.

Edge   In a space figure, a segment where two faces meet.

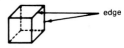

Endpoint The end of a line segment or a ray.

Equilateral triangle A triangle whose three sides are congruent.

Even number A whole number with a factor of 2.

Exponent In 4^3, 3 is the exponent. It tells that 4 is to be used as a factor three times.
$$4^3 = 4 \times 4 \times 4 = 64$$

Face A plane region of a space figure.

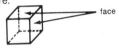
face

Factor A number used in multiplication. In $3 \times 8 = 24$, 3 and 8 are factors.

Factorial The product of a whole number and every whole number less than itself.
$$4! = 4 \times 3 \times 2 \times 1 = 24$$

Frequency table In statistics, a listing of the data and how many times each item of data occurred.

Grouping property See Associative property of addition *and* Associative property of multiplication.

Hexagon A six-sided polygon.

Hypotenuse In a right triangle, the side opposite the right angle.

Improper fraction A fraction whose numerator is equal to or greater than its denominator. Examples are $\frac{4}{4}$, $\frac{15}{2}$, and $\frac{8}{1}$.

Inscribed angle An angle whose vertex is on a circle and whose sides cut off an arc of the circle.

Inscribed polygon A polygon inside a circle, with its vertices on the circle.

Integer A number such as $^-183$, $^-6$, 0, $^+32$, or $^+14{,}029$.

Intersecting lines Two lines with exactly one point in common.

Isosceles triangle A triangle with two congruent sides.

Least common multiple The smallest number that is a common multiple of two given numbers. The least common multiple of 6 and 8 is 24.

Lowest terms A fraction is in lowest terms if the only common factor of the numerator and the denominator is 1.

Mean Another name for "average." The mean of the set 2, 4, 5, 6, 6 is $23 \div 5$, or 4.6.

Median The middle number in a set of numbers when the numbers are in order. The median of the set 2, 4, 5, 6, 6 is 5.

Midpoint The point in a segment that divides it into two equal parts.

Mode The number that occurs most often in a set of numbers. The mode of the set 2, 4, 5, 6, 6 is 6.

Multiple The product of a given number and a whole number. The multiples of 3 are 3, 6, 9, 12, and so on.

Obtuse angle An angle whose measure is greater than 90°.

Octagon An eight-sided polygon.

Odd number A whole number that does not have 2 as a factor.

Opposite angles In this quadrilateral, angles J and L are opposite angles.

opposite angles

Opposites Two numbers whose sum is zero. 5 and $^-5$ are opposites.

Order property See Commutative property of addition *and* Commutative property of multiplication.

Origin On a coordinate grid, the point (0, 0) where the two number lines, or axes, intersect.

Parallel lines Lines in the same plane that do not intersect.

Parallelogram A quadrilateral whose opposite sides are parallel.

Pentagon A five-sided polygon.

Percent A fraction whose denominator is 100. $45\% = \frac{45}{100}$

Perimeter The distance around a closed figure.

Permutations The ordered arrangements of a set of objects or numbers. The permutations of the set A, B, C are:
ABC   BAC   CAB
ACB   BCA   CBA

Perpendicular lines Two lines that intersect to form right angles.

Polygon A closed figure made up of segments.

Polyhedron A space figure whose faces are regions shaped like polygons.

Power 2^3 is read "2 to the third power." $2^3 = 2 \times 2 \times 2 = 8$. The third power of 2 is 8. See *also* Exponent.

Precision A property of measurement that depends upon the size of the unit of measure. The smaller the unit, the more precise the measurement.

Prime factor A factor that is a prime number.

Prime number A whole number, such as 17, that has only two factors, itself and 1.

Prism A polyhedron with two parallel faces, called bases, that are congruent.

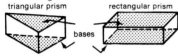
triangular prism   rectangular prism
bases

Probability A number that tells how likely it is that a certain event will happen. It is the number of favorable outcomes divided by the number of possible outcomes.

Proportion A statement that two ratios are equal.

$$\frac{2}{5} = \frac{12}{30}$$

Pyramid A polyhedron with one base. The other faces are triangular.

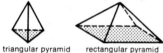
triangular pyramid   rectangular pyramid

Quadrant One of the four parts into which a plane is divided by two perpendicular lines.

Quadrilateral A polygon with four sides.

Radius A segment whose endpoints are the center of a circle and a point on the circle.

Ratio A pair of numbers that expresses a rate or a comparison.

Rational number Any number that can be expressed as either a terminating decimal or a repeating decimal.

$$4\frac{3}{4} = 4.75 \quad \frac{1}{3} = .33 \ldots$$

Ray Part of a line that has one endpoint and extends in one direction.

Reciprocals Two numbers whose product is 1; for example, $\frac{3}{4}$ and $\frac{4}{3}$.

Rectangle A parallelogram with four right angles.

Regular polygon A polygon that has all its sides congruent and all its angles congruent.

Repeating decimal A decimal in which one or more digits keep repeating.
.5181818 . . .

Repetend The part of a repeating decimal that keeps repeating. A bar is often shown above the repetend.
.5181818 . . . = .5$\overline{18}$

Rhombus A parallelogram whose sides are congruent.

Right angle An angle whose measure is 90°.

Scalene triangle A triangle in which no two sides are congruent.

Scientific notation A way of expressing a number by writing it as a decimal between 1 and 10 times a power of 10.
$352 = 3.52 \times 10^2$

Segment Two points in a line and all the points between them.

Semicircle An arc that is one-half of a circle.

Significant digits In a measurement, the digits needed to tell how many times the unit of measure is used. The measurement 7.60 meters has three significant digits, 7, 6, and 0.

Similar figures Figures having the same shape but not necessarily the same size.

Sine For a given acute angle in a right triangle, the ratio:

$$\frac{\text{length of opposite side}}{\text{length of hypotenuse}}$$

Square A rectangle with four congruent sides.

Square root A number a is the square root of a number b if $a \times a = b$. 3 is the square root of 9.

Surface area The total area of all the faces of a space figure.

Tangent For a given acute angle in a right triangle, the ratio:

$$\frac{\text{length of opposite side}}{\text{length of adjacent side}}$$

Terminating decimal A decimal with a limited number of nonzero digits. Examples are .5 and .0082.

Transversal A line that intersects two or more lines in the same plane.

Trapezoid A quadrilateral with one pair of parallel sides.

Triangle A polygon with three sides.

Trigonometric ratios See Cosine, Sine, and Tangent.

Variable In an expression or an equation, a letter that represents a number.

Vertex (1) The common endpoint of two rays that form an angle. (2) The point of intersection of two sides of a polygon. (3) The point of intersection of three or more edges of a space figure.

(1)   (2)   (3)

Volume A number indicating amount of space inside a space figure.

Index